Radiate Science knowledge with CGP...

OK, so there's a lot to learn in GCSE Combined Science — it is worth two GCSEs, after all.

Not to worry. This chunky CGP book explains all the facts, theory and practical skills you'll need, with essential exam practice questions on every page. It's a beautiful thing.

How to access your free Online Edition

This book includes a free Online Edition to read on your PC, Mac or tablet.
To access it, just go to **cgpbooks.co.uk/extras** and enter this code...

7437 2678 8734 9521

Fashion

By the way, this code only works for one person. If somebody else has used
this book before you, they might have already claimed the Online Edition.

CGP — still the best! ☺

Our sole aim here at CGP is to produce the highest quality books —
carefully written, immaculately presented and dangerously close to being funny.

Then we work our socks off to get them out to you
— at the cheapest possible prices.

Contents

Published by CGP

From original material by Richard Parsons.

Editors: Jane Ellingham, Mary Falkner, Emily Garrett, Paul Jordin, Christopher Lindle, Rachael Marshall, Sam Pilgrim, Claire Plowman, Rachael Rogers, Sophie Scott and Camilla Simson.

Contributor: Paddy Gannon

ISBN: 978 1 78294 569 7

With thanks to Katherine Faudemer, Emily Howe and Sarah Williams for the proofreading.

Printed by Elanders Ltd, Newcastle upon Tyne.
Clipart from Corel®

The Scientific Method

This section isn't about how to 'do' science — but it does show you the way most scientists work.

Scientists Come Up With Hypotheses — Then Test Them

1) Scientists try to explain things. They start by observing something they don't understand.

2) They then come up with a hypothesis — a possible explanation for what they've observed.

3) The next step is to test whether the hypothesis might be right or not. This involves making a prediction based on the hypothesis and testing it by gathering evidence (i.e. data) from investigations. If evidence from experiments backs up a prediction, you're a step closer to figuring out if the hypothesis is true.

About 100 years ago, scientists hypothesised that atoms looked like this.

Several Scientists Will Test a Hypothesis

1) Normally, scientists share their findings in peer-reviewed journals, or at conferences.

2) Peer-review is where other scientists check results and scientific explanations to make sure they're 'scientific' (e.g. that experiments have been done in a sensible way) before they're published. It helps to detect false claims, but it doesn't mean that findings are correct — just that they're not wrong in any obvious way.

3) Once other scientists have found out about a hypothesis, they'll start basing their own predictions on it and carry out their own experiments. They'll also try to reproduce the original experiments to check the results — and if all the experiments in the world back up the hypothesis, then scientists start to think the hypothesis is true.

4) However, if a scientist does an experiment that doesn't fit with the hypothesis (and other scientists can reproduce the results) then the hypothesis may need to be modified or scrapped altogether.

After more evidence was gathered, scientists changed their hypothesis to this.

If All the Evidence Supports a Hypothesis, It's Accepted — For Now

1) Accepted hypotheses are often referred to as theories. Our currently accepted theories are the ones that have survived this 'trial by evidence' — they've been tested many times over the years and survived.

2) However, theories never become totally indisputable fact. If new evidence comes along that can't be explained using the existing theory, then the hypothesising and testing is likely to start all over again.

Now we think it's more like this.

Theories Can Involve Different Types of Models

1) A representational model is a simplified description or picture of what's going on in real life. Like all models, it can be used to explain observations and make predictions. E.g. the Bohr model of an atom is a simplified way of showing the arrangement of electrons in an atom (see p.83). It can be used to explain trends down groups in the periodic table.

Scientists test models by carrying out experiments to check that the predictions made by the model happen as expected.

2) Computational models use computers to make simulations of complex real-life processes, such as climate change. They're used when there are a lot of different variables (factors that change) to consider, and because you can easily change their design to take into account new data.

3) All models have limitations on what they can explain or predict. E.g. ball and stick models (a type of spatial model) can be used to show how ions are arranged in an ionic compound. One of their limitations is that they don't show the relative sizes of the ions (see p.89).

I'm off to the zoo to test my hippo-thesis...

The scientific method has developed over time, and many people have helped to develop it. From Aristotle to modern day scientists, lots of people have contributed. And many more are likely to contribute in the future.

Communication & Issues Created by Science

Scientific developments can be great, but they can sometimes <u>raise more questions</u> than they answer...

It's Important to Communicate Scientific Discoveries to the General Public

Some scientific discoveries show that people should <u>change their habits</u>, or they might provide ideas that could be <u>developed</u> into new <u>technology</u>. So scientists need to <u>tell the world</u> about their discoveries.

<u>Gene technologies</u> are used in <u>genetic engineering</u>, to produce <u>genetically modified crops</u>. Information about these crops needs to be communicated to <u>farmers</u> who might <u>benefit</u> from growing them and to the <u>general public</u>, so they can make <u>informed decisions</u> about the food they buy and eat.

Scientific Evidence can be Presented in a Biased Way

1) <u>Reports</u> about scientific discoveries in the <u>media</u> (e.g. newspapers or television) <u>aren't</u> peer-reviewed.
2) This means that, even though news stories are often <u>based</u> on data that has been peer-reviewed, the data might be <u>presented</u> in a way that is <u>over-simplified</u> or <u>inaccurate</u>, making it open to <u>misinterpretation</u>.
3) People who want to make a point can sometimes <u>present data</u> in a <u>biased way</u>. (Sometimes <u>without knowing</u> they're doing it.) For example, a scientist might overemphasise a relationship in the data, or a newspaper article might describe details of data <u>supporting</u> an idea without giving any evidence <u>against</u> it.

Scientific Developments are Great, but they can Raise Issues

Scientific <u>knowledge is increased</u> by doing experiments. And this knowledge leads to <u>scientific developments</u>, e.g. new technologies or new advice. These developments can create <u>issues</u> though. For example:

<u>Economic issues:</u> Society <u>can't</u> always <u>afford</u> to do things scientists recommend (e.g. investing in alternative energy sources) without <u>cutting back elsewhere</u>.

<u>Social issues:</u> Decisions based on scientific evidence affect <u>people</u> — e.g. should alcohol be banned (to prevent health problems)? Would the <u>effect on people's lifestyles be acceptable...?</u>

<u>Personal issues:</u> Some decisions will affect <u>individuals</u>. For example, someone might support <u>alternative energy</u>, but object if a <u>wind farm</u> is built next to their house.

<u>Environmental issues:</u> <u>Human activity</u> often affects the <u>natural environment</u> — e.g. <u>genetically modified crops</u> may help us to produce <u>more food</u> — but some people think they could cause <u>environmental problems</u> (see p.67).

Science Can't Answer Every Question — Especially Ethical Ones

1) We don't <u>understand everything</u>. We're always finding out <u>more</u>, but we'll never know <u>all</u> the answers.
2) In order to answer scientific questions, scientists need <u>data</u> to provide <u>evidence</u> for their hypotheses.
3) Some questions can't be answered <u>yet</u> because the data <u>can't</u> currently be <u>collected</u>, or because there's <u>not enough</u> data to <u>support</u> a theory.
4) <u>Eventually</u>, as we get <u>more evidence</u>, we'll answer some of the questions that <u>currently</u> can't be answered, e.g. what the impact of global warming on sea levels will be. But there will always be the "<u>Should we be doing this at all?</u>"-type questions that experiments <u>can't</u> help us to answer...

Think about <u>new drugs which can be taken to boost your 'brain power'</u>.
- Some people think they're <u>good</u> as they could improve concentration or memory. New drugs could let people think in ways beyond the powers of normal brains.
- Other people say they're <u>bad</u> — they could give you an <u>unfair advantage</u> in exams. And people might be <u>pressured</u> into taking them so that they could work more <u>effectively</u>, and for <u>longer hours</u>.

THE GAZETTE: BRAIN-BOOSTING DRUGS MAKE A MOCKERY OF EXAMS
THE POST: GENIUS PILLS TO BECOME THE NEW COFFEE

Tea to milk or milk to tea? — Totally unanswerable by science...

Science can't tell you whether or not you should do something. That's for you and society to decide. But there are tons of questions science might be able to answer, like where life came from and where my superhero socks are.

Risk

By reading this page you are agreeing to the risk of a paper cut or severe drowsiness...

Nothing is Completely Risk-Free

1) A hazard is something that could potentially cause harm.

2) All hazards have a risk attached to them — this is the chance that the hazard will cause harm.

3) The risks of some things seem pretty obvious, or we've known about them for a while, like the risk of causing acid rain by polluting the atmosphere, or of having a car accident when you're travelling in a car.

4) New technology arising from scientific advances can bring new risks, e.g. scientists are unsure whether nanoparticles that are being used in cosmetics and suncream might be harming the cells in our bodies. These risks need to be considered alongside the benefits of the technology, e.g. improved sun protection.

5) You can estimate the size of a risk based on how many times something happens in a big sample (e.g. 100 000 people) over a given period (e.g. a year). For example, you could assess the risk of a driver crashing by recording how many people in a group of 100 000 drivers crashed their cars over a year.

6) To make a decision about activities that involve hazards, we need to take into account the chance of the hazard causing harm, and how serious the consequences would be if it did. So if an activity involves a hazard that's very likely to cause harm, with serious consequences if it does, it's considered high-risk.

People Make Their Own Decisions About Risk

1) Not all risks have the same consequences, e.g. if you chop veg with a sharp knife you risk cutting your finger, but if you go scuba-diving you risk death. You're much more likely to cut your finger during half an hour of chopping than to die during half an hour of scuba-diving. But most people are happier to accept a higher probability of an accident if the consequences are short-lived and fairly minor.

2) People tend to be more willing to accept a risk if they choose to do something (e.g. go scuba diving), compared to having the risk imposed on them (e.g. having a nuclear power station built next door).

3) People's perception of risk (how risky they think something is) isn't always accurate. They tend to view familiar activities as low-risk and unfamiliar activities as high-risk — even if that's not the case. For example, cycling on roads is often high-risk, but many people are happy to do it because it's a familiar activity. Air travel is actually pretty safe, but a lot of people perceive it as high-risk.

4) People may over-estimate the risk of things with long-term or invisible effects, e.g. ionising radiation.

Investigations Can be Hazardous

1) Hazards from science experiments might include:

- Microorganisms, e.g. some bacteria can make you ill.
- Chemicals, e.g. sulfuric acid can burn your skin and alcohols catch fire easily.
- Fire, e.g. an unattended Bunsen burner is a fire hazard.
- Electricity, e.g. faulty electrical equipment could give you a shock.

Hmm... Where did my bacteria sample go?

2) Part of planning an investigation is making sure that it's safe.

3) You should always make sure that you identify all the hazards that you might encounter. Then you should think of ways of reducing the risks from the hazards you've identified. For example:

- If you're working with sulfuric acid, always wear gloves and safety goggles. This will reduce the risk of the acid coming into contact with your skin and eyes.
- If you're using a Bunsen burner, stand it on a heat proof mat. This will reduce the risk of starting a fire.

You can find out about potential hazards by looking in textbooks, doing some internet research, or asking your teacher.

Not revising — an unacceptable exam hazard...

The world's a dangerous place, but if you can recognise hazards, decide how to reduce their risks, and be happy to accept some risks, you can still have fun. Just maybe don't go skydiving with a great white shark on Friday 13th.

Designing Investigations

Dig out your lab coat and dust down your badly-scratched safety goggles... it's investigation time.

Investigations Produce Evidence to Support or Disprove a Hypothesis

1) Scientists observe things and come up with hypotheses to explain them (see p.1).
   You need to be able to do the same. For example:

   > Observation: People have big feet and spots. Hypothesis: Having big feet causes spots.

2) To determine whether or not a hypothesis is right, you need to do an investigation to gather evidence. To do this, you need to use your hypothesis to make a prediction — something you think will happen that you can test. E.g. people who have bigger feet will have more spots.

3) Investigations are used to see if there are patterns or relationships between two variables, e.g. to see if there's a pattern or relationship between the variables 'number of spots' and 'size of feet'.

Evidence Needs to be Repeatable, Reproducible and Valid

1) Repeatable means that if the same person does an experiment again using the same methods and equipment, they'll get similar results.

Investigations include experiments and studies.

2) Reproducible means that if someone else does the experiment, or a different method or piece of equipment is used, the results will still be similar.

3) If data is repeatable and reproducible, it's reliable and scientists are more likely to have confidence in it.

4) Valid results are both repeatable and reproducible AND they answer the original question. They come from experiments that were designed to be a FAIR TEST...

To Make an Investigation a Fair Test You Have to Control the Variables

1) In a lab experiment you usually change one variable and measure how it affects another variable.

2) To make it a fair test, everything else that could affect the results should stay the same — otherwise you can't tell if the thing you're changing is causing the results or not.

3) The variable you CHANGE is called the INDEPENDENT variable.

4) The variable you MEASURE when you change the independent variable is the DEPENDENT variable.

5) The variables that you KEEP THE SAME are called CONTROL variables.

   > You could find how temperature affects the rate of an enzyme-controlled reaction. The independent variable is the temperature. The dependent variable is the rate of reaction. Control variables include the concentration and amounts of reactants, pH, the time period you measure, etc.

6) Because you can't always control all the variables, you often need to use a control experiment. This is an experiment that's kept under the same conditions as the rest of the investigation, but doesn't have anything done to it. This is so that you can see what happens when you don't change anything at all.

The Bigger the Sample Size the Better

1) Data based on small samples isn't as good as data based on large samples. A sample should represent the whole population (i.e. it should share as many of the characteristics in the population as possible) — a small sample can't do that as well. It's also harder to spot anomalies if your sample size is too small.

2) The bigger the sample size the better, but scientists have to be realistic when choosing how big. For example, if you were studying how lifestyle affects people's weight it'd be great to study everyone in the UK (a huge sample), but it'd take ages and cost a bomb. It's more realistic to study a thousand people, with a mixture of ages, gender and race.

This is no high street survey — it's a designer investigation...

Not only do you need to be able to plan your own investigations, you should also be able to look at someone else's plan and decide whether or not it needs improving. Those examiners aren't half demanding.

Collecting Data

You've designed the perfect investigation — now it's time to get your hands mucky and collect some data.

Your Data Should be Repeatable, Reproducible, Accurate and Precise

1) To check repeatability you need to repeat the readings and check that the results are similar. You need to repeat each reading at least three times.

2) To make sure your results are reproducible you can cross check them by taking a second set of readings with another instrument (or a different observer).

Brian's result was a curate.

3) Your data also needs to be ACCURATE. Really accurate results are those that are really close to the true answer. The accuracy of your results usually depends on your method — you need to make sure you're measuring the right thing and that you don't miss anything that should be included in the measurements. E.g. estimating the amount of gas released from a reaction by counting the bubbles isn't very accurate because you might miss some of the bubbles and they might have different volumes. It's more accurate to measure the volume of gas released using a gas syringe (see p.222).

Repeat	Data set 1	Data set 2
1	12	11
2	14	17
3	13	14
Mean	13	14

Data set 1 is more precise than data set 2.

4) Your data also needs to be PRECISE. Precise results are ones where the data is all really close to the mean (average) of your repeated results (i.e. not spread out).

Your Equipment has to be Right for the Job

1) The measuring equipment you use has to be sensitive enough to measure the changes you're looking for. For example, if you need to measure changes of 1 cm³ you need to use a measuring cylinder that can measure in 1 cm³ steps — it'd be no good trying with one that only measures in 10 cm³ steps.

2) The smallest change a measuring instrument can detect is called its RESOLUTION. E.g. some mass balances have a resolution of 1 g, some have a resolution of 0.1 g, and some are even more sensitive.

3) Also, equipment needs to be calibrated by measuring a known value. If there's a difference between the measured and known value, you can use this to correct the inaccuracy of the equipment.

You Need to Look out for Errors and Anomalous Results

1) The results of your experiment will always vary a bit because of RANDOM ERRORS — unpredictable differences caused by things like human errors in measuring. E.g. the errors you make when reading from a measuring cylinder are random. You have to estimate or round the level when it's between two marks — so sometimes your figure will be a bit above the real one, and sometimes it will be a bit below.

2) You can reduce the effect of random errors by taking repeat readings and finding the mean. This will make your results more precise.

If there's no systematic error, then doing repeats and calculating a mean can make your results more accurate.

3) If a measurement is wrong by the same amount every time, it's called a SYSTEMATIC ERROR. For example, if you measured from the very end of your ruler instead of from the 0 cm mark every time, all your measurements would be a bit small. Repeating the experiment in the exact same way and calculating a mean won't correct a systematic error.

4) Just to make things more complicated, if a systematic error is caused by using equipment that isn't zeroed properly, it's called a ZERO ERROR. For example, if a mass balance always reads 1 gram before you put anything on it, all your measurements will be 1 gram too heavy.

5) You can compensate for some systematic errors if you know about them though, e.g. if your mass balance always reads 1 gram before you put anything on it you can subtract 1 gram from all your results.

6) Sometimes you get a result that doesn't fit in with the rest at all. This is called an ANOMALOUS RESULT. You should investigate it and try to work out what happened. If you can work out what happened (e.g. you measured something totally wrong) you can ignore it when processing your results.

Watch what you say to that mass balance — it's very sensitive...

Weirdly, data can be really precise but not very accurate. For example, a fancy piece of lab equipment might give results that are really precise, but if it's not been calibrated properly those results won't be accurate.

Processing and Presenting Data

Processing your data means doing some <u>calculations</u> with it to make it <u>more useful</u>. Once you've done that, you can present your results in a nice <u>chart</u> or <u>graph</u> to help you <u>spot any patterns</u> in your data.

Data Needs to be Organised

Tables are dead useful for <u>organising data</u>. When you draw a table <u>use a ruler</u> and make sure <u>each column</u> has a <u>heading</u> (including the <u>units</u>).

You Might Have to Process Your Data

1) When you've done repeats of an experiment you should always calculate the <u>mean</u> (a type of average). To do this <u>add together</u> all the data values and <u>divide</u> by the total number of values in the sample.

2) You might also need to calculate the <u>range</u> (how spread out the data is). To do this find the <u>largest</u> number and <u>subtract</u> the <u>smallest</u> number from it. 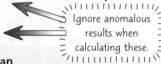 Ignore anomalous results when calculating these.

EXAMPLE: The results of an experiment to find the volume of gas produced in an enzyme-controlled reaction are shown below. Calculate the mean volume and the range.

Repeat 1 (cm³)	Repeat 2 (cm³)	Repeat 3 (cm³)	Mean (cm³)	Range (cm³)
28	37	32	(28 + 37 + 32) ÷ 3 = 32	37 − 28 = 9

3) You might also need to calculate the <u>median</u> or <u>mode</u> (two more types of average). To calculate the <u>median</u>, put all your data in <u>numerical order</u> — the median is the <u>middle value</u>. The number that appears <u>most often</u> in a data set is the <u>mode</u>.

> E.g. If you have the data set: 1 2 1 1 3 4 2
> The <u>median</u> is: 1 1 1 <u>2</u> 2 3 4. The <u>mode</u> is <u>1</u> because 1 appears most often.

If you have an even number of values, the median is halfway between the middle two values.

Round to the Lowest Number of Significant Figures

The <u>first significant figure</u> of a number is the first digit that's <u>not zero</u>. The second and third significant figures come <u>straight after</u> (even if they're zeros). You should be aware of significant figures in calculations.

1) In <u>any</u> calculation, you should round the answer to the <u>lowest number of significant figures</u> (s.f.) given.

2) Remember to write down <u>how many</u> significant figures you've rounded to after your answer.

3) If your calculation has multiple steps, <u>only</u> round the <u>final</u> answer, or it won't be as accurate.

EXAMPLE: The mass of a solid is 0.24 g and its volume is 0.715 cm³. Calculate the density of the solid.

Density = 0.24 g ÷ 0.715 cm³ = 0.33566... = 0.34 g/cm³ (2 s.f.)
      2 s.f.   3 s.f.

— Final answer should be rounded to 2 s.f.

If Your Data Comes in Categories, Present It in a Bar Chart

1) If the independent variable is <u>categoric</u> (comes in distinct categories, e.g. flower colour, blood group) you should use a <u>bar chart</u> to display the data.

2) You also use them if the independent variable is <u>discrete</u> (the data can be counted in chunks, where there's no in-between value, e.g. number of bacteria is discrete because you can't have half a bacterium).

3) There are some <u>golden rules</u> you need to follow for <u>drawing</u> bar charts:

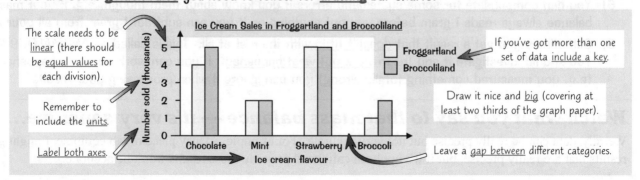

The scale needs to be <u>linear</u> (there should be <u>equal values</u> for each division).

Remember to include the <u>units</u>.

<u>Label both axes</u>.

If you've got more than one set of data <u>include a key</u>.

Draw it nice and <u>big</u> (covering at least two thirds of the graph paper).

Leave a <u>gap between</u> different categories.

If Your Data is Continuous, Plot a Graph

If both variables are <u>continuous</u> (numerical data that can have any value within a range, e.g. length, volume, temperature) you should use a <u>graph</u> to display the data.

Here are the rules for plotting points on a graph:

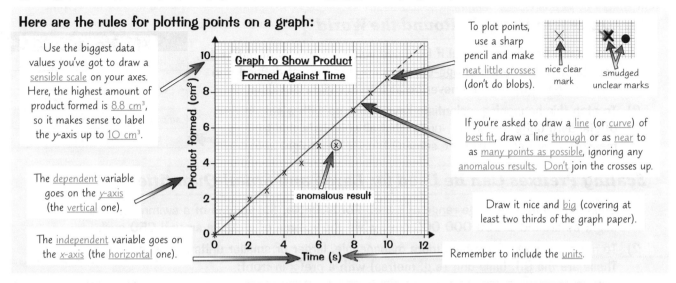

Use the biggest data values you've got to draw a <u>sensible scale</u> on your axes. Here, the highest amount of product formed is <u>8.8 cm³</u>, so it makes sense to label the y-axis up to <u>10 cm³</u>.

The <u>dependent</u> variable goes on the <u>y-axis</u> (the <u>vertical</u> one).

The <u>independent</u> variable goes on the <u>x-axis</u> (the <u>horizontal</u> one).

To plot points, use a sharp pencil and make <u>neat little crosses</u> (don't do blobs).

nice clear mark

smudged unclear marks

If you're asked to draw a <u>line</u> (or <u>curve</u>) of <u>best fit</u>, draw a line <u>through</u> or as <u>near</u> to as <u>many points as possible</u>, ignoring any <u>anomalous results</u>. <u>Don't</u> join the crosses up.

Draw it nice and <u>big</u> (covering at least two thirds of the graph paper).

Remember to include the <u>units</u>.

Graphs Can Give You a Lot of Information About Your Data

1) The <u>gradient</u> (slope) of a graph tells you how quickly the <u>dependent variable</u> changes if you change the <u>independent variable</u>.

$$\text{gradient} = \frac{\text{change in } y}{\text{change in } x}$$

This <u>graph</u> shows the <u>volume of gas</u> produced in a reaction against <u>time</u>. The graph is <u>linear</u> (it's a straight line graph), so you can simply calculate the <u>gradient</u> of the line to find out the <u>rate of reaction</u>.

1) To calculate the gradient, pick <u>two points</u> on the line that are easy to read and a <u>good distance</u> apart.

2) <u>Draw a line down</u> from one of the points and a <u>line across</u> from the other to make a <u>triangle</u>. The line drawn down the side of the triangle is the <u>change in y</u> and the line across the bottom is the <u>change in x</u>.

Change in y = 6.8 − 2.0 = 4.8 cm³   Change in x = 5.2 − 1.6 = 3.6 s

$$\text{Rate} = \text{gradient} = \frac{\text{change in } y}{\text{change in } x} = \frac{4.8 \text{ cm}^3}{3.6 \text{ s}} = \underline{1.3 \text{ cm}^3 \text{ s}^{-1}}$$

The units of the gradient are (units of y)/(units of x). cm³ s⁻¹ can also be written as cm³/s.

You can use this method to calculate other rates from a graph, not just the rate of a reaction. Just remember that a rate is how much something changes over time, so x needs to be the time.

2) To find the <u>gradient of a curve</u> at a <u>certain point</u>, draw a <u>tangent</u> to the curve at that point and then find the <u>gradient of the tangent</u>. See page 131 for details on how to do this.

3) The <u>intercept</u> of a graph is where the line of best fit crosses one of the <u>axes</u>. The <u>x-intercept</u> is where the line of best fit crosses the x-axis and the <u>y-intercept</u> is where it crosses the <u>y-axis</u>.

Graphs Show the Relationship Between Two Variables

1) You can get <u>three</u> types of <u>correlation</u> (relationship) between variables:

2) Just because there's correlation, it doesn't mean the change in one variable is <u>causing</u> the change in the other — there might be <u>other factors</u> involved (see page 9).

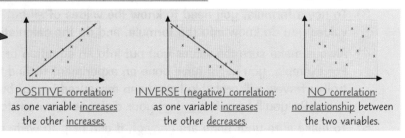

<u>POSITIVE</u> correlation: as one variable <u>increases</u> the other <u>increases</u>.

<u>INVERSE</u> (negative) correlation: as one variable <u>increases</u> the other <u>decreases</u>.

<u>NO</u> correlation: <u>no relationship</u> between the two variables.

I love eating apples — I call it core elation...

Science is all about finding relationships between things. And I don't mean that chemists gather together in corners to discuss whether or not Devini and Sebastian might be a couple... though they probably do that too.

Units and Equations

Graphs and maths skills are all very well, but the numbers don't mean much if you can't get the <u>units</u> right.

S.I. Units Are Used All Round the World

1) It wouldn't be all that useful if I defined volume in terms of <u>bath tubs</u>, you defined it in terms of <u>egg-cups</u> and my pal Sarwat defined it in terms of <u>balloons</u> — we'd never be able to compare our data.

2) To stop this happening, scientists have come up with a set of <u>standard units</u>, called S.I. units, that all scientists use to measure their data. Here are some S.I. units you might see:

Quantity	S.I. Base Unit
mass	kilogram, kg
length	metre, m
time	second, s
amount of substance	mole, mol
temperature	kelvin, K

Scaling Prefixes Can Be Used for Large and Small Quantities

1) Quantities come in a huge <u>range</u> of sizes. For example, the volume of a swimming pool might be around 2 000 000 000 cm³, while the volume of a cup is around 250 cm³.

2) To make the size of numbers more <u>manageable</u>, larger or smaller units are used. These are the <u>S.I. base unit</u> (e.g. metres) with a <u>prefix</u> in front:

prefix	tera (T)	giga (G)	mega (M)	kilo (k)	deci (d)	centi (c)	milli (m)	micro (μ)	nano (n)
multiple of unit	10^{12}	10^9	1 000 000 (10^6)	1000	0.1	0.01	0.001	0.000001 (10^{-6})	10^{-9}

3) These <u>prefixes</u> tell you <u>how much bigger</u> or <u>smaller</u> a unit is than the base unit. So one <u>kilo</u>metre is <u>one thousand</u> metres.

The conversion factor is the number of times the smaller unit goes into the larger unit.

4) To <u>swap</u> from one unit to another, all you need to know is what number you have to divide or multiply by to get from the original unit to the new unit — this is called the <u>conversion factor</u>.

- To go from a <u>bigger unit</u> (like m) to a <u>smaller unit</u> (like cm), you <u>multiply</u> by the conversion factor.
- To go from a <u>smaller unit</u> (like g) to a <u>bigger unit</u> (like kg), you <u>divide</u> by the conversion factor.

5) Here are some conversions that'll be useful for GCSE science:

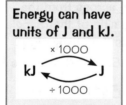

Mass can have units of kg and g.

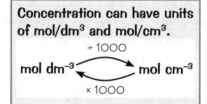

Energy can have units of J and kJ.

Concentration can have units of mol/dm³ and mol/cm³.

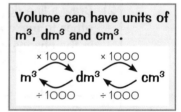

Volume can have units of m³, dm³ and cm³.

6) Numbers can also be written in <u>standard form</u>, e.g. 1×10^2 m = 100 m. There's more on this on p.13 and p.150. Make sure you know how to work with standard form on <u>your calculator</u>.

Always Check The Values in Equations and Formulas Have the Right Units

1) Equations show <u>relationships</u> between <u>variables</u>.

2) To <u>rearrange</u> an equation — whatever you do to <u>one side</u> of the equation also do to the <u>other</u>.

wave speed = frequency × wavelength. You can <u>rearrange</u> this equation to find the <u>frequency</u> by <u>dividing each side</u> by wavelength to give: frequency = wave speed ÷ wavelength.

3) To use a formula, you need to know the values of <u>all but one</u> of the variables. <u>Substitute</u> the values you do know into the formula, and do the calculation to work out the final variable.

4) Always make sure the values you put into an equation or formula have the <u>right units</u>. For example, you might have done an experiment to find the speed of a trolley. The distance the trolley travels will probably have been measured in cm, but the equation to find speed uses distance in m. So you'll have to <u>convert</u> your distance from cm to m before you put it into the equation.

5) To make sure your units are <u>correct</u>, it can help to write down the <u>units</u> on each line of your <u>calculation</u>.

I wasn't sure I liked units, but now I'm converted...

It's easy to get in a muddle when converting between units, but there's a handy way to check you've done it right. If you're moving from a smaller unit to a larger unit (e.g. g to kg) the number should get smaller, and vice versa.

Drawing Conclusions

Congratulations — you're nearly at the end of a gruelling investigation, time to <u>draw conclusions</u>.

You Can Only Conclude What the Data Shows and NO MORE

1) Drawing conclusions might seem pretty straightforward — you just <u>look at your data</u> and <u>say what pattern or relationship you see</u> between the dependent and independent variables.

The table on the right shows the heights of pea plant seedlings grown for three weeks with <u>different fertilisers</u>.

Fertiliser	Mean growth / mm
A	13.5
B	19.5
No fertiliser	5.5

<u>CONCLUSION</u>:
Fertiliser <u>B</u> makes <u>pea plant</u> seedlings grow taller over a <u>three week</u> period than fertiliser A.

2) But you've got to be really careful that your conclusion <u>matches the data</u> you've got and <u>doesn't go any further</u>.

You <u>can't</u> conclude that fertiliser B makes <u>any other type of plant</u> grow taller than fertiliser A — the results could be totally different.

3) You also need to be able to <u>use your results</u> to <u>justify your conclusion</u> (i.e. back up your conclusion with some specific data).

Over the three week period, fertiliser B made the pea plants grow <u>6 mm more</u> on average than fertiliser A.

4) When writing a conclusion you need to <u>refer back</u> to the original hypothesis and say whether the data <u>supports it</u> or not:

The hypothesis for this experiment might have been that adding fertiliser would increase the growth of plants and that different types of fertiliser would affect growth by different amounts. If so, the data <u>supports</u> the hypothesis.

Correlation DOES NOT Mean Cause

If two things are correlated (i.e. there's a relationship between them) it <u>doesn't</u> necessarily mean a change in one variable is <u>causing</u> the change in the other — this is <u>REALLY IMPORTANT</u> — <u>DON'T FORGET IT</u>. There are <u>three possible reasons</u> for a correlation:

1) <u>CHANCE</u>: It might seem strange, but two things can show a correlation purely due to <u>chance</u>.

For example, one study might find a correlation between people's hair colour and how good they are at frisbee. But other scientists <u>don't</u> get a correlation when they investigate it — the results of the first study are just a <u>fluke</u>.

2) <u>LINKED BY A 3RD VARIABLE</u>: A lot of the time it may <u>look</u> as if a change in one variable is causing a change in the other, but it <u>isn't</u> — a <u>third variable links</u> the two things.

For example, there's a correlation between <u>water temperature</u> and <u>shark attacks</u>. This isn't because warmer water makes sharks crazy. Instead, they're linked by a third variable — the <u>number of people swimming</u> (more people swim when the water's hotter, and with more people in the water you get more shark attacks).

3) <u>CAUSE</u>: Sometimes a change in one variable does <u>cause</u> a change in the other. You can only conclude that a correlation is due to cause when you've <u>controlled all the variables</u> that could, just could, be affecting the result.

For example, there's a correlation between <u>smoking</u> and <u>lung cancer</u>. This is because chemicals in tobacco smoke cause lung cancer. This conclusion was only made once <u>other variables</u> (such as age and exposure to other things that cause cancer) had been <u>controlled</u> and shown <u>not</u> to affect people's risk of getting lung cancer.

I conclude that this page is a bit dull...

...although, just because I find it dull doesn't mean that I can conclude it's dull (you might think it's the most interesting thing since that kid got his head stuck in the railings near school). In the exams you could be given a conclusion and asked whether some data supports it — so make sure you understand how far conclusions can go.

Uncertainties and Evaluations

Hurrah! The end of another investigation. Well, now you have to work out all the things you did <u>wrong</u>.

Uncertainty is the Amount of Error Your Measurements Might Have

1) When you <u>repeat</u> a measurement, you often get a <u>slightly different</u> figure each time you do it due to <u>random error</u>. This means that <u>each result</u> has some <u>uncertainty</u> to it.

2) The measurements you make will also have some uncertainty in them due to <u>limits</u> in the <u>resolution</u> of the equipment you use (see page 5).

3) This all means that the <u>mean</u> of a set of results will also have some uncertainty to it. You can calculate the uncertainty of a <u>mean result</u> using the equation:

4) The <u>larger</u> the range, the <u>less precise</u> your results are and the <u>more uncertainty</u> there will be in your results. Uncertainties are shown using the '±' symbol.

The range is the largest value minus the smallest value (p.6).

$$\text{uncertainty} = \frac{\text{range}}{2}$$

**EXAMPLE:** The table below shows the results of a trolley experiment to determine the speed of the trolley as it moves along a horizontal surface. Calculate the uncertainty of the mean.

Repeat	1	2	3	mean
Speed (m/s)	2.02	1.98	2.00	2.00

1) First work out the range:
   Range = 2.02 − 1.98
          = 0.04 m/s

2) Use the range to find the uncertainty:
Uncertainty = range ÷ 2 = 0.04 ÷ 2 = 0.02 m/s   So, uncertainty of the mean = 2.00 ± 0.02 m/s

5) Measuring a <u>greater amount</u> of something helps to <u>reduce uncertainty</u>. For example, in a rate of reaction experiment, measuring the amount of product formed over a <u>longer period</u> compared to a shorter period will <u>reduce</u> the <u>percentage uncertainty</u> in your results.

Evaluations — Describe How it Could be Improved

An evaluation is a <u>critical analysis</u> of the whole investigation.

1) You should comment on the <u>method</u> — was it <u>valid</u>? Did you control all the other variables to make it a <u>fair test</u>?

2) Comment on the <u>quality</u> of the <u>results</u> — was there <u>enough evidence</u> to reach a valid <u>conclusion</u>? Were the results <u>repeatable</u>, <u>reproducible</u>, <u>accurate</u> and <u>precise</u>?

3) Were there any <u>anomalous</u> results? If there were <u>none</u> then <u>say so</u>. If there were any, try to <u>explain</u> them — were they caused by <u>errors</u> in measurement? Were there any other <u>variables</u> that could have <u>affected</u> the results? You should comment on the level of <u>uncertainty</u> in your results too.

4) All this analysis will allow you to say how <u>confident</u> you are that your conclusion is <u>right</u>.

5) Then you can suggest any <u>changes</u> to the <u>method</u> that would <u>improve</u> the quality of the results, so that you could have <u>more confidence</u> in your conclusion. For example, you might suggest <u>changing</u> the way you controlled a variable, or <u>increasing</u> the number of <u>measurements</u> you took. Taking more measurements at <u>narrower intervals</u> could give you a <u>more accurate result</u>. For example:

<u>Enzymes</u> have an <u>optimum temperature</u> (a temperature at which they <u>work best</u>). Say you do an experiment to find an enzyme's optimum temperature and take measurements at 10 °C, 20 °C, 30 °C, 40 °C and 50 °C. The results of this experiment tell you the optimum is <u>40 °C</u>. You could then <u>repeat</u> the experiment, taking <u>more measurements around 40 °C</u> to a get a <u>more accurate</u> value for the optimum.

6) You could also make more <u>predictions</u> based on your conclusion, then <u>further experiments</u> could be carried out to test them.

When suggesting improvements to the investigation, always make sure that you say why you think this would make the results better.

Evaluation — next time, I'll make sure I don't burn the lab down...

So there you have it — Working Scientifically. Make sure you know this stuff like the back of your hand. It's not just in the lab that you'll need to know how to work scientifically. You can be asked about it in the exams as well.

Cells and Microscopy

Biology's all about <u>living stuff</u>. And all living stuff contains <u>cells</u>. So let's make a <u>start</u> with cells...

Organisms can be Eukaryotes or Prokaryotes

1) <u>Eukaryotes</u> (e.g. all animals and plants) are made from <u>complex cells</u> called <u>eukaryotic</u> cells.

2) <u>Prokaryotes</u> (e.g. bacteria) are smaller and <u>simpler cells</u> called <u>prokaryotic</u> cells.

3) Both types of cells contain <u>sub-cellular structures</u> — parts of cells that each have a <u>specific function</u>.

You Need to Learn the Structures Within Eukaryotic Cells...

<u>ANIMAL CELL</u>

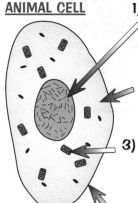

1) <u>NUCLEUS</u> — contains <u>DNA</u> (genetic material) in the form of <u>chromosomes</u> (see p.49) that controls the cell's activities.

2) <u>CYTOPLASM</u> — gel-like substance where most of the <u>chemical reactions</u> happen.

3) <u>MITOCHONDRIA</u> — these are the site of cellular <u>respiration</u> (see p.18) and contain the <u>enzymes</u> needed for the reactions involved.

4) <u>CELL MEMBRANE</u> — holds the cell together and <u>controls</u> what goes <u>in and out</u> by providing a <u>selective barrier</u> (see p.26). They also contain <u>receptor molecules</u> that are used for <u>cell communication</u>, e.g. by hormones.

<u>PLANT CELL</u> — plant cells include <u>everything</u> animal cells have as well as these <u>extras</u>:

1) <u>RIGID CELL WALL</u> — made of <u>cellulose</u>, gives support for the cell.

2) <u>CHLOROPLASTS</u> — where <u>photosynthesis</u> occurs (see p.21). They contain a green substance called <u>chlorophyll</u>.

...and Within Prokaryotic Cells

1) <u>CHROMOSOMAL DNA</u> — (<u>one</u> long circular chromosome) controls the cell's <u>activities</u> and <u>replication</u>. It <u>floats free</u> in the <u>cytoplasm</u> (not in a nucleus).

2) <u>PLASMIDS</u> — <u>small loops</u> of <u>extra DNA</u> that aren't part of the chromosome. Plasmids contain genes for things like <u>drug resistance</u>, and can be <u>passed</u> between bacteria.

<u>A bacterial cell</u>

3) <u>CELL MEMBRANE</u> — <u>controls</u> what goes <u>in and out</u>. The cell is also <u>supported</u> by a <u>cell wall</u>.

Cells are Studied Using Microscopes

There's loads more on light microscopes coming up on the next two pages.

1) <u>Microscopes</u> use lenses to <u>magnify</u> images (make them look bigger).

2) They also increase the <u>resolution</u> of an image. This means they <u>increase the detail</u> you can see. Resolution is how well a microscope distinguishes between <u>two points</u> that are <u>close together</u>.

3) <u>Light microscopes</u> were invented in the 1590s. They let us see things like <u>nuclei</u> and <u>chloroplasts</u>.

4) <u>Electron microscopes</u> were invented in the 1930s. They let us see much <u>smaller things</u> in <u>more detail</u> like the <u>internal structure</u> of mitochondria. This has allowed us to have a much <u>greater understanding</u> of <u>sub-cellular structures</u>. Only electron microscopes will let us see things as tiny as <u>plasmids</u> or <u>viruses</u>.

5) <u>Transmission electron microscopes</u> (<u>TEMs</u>) have a <u>higher magnification</u> and <u>resolution</u> than light microscopes but they're <u>not portable</u>, they're <u>expensive</u> and it's a <u>complicated process</u> to <u>prepare</u> specimens for use (which means they <u>can't</u> be used to look at <u>living tissue</u>, unlike light microscopes).

Cell structures — become an estate agent...

The number of some sub-cellular structures will depend on the cell's function, e.g. muscle cells, which respire lots, will have more mitochondria than other cells, and plant cells that don't get any light won't have chloroplasts.

Q1   Give two functions of the cell membrane in an animal cell.   [2 marks]

Light Microscopy

Ah, the light microscope — that great scientific invention that has enabled us to get up close and personal with the humble cell (and other really small things). Here's how to use one...

You Need to Be Familiar with the Parts of a Light Microscope

Here are the main parts of a light microscope and what they do:

- **Eyepiece lens** — looked through to see the image and also magnifies the image.
- **Objective lens** — magnifies the image. Usually there are three different objective lenses (e.g. ×4, ×10 and ×40).
- **Stage** — supports the slide (see below).
- **Clip** — holds the slide in place.
- **Handle** — to carry the microscope with.
- **Lamp** — shines light through the slide so the image can be seen more easily.
- **Focusing knobs** — move the stage up and down to bring the image into focus.

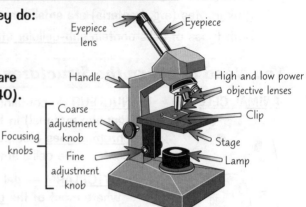

Specimens Need to be Prepared Before Investigation...

1) Your specimen (the sample you're looking at) needs to let light through it for you to be able to see it clearly — if you've got quite a thick specimen, you'll need to take a thin slice of it to start with.

2) Next, take a clean slide (a strip of clear glass or plastic) and use a pipette to put one drop of water or mountant (a clear, gloopy liquid) in the middle of it — this will secure the specimen in place.

3) Use tweezers to place your specimen on the slide.

4) Add a drop of stain if needed — if your specimen is completely transparent or colourless, a drop of stain is added to make the specimen easier to see. Different stains are used to highlight different structures or tissues. For example, eosin is used to stain cytoplasm and methylene blue stains DNA.

5) Place a cover slip (a square of thin, transparent plastic or glass) at one end of the specimen, holding it at an angle with a mounted needle.

6) Carefully lower the cover slip onto the slide. Press it down gently with the needle so that no air bubbles are trapped under it.

... Then You're Ready for Viewing

1) Start by clipping the slide containing your specimen onto the stage.

2) Select the lowest-powered objective lens (i.e. the one that produces the lowest magnification).

3) Use the coarse adjustment knob to move the stage up to just below the objective lens. Then, looking down the eyepiece, move the stage downwards (so you don't accidentally crash the slide into the lens) until the specimen is just about in focus.

4) Then, still looking down the eyepiece, adjust the focus with the fine adjustment knob, until you get a clear image of your specimen.

5) If you need to see your specimen with greater magnification, swap to a higher-powered objective lens and refocus.

> A higher magnification isn't always a good thing — if your specimen is relatively big you might not be able to see the whole thing. It can also be difficult to focus at high magnifications.

Once you're happy with what you can see, you can make a scientific drawing of your specimen (see p.220).

Mi-cros-copy — when my twin gets annoyed...

Yowch. Sorry. Anyway, there's some important stuff about using microscopes here, so get learning.

Q1   A scientist wants to use a light microscope to view the cell walls of a colourless sample of plant tissue. Describe how she could prepare a slide containing the tissue, where the cell walls are visible.   [4 marks]

More on Light Microscopy

Sometimes you need to do a bit of <u>maths</u> with microscope images. It's time to get your <u>numbers head on</u>...

Magnification is How Many Times Bigger the Image is than its Real Size

1) If you know the <u>power of the lenses</u> used by a microscope to view an image, you can work out the <u>total magnification</u> of the image using this simple formula:

What are you looking at?

> **total magnification = eyepiece lens magnification × objective lens magnification**

> **EXAMPLE:**
>
> What is the total magnification of an image viewed with an eyepiece lens magnification of ×10 and an objective lens magnification of ×40?
>
> 10 × 40 = 400, so the total magnification is ×400

2) If you don't know which lenses were used, you can still work out the magnification of an image as long as you can <u>measure the image</u> and know the <u>real size of the specimen</u>. This is the <u>formula</u> you need:

> $$\text{magnification} = \frac{\text{image size}}{\text{real size}}$$

Both measurements should have the same units. If they don't, you'll need to convert them first (see p.8).

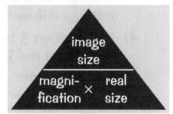

If you want to work out the image size or the real size of the object, you can rearrange the equation using the <u>formula triangle</u>. <u>Cover up</u> the thing you're trying to find. The parts you can <u>still see</u> are the formula you need to use.

> **EXAMPLE:** A specimen is 50 μm wide. Calculate the width of the image of the specimen under a magnification of ×100. Give your answer in mm.
>
> 1) <u>Rearrange</u> the magnification formula. image size = magnification × real size
> 2) Fill in the <u>values</u> you know. image size = 100 × 50
> 3) Remember the <u>units</u> in your answer. = 5000 μm
> 4) <u>Convert</u> the units. = 5 mm

Remember, to convert from micrometres (μm) to millimetres (mm), you need to divide by 1000 (see p.8).

You Need to Know How to Work With Numbers in Standard Form

1) Because microscopes can see such <u>tiny objects</u> sometimes it's useful to write numbers in <u>standard form</u>.

2) This is where you change <u>very big</u> or <u>small</u> numbers with <u>lots of zeros</u> into something more manageable, e.g. 0.017 can be written 1.7×10^{-2}.

3) To do this you just need to <u>move</u> the <u>decimal point</u> left or right.

4) The number of places the decimal point moves is then represented by a <u>power of 10</u> — this is <u>positive</u> if the decimal point's moved to the <u>left</u>, and <u>negative</u> if it's moved to the <u>right</u>.

> **EXAMPLE:** A mitochondrion is approximately 0.0025 mm long. Write this figure in standard form.
>
> 1) The first number needs to be <u>between 1 and 10</u> so the decimal point needs to move after the '2'. 0.0025
> 2) <u>Count</u> how many places the decimal point has <u>moved</u> — this is the power of 10. Don't forget the <u>minus</u> sign because the decimal point has moved <u>right</u>. 2.5×10^{-3}

You can put standard form numbers into your calculator using the 'EXP' or the '×10^x' button. E.g. enter 2.67×10^{15} by pressing 2.67 then 'EXP' then 15.

Gather your microscopes, comrades — it's the bio resolution...

Congratulations — you've made it to the end of the microscopy pages. If the whole concept of microscopy has yet to swim into focus, go back and have another read through. Then make yourself a nice cup of tea.

Q1   Calculate the magnification of images viewed with an eyepiece lens magnification of ×8 and an objective lens magnification of ×15.

[1 mark]

DNA

DNA is a big, big deal in biology, but the mystery of its structure was only solved relatively recently. Luckily, you get to learn all about it, so pen at the ready, thinking cap on... woah there, we nearly forgot the biscuits...

DNA — a Double Helix of Paired Bases

DNA contains all of an organism's genetic material — the chemical instructions it needs to grow and develop. DNA is arranged into chromosomes.

1) Chromosomes are long molecules of coiled up DNA. The DNA is divided up into short sections called genes (see page 49).

2) DNA is a double helix (a double-stranded spiral). Each of the two DNA strands is made up of lots of nucleotides joined together in a long chain — this makes DNA a polymer (see below).

3) Each nucleotide contains a small molecule called a "base". DNA has just four different bases.

4) The bases are A (adenine), C (cytosine), G (guanine) and T (thymine).

5) Each base forms cross links to a base on the other strand. This keeps the two DNA strands tightly wound together.

6) A always pairs up with T, and C always pairs up with G. This is called complementary base-pairing.

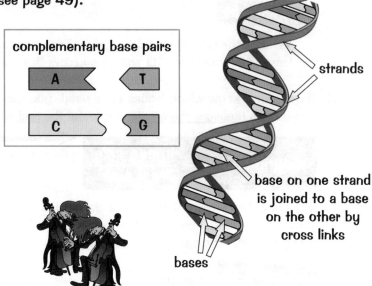

complementary base pairs

A   T

C   G

A DNA Double Helix

strands

base on one strand is joined to a base on the other by cross links

bases

Nucleotides Contain a Sugar, a Phosphate Group and a Base

1) Each DNA nucleotide has the same sugar and a phosphate group. The base on each nucleotide is the only part of the molecule that varies (i.e. it's either A, C, G or T).

2) The base is attached to the sugar.

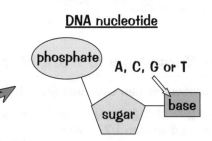

DNA nucleotide

phosphate

A, C, G or T

sugar   base

DNA is a Polymer

1) Polymers are large, complex molecules composed of long chains of monomers joined together.

2) Monomers are small, basic molecular units.

3) DNA is a polymer made up of nucleotide monomers.

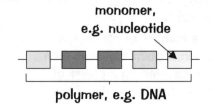

monomer, e.g. nucleotide

polymer, e.g. DNA

Complementary base pairs — oh A, darling, you are stunning...

The complementary base-pairing thing is a mega important idea in biology so make sure you've got your head around it. Then you can treat yourself to some twisty crisps and imagine you're eating DNA.

Q1   Why can DNA be described as a polymer?   [1 mark]

Q2   a) Which base does 'C' pair with in DNA?   [1 mark]
      b) Explain the effect of base-pairing on the structure of DNA.   [2 marks]

Enzymes

Enzymes are the magicians of the protein world — they make reactions happen faster without being changed themselves. Surely that's not possible without a little bit of magic... though here's what science says...

Enzymes Control Cell Reactions

1) Cells have thousands of different chemical reactions going on inside them all the time — like respiration, photosynthesis and protein synthesis. Together these make up the cell's metabolism.

2) These reactions need to be carefully controlled — to get the right amounts of substances and keep the organism working properly.

3) You can usually make a reaction happen more quickly by raising the temperature. This would speed up the useful reactions but also the unwanted ones too... not good. There's also a limit to how far you can raise the temperature inside a living creature before its cells start getting damaged.

4) So living things produce enzymes, which act as biological catalysts. A catalyst is a substance that speeds up a reaction, without being changed or used up in the reaction itself.

5) Enzymes reduce the need for high temperatures and we only have enzymes to speed up the useful chemical reactions in the body.

6) Every different biological reaction has its own enzyme especially for it.

7) Each enzyme is a protein coded for by a different gene, and has a unique shape which it needs to do its job.

Enzymes are Very Specific

1) Chemical reactions usually involve things either being split apart or joined together.

2) The substrate is the molecule changed in the reaction.

3) Every enzyme has an active site — the part where it joins on to its substrate to catalyse the reaction.

4) Enzymes are really picky — they usually only work with one substrate. The posh way of saying this is that enzymes have a high specificity for their substrate.

5) This is because, for the enzyme to work, the substrate has to fit into the active site. If the substrate's shape doesn't match the active site's shape, then the reaction won't be catalysed. This is called the 'lock and key' hypothesis, because the substrate fits into the enzyme just like a key fits into a lock.

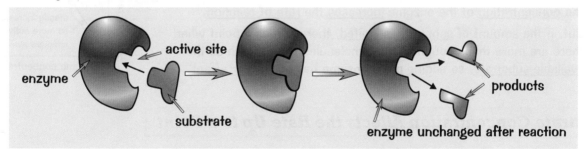

If the lock and key mechanism fails, there's always the window...

Enzymes aren't just useful for controlling chemical reactions in the body — we even put them in things like biological washing powders to catalyse the breakdown of nasty stains (like tomato ketchup). Useful, eh?

Q1 Which statement best describes the role of enzymes in the body?

   A Enzymes speed up the rate of all the body's reactions.

   B Enzymes raise the temperature allowing reactions to happen faster.

   C Enzymes speed up specific reactions without being used up themselves.

   D Each enzyme can speed up of lots of different chemical reactions.   [1 mark]

Q2 Enzymes are described as having a 'high specificity' for their substrate. What is meant by this?   [3 marks]

More on Enzymes

Enzymes are _fussy_ little blighters — they like just the _right temperature_, _pH_, _concentration_...

Enzymes Like it Warm but Not Too Hot

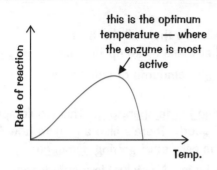

this is the optimum temperature — where the enzyme is most active

1) Changing the _temperature_ changes the _rate_ of an enzyme-controlled reaction.

2) Like with any reaction, a higher temperature _increases_ the rate at first. The enzymes and the substrate _move about_ more, so they're more likely to meet up and react. But if it gets _too hot_, some of the _bonds_ holding the enzyme together _break_. This makes the enzyme become _denatured_ — it _loses its shape_ and the substrate _doesn't fit_ the active site any more. This means the enzyme _can't_ catalyse the reaction and the reaction _stops_. The enzyme is _denatured irreversibly_ — it won't go back to its normal shape if things _cool down_ again.

3) Each enzyme has its own _optimum_ temperature when the reaction goes _fastest_. This is the temperature just before it gets too hot and starts to denature. The optimum temperature for the most important _human_ enzymes is about _37 °C_ — the same temperature as our _bodies_. Lucky for us.

Enzymes Like it the Right pH Too

1) The _pH_ also has an effect on enzymes. If it's too _high_ or too _low_, it interferes with the _bonds_ holding the enzyme together. This changes the _shape_ of the _active site_ and can _irreversibly denature_ the enzyme.

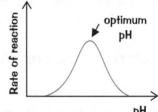

optimum pH

2) All enzymes have an _optimum_ pH that they work best at. It's often _neutral pH 7_, but _not always_. For example, _pepsin_ is an enzyme used to break down _proteins_ in the _stomach_. It works best at _pH 2_, which means it's well-suited to the _acidic_ conditions in the stomach.

Enzyme Concentration Affects the Rate of Reaction

1) The more _enzyme molecules_ there are in a solution, the _more likely_ a substrate molecule will meet up with one and join with it. So increasing the _concentration_ of the enzyme _increases_ the _rate of reaction_.

2) But, if the amount of _substrate_ is _limited_, there comes a point when there are more than enough enzyme molecules to deal with all the _available substrate_, so adding more enzyme has _no further effect_.

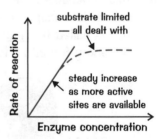

substrate limited — all dealt with

steady increase as more active sites are available

Enzyme concentration

Substrate Concentration Affects the Rate Up to a Point

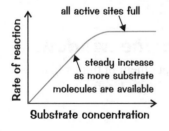

all active sites full

steady increase as more substrate molecules are available

Substrate concentration

1) The higher the _substrate concentration_, the _faster_ the reaction — it's _more likely_ the enzyme will meet up and react with a substrate molecule.

2) This is only true _up to a point_ though. After that, there are so many substrate molecules that the enzymes have about as much as they can cope with (all the _active sites_ are _full_), and adding _more_ makes _no difference_.

My concentration — affects rate of revision up to a point...

With enzymes it's all about the active sites. Anything that changes their shape stops the reaction. Simple.

Q1   Enzyme A's optimum pH is 4. Explain what might happen to enzyme A's activity in conditions above pH 4.

[5 marks]

Investigating Enzyme Activity

You'll soon know how to investigate the effect of a <u>variable</u> on the rate of <u>enzyme activity</u>... I bet you're thrilled.

You Can Investigate How Temperature Affects Enzyme Activity

There are a couple of <u>different ways</u> to investigate how <u>temperature</u> affects <u>enzyme activity</u>. You can also <u>adapt</u> these experiments to measure variables <u>other than temperature</u>. For example:

1) To investigate the effect of <u>pH</u>, add a <u>buffer solution</u> with a different <u>pH level</u> to a series of different tubes containing the enzyme-substrate mixture.

2) Vary the initial <u>concentrations</u> of the <u>substrate</u> to investigate the effect of <u>substrate concentration</u>.

3) Vary the initial <u>concentrations</u> of the <u>enzyme</u> to investigate the effect of <u>enzyme concentration</u>.

You Can Measure How Fast a Product Appears...

1) The enzyme <u>catalase</u> catalyses the <u>breakdown</u> of <u>hydrogen peroxide</u> into <u>water</u> and <u>oxygen</u>.

2) You can collect the <u>oxygen</u> and measure <u>how much</u> is produced in a <u>set time</u>.

3) Use a <u>pipette</u> to add a set amount of <u>hydrogen peroxide</u> to a <u>boiling tube</u>. Put the tube in a <u>water bath</u> at 10 °C.

4) <u>Set up</u> the rest of the apparatus as shown. Add a source of <u>catalase</u> (e.g. 1 cm³ of potato) to the <u>hydrogen peroxide</u> and quickly <u>attach the bung</u>.

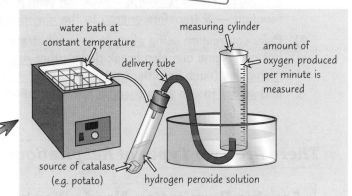

5) Record how much <u>oxygen</u> is produced in the <u>first minute</u>. <u>Repeat three times</u> and calculate the <u>mean</u>.

6) <u>Repeat</u> at 20 °C, 30 °C and 40 °C.

7) <u>Control any variables</u> (e.g. pH, the potato used, the size of potato pieces, etc.) to make it a <u>fair test</u>.

8) Calculate the <u>mean rate of reaction</u> at each temperature by <u>dividing</u> the mean <u>volume of oxygen</u> produced (in cm³) by the <u>time taken</u> (i.e. 60 s). The units will be cm³/second.

...Or How Fast a Substrate Disappears

1) The enzyme <u>amylase</u> catalyses the breakdown of <u>starch</u> to <u>maltose</u>.

2) It's easy to <u>detect starch</u> using <u>iodine solution</u> — if starch is present, the iodine solution will change from <u>browny-orange</u> to <u>blue-black</u>.

3) <u>Set up</u> the apparatus as in the diagram. Put a drop of iodine solution into <u>each well</u> on the spotting tile. Every ten seconds, <u>drop</u> a sample of the <u>mixture</u> into a well using a <u>pipette</u>. When the iodine solution <u>remains browny-orange</u> (i.e. starch is no longer present) record the total time taken.

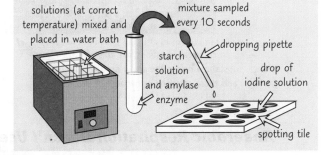

4) <u>Repeat</u> with the water bath at <u>different temperatures</u> to see how it <u>affects</u> the time taken for the starch to be broken down. Remember to <u>control</u> all of the <u>variables</u> each time.

You could improve the <u>accuracy</u> of this experiment by using a <u>colorimeter</u> — a piece of electronic equipment that measures the <u>strength</u> of a <u>coloured solution</u> so measurements <u>aren't</u> just based on somebody's <u>judgement</u> of when the colour has changed.

Mad scientists — they're experi-mental...

The key thing with experiments is to only change the thing you're testing — and absolutely nothing else. Sorted.

Q1 An enzyme-controlled reaction was carried out at 25 °C. After 60 seconds, 33 cm³ of product had been released. Calculate the rate of reaction in cm³/second. [1 mark]

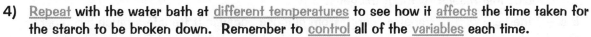

Respiration

You need energy to keep your body going. Energy comes from food, and it's transferred by respiration. This page and the following one cover two types of respiration — aerobic and anaerobic.

Respiration is NOT "Breathing In and Out"

1) Respiration is the process of transferring energy from the breakdown of glucose (a sugar). It goes on in every cell in all living organisms, all the time — it's a universal chemical process.

2) The energy transferred by respiration can't be used directly by cells — so it's used to make a substance called ATP. ATP stores the energy needed for many cell processes.

3) Respiration is controlled by enzymes, so the rate of respiration is affected by both temperature and pH (see p.16). It's an exothermic reaction — it transfers energy to the environment (by heat).

4) Cells can respire using glucose as a substrate, but organisms can also break down other organic molecules (such as other carbohydrates, proteins and lipids) to use as substrates for respiration.

Carbohydrates, proteins and lipids are all biological molecules (see page 20). They're organic because they contain carbon.

There Are Two Types of Respiration:

In eukaryotic cells, respiration takes place in the mitochondria.

Aerobic Respiration Needs Plenty of Oxygen

1) Aerobic respiration is what happens when there's plenty of oxygen available.

2) "Aerobic" just means "with oxygen" and it's the most efficient way to transfer energy from glucose. Aerobic respiration produces lots of ATP — 32 molecules per molecule of glucose.

3) This is the type of respiration that you're using most of the time.

4) Here is the equation for aerobic respiration:

$$\text{glucose} + \text{oxygen} \longrightarrow \text{carbon dioxide} + \text{water}$$
$$C_6H_{12}O_6 + 6O_2 \longrightarrow 6CO_2 + 6H_2O$$

In chemical equations, like this one, the substances before the arrow are the reactants and those after the arrow are the products.

Anaerobic Respiration Doesn't Use Oxygen At All

1) "Anaerobic" just means "without oxygen".

2) It's not the best way to transfer energy from glucose because it transfers much less energy per glucose molecule than aerobic respiration — just 2 molecules of ATP are produced.

3) The process of anaerobic respiration is slightly different in different organisms. See the next page for how it works in both animals, plants and fungi.

Respiration transfers energy — but this page has worn me out...

Thank goodness for respiration — transferring the energy stored in my tea and biscuits to my brain cells. Great.

Q1   Give the word equation for aerobic respiration.   [2 marks]

More on Respiration

Now more on the second type of respiration — anaerobic respiration. If you've ever really felt 'the burn' while you're exercising you're about to find out why. See, biology can actually be really interesting...

Animals Produce Lactic Acid During Anaerobic Respiration...

1) When you do really vigorous exercise your body can't supply enough oxygen to your muscles for aerobic respiration — even though your heart rate and breathing rate increase as much as they can. Your muscles have to start respiring anaerobically as well.

2) In anaerobic respiration, the glucose is only partially broken down, and lactic acid is also produced. All animals that respire anaerobically produce lactic acid by the same process. This is the word equation for anaerobic respiration in animals:

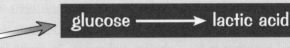

glucose ⟶ lactic acid

3) The lactic acid builds up in the muscles, which gets painful and makes your muscles fatigued.

4) The advantage is that at least you can keep on using your muscles.

5) After resorting to anaerobic respiration, when you stop exercising you'll have an oxygen debt. Basically you need extra oxygen to break down all the lactic acid that's built up and to allow aerobic respiration to begin again. So you need to keep breathing hard for a while.

...While Plants and Fungi Produce Ethanol and Carbon Dioxide

1) Under certain conditions plants may also have to resort to anaerobic respiration, e.g. in waterlogged soil (where there is little or no oxygen) plant root cells respire anaerobically.

2) Some fungi (such as yeast) can respire anaerobically too.

3) Anaerobic respiration in plants and fungi produces ethanol and carbon dioxide instead of lactic acid. This is the word equation:

glucose ⟶ ethanol + carbon dioxide

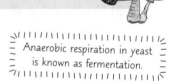

Anaerobic respiration in yeast is known as fermentation.

You Need to Compare Aerobic and Anaerobic Respiration

This handy table shows the differences and similarities between aerobic and anaerobic respiration:

	Aerobic	Anaerobic
Conditions	Oxygen present	Not enough oxygen present, e.g. during vigorous exercise, in waterlogged soils
Substrate	Glucose (or another organic molecule)	
Products	Carbon dioxide and water	In animals — lactic acid. In plants and some fungi (e.g. yeast) — ethanol and carbon dioxide
Energy transferred	Lots — 32 ATP made	Much less — 2 ATP made

My friend Anne O'Robic is rather odd — I only see her at the gym...

Make sure you know those word equations and can compare the processes of aerobic and anaerobic respiration.

Q1   Name the product(s) of anaerobic respiration in plants. [1 mark]

Q2   Why is it advantageous for organisms to respire aerobically rather than anaerobically? [1 mark]

Biological Molecules

Biological molecules are molecules found in living organisms — things like carbohydrates, proteins and lipids. They're generally long, complex molecules made up from smaller basic units.

Biological Molecules Can be Broken Down to Fuel Respiration

As you may remember from page 18, carbohydrates, proteins and lipids can be broken down so that energy can be transferred to ATP through respiration — the energy stored in ATP is then available for the cell to use. You need to know how the structures of these biological molecules are formed from their basic units:

Carbohydrates are Made up of Simple Sugars

1) Carbohydrate molecules contain the elements carbon, hydrogen and oxygen.

2) The smallest units, monomers (see page 14), are simple sugars, e.g. glucose or fructose molecules.

3) These can be joined together in long chains, polymers, to make large, complex carbohydrates, e.g. starch and glycogen.

4) The polymer molecules can be broken down back into sugars again when the chemical bonds between the monomers are broken.

5) In the body, carbohydrates are broken down (digested) by enzymes in the mouth and small intestine.

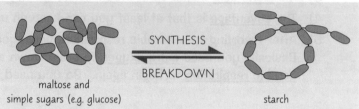

maltose and simple sugars (e.g. glucose)   starch

Proteins are Made Up of Amino Acids

1) Proteins are polymers that are made up of long chains of monomers called amino acids.

2) Amino acids all contain carbon, nitrogen, hydrogen and oxygen atoms.

3) In the body, proteins are broken down by enzymes in the stomach and small intestine.

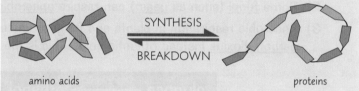

amino acids   proteins

Lipids are Made Up of Fatty Acids and Glycerol

1) Lipids (fats and oils) are made from glycerol and three fatty acids.

2) Unlike carbohydrates and proteins they are NOT polymers because they don't form a long chain of repeating units.

3) Lipids contain carbon, hydrogen and oxygen atoms.

4) In the body, lipids are broken down by enzymes in the small intestine.

When lipids are broken down, the fatty acids will make the solution they are in more acidic (it will have a lower pH).

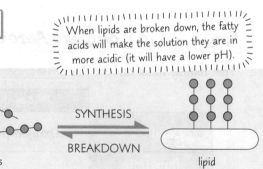

glycerol & fatty acids   lipid

What do you call an acid that's eaten all the pies...

This page isn't too bad really, once you've got the whole monomer/polymer thing sorted. But you still need to make sure you learn it properly. So look, cover and scribble 'til you can do the whole lot standing on your head.

Q1   Name the monomers that result from the breakdown of:
      a) carbohydrates,   b) proteins.   [2 marks]

Q2   Give one reason why it's important for the body to be able to break down
      large, complex molecules, such as starch.   [1 mark]

Photosynthesis

You don't know <u>photosynthesis</u> 'til you know its <u>equation</u>. It's in a nice <u>green box</u> so you can't possibly miss it.

Plants are Able to Make Their Own Food by Photosynthesis

1) During photosynthesis, <u>photosynthetic organisms</u>, such as <u>green plants</u> and <u>algae</u>, use <u>energy</u> from the Sun or an artificial source to make <u>glucose</u>.

2) Some of the glucose is used to make <u>larger</u>, <u>complex molecules</u> that the plants or algae need to <u>grow</u>. These make up the organism's <u>biomass</u> — the mass of <u>living material</u>.

3) The <u>energy stored</u> in the organisms' <u>biomass</u> then works its way through the <u>food chain</u> as animals <u>eat</u> them and each other. So ultimately, photosynthetic organisms <u>support nearly all life on Earth</u>.

4) Photosynthesis happens inside <u>chloroplasts</u> — they contain <u>chlorophyll</u> which <u>absorbs light</u>. Energy is <u>transferred</u> to the <u>chloroplasts</u> from the environment by <u>light</u>. This is the <u>equation</u> for photosynthesis:

$$\text{carbon dioxide} + \text{water} \xrightarrow[\text{chlorophyll}]{\text{LIGHT}} \text{glucose} + \text{oxygen}$$
$$6CO_2 + 6H_2O \xrightarrow[\text{chlorophyll}]{\text{LIGHT}} C_6H_{12}O_6 + 6O_2$$

5) Photosynthesis is an <u>endothermic</u> reaction — <u>energy</u> is <u>transferred</u> from the <u>environment</u> during it.

6) Photosynthesis actually happens in <u>two main stages</u>. First, energy transferred by <u>light</u> is used to split <u>water</u> into <u>oxygen gas</u> and <u>hydrogen ions</u>.

7) <u>Carbon dioxide gas</u> then combines with the <u>hydrogen ions</u> to make <u>glucose</u>.

Oxygen Production Shows the Rate of Photosynthesis   PRACTICAL

1) The rate of photosynthesis is affected by <u>light intensity</u>, <u>concentration of CO_2</u> and <u>temperature</u>. Any of these three factors can become the <u>limiting factor</u>. This just means that it's stopping photosynthesis from happening any <u>faster</u>.

2) You can <u>investigate</u> how each of the different factors affect the <u>rate of photosynthesis</u>. A classic way to do this is to use <u>pondweed</u> and to measure <u>oxygen production</u>.

3) The rate at which the pondweed produces <u>oxygen</u> corresponds to the rate at which it's photosynthesising — the <u>faster</u> the rate of oxygen production, the <u>faster</u> the rate of photosynthesis.

4) The box below describes the <u>basic method</u> you could use — the ways in which you could <u>alter</u> the experiment to <u>test the different factors</u> are described on the next page.

1) The experiment is <u>set up</u> as shown in the <u>diagram</u>.

2) The pondweed is left to photosynthesise for a <u>set amount of time</u>. As it photosynthesises, the oxygen released will collect in the <u>capillary tube</u>.

3) At the end of the experiment, the <u>syringe</u> is used to draw the gas bubble in the tube up alongside a ruler and the <u>length</u> of the <u>gas bubble</u> is <u>measured</u>. This is <u>proportional</u> to the <u>volume of O_2</u> produced.

4) The experiment is then <u>repeated</u> to test a <u>range</u> of values for the <u>factor being investigated</u>, e.g. a range of different temperatures.

5) Variables other than the one being investigated should be kept the <u>same</u>, e.g. the other limiting factors, the time the pondweed is left for.

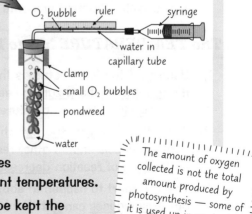

The amount of oxygen collected is not the total amount produced by photosynthesis — some of it is used up in respiration.

I'm working on sunshine — woah oh...

You could also measure how much oxygen's produced by counting the bubbles — fun, but it's not as accurate.

Q1 Explain how photosynthesis contributes to a plant's biomass.   [2 marks]

The Rate of Photosynthesis

Before you start on this page, make sure you've read the photosynthesis experiment from the last page. OK...

Three Important Graphs for Rate of Photosynthesis

Not Enough LIGHT Slows Down the Rate of Photosynthesis

1) Light transfers the energy needed for photosynthesis.

2) As the light level is raised, the rate of photosynthesis increases steadily — but only up to a certain point.

3) Beyond that, it won't make any difference — it'll be either the temperature or the CO_2 level which is the limiting factor.

4) In the lab you can investigate light intensity by moving a lamp closer to or further away from your plant.

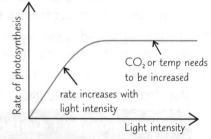

5) But if you just plot the rate of photosynthesis against "distance of lamp from the plant", you get a weird-shaped graph. To get a graph like the one above you either need to measure the light intensity at the plant using a light meter or do a bit of nifty maths with your results. Here's why:

The distance from the lamp and light intensity are inversely proportional to each other — this means that as the distance increases, the light intensity decreases. However, light intensity decreases in proportion to the square of the distance. This is called the inverse square law and is written like this:

Putting one over the distance shows the inverse.

$$\text{light intensity (i)} \propto \frac{1}{\text{distance (d)}^2}$$

Halving the distance → intensity is 2×2 = 4 times greater
Tripling the distance → intensity is 3×3 = 9 times smaller

Too Little CARBON DIOXIDE Also Slows it Down

1) CO_2 is one of the raw materials needed for photosynthesis.

2) As with light intensity the concentration of CO_2 will only increase the rate of photosynthesis up to a point. After this the graph flattens out showing that CO_2 is no longer the limiting factor.

3) As long as light and CO_2 are in plentiful supply then the factor limiting photosynthesis must be temperature.

4) There are loads of different ways to control the concentration of CO_2. E.g. dissolve different amounts of sodium hydrogen-carbonate (which gives off CO_2) in the water.

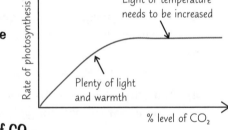

The TEMPERATURE has to be Just Right

1) Usually, if the temperature is the limiting factor it's because it's too low — the enzymes needed for photosynthesis work more slowly at low temperatures.

2) But if the plant gets too hot, the enzymes it needs for photosynthesis and its other reactions will be denatured — the rate of reaction decreases dramatically.

3) This can start to happen at about 45 °C (pretty hot for outdoors, but greenhouses can get that hot if you're not careful).

4) Experimentally, the best way to control the temperature of a boiling tube is to put it in a water bath.

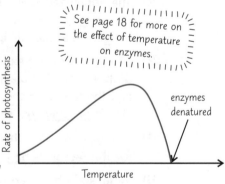

Don't blame it on the sunshine, don't blame it on the CO_2...

...don't blame it on the temperature, blame it on the plant. And now you'll never forget these three limiting factors. in photosynthesis. No... well, make sure you read these pages over and over again 'til you're sure you won't.

Q1   Explain the effect of increasing temperature on the rate of photosynthesis.   [4 marks]

Revision Questions for Topic B1

Well, that's Topic B1 covered — time to see how much stayed in and didn't go in one eye and out the other.

- Try these questions and tick off each one when you get it right.
- When you've done all the questions under a heading and are completely happy with it, tick it off.

Cells and Microscopy (p11-13) ☑

1) List four features that animal and plant cells have in common. ☑
2) Give two sub-cellular structures that are present in prokaryotic cells but not eukaryotic cells. ☑
3) How have electron microscopes been able to increase our understanding of sub-cellular structures? ☑
4) Why is it important to take a thin slice of a sample before viewing it under a light microscope? ☑
5) How can you calculate the magnification of an image if you don't know which lenses were used? ☑

DNA (p14) ☑

6) Give the initials of the four bases present in DNA. ☑
7) Describe the structure of a nucleotide. ☑
8) What is a gene? ☑

Enzymes (p15-17) ☑

9) Draw a diagram to show how the 'lock and key' mechanism of enzymes works. ☑
10) What does it mean when an enzyme has been 'denatured'? ☑
11) Sketch a graph to show how substrate concentration affects the rate of an enzyme-controlled reaction. ☑
12) Give two things that you could measure when investigating the rate of an enzyme-controlled reaction. ☑
13) Give two variables that need controlling when investigating the effect of pH on an enzyme-controlled reaction. ☑

Respiration (p18-19) ☐

14) What is respiration? ☑
15) What is the function of ATP in a cell? ☑
16) Is respiration an exothermic or an endothermic reaction? ☑
17) Name the type of respiration that requires oxygen. ☑
18) Give an example of when lactic acid would be produced as a product of respiration. ☑
19) Which form of respiration transfers more energy per glucose molecule? ☑

Biological Molecules (p20) ☐

20) What type of polymer do you get when you join together simple sugars? ☑
21) What type of biological molecule are oils? ☑
22) Name the basic units that lipids are made from. ☑

Photosynthesis (p21-22) ☑

23) In what part of a cell does photosynthesis take place? ☑
24) Give three factors that can limit the rate of photosynthesis. ☑
25) Describe how you could investigate the effect of CO_2 concentration on the rate of photosynthesis. ☑

The Cell Cycle and Mitosis

Your cells have to be able to <u>divide</u> for your body to <u>grow</u>. And that means your <u>DNA</u> has to be <u>copied</u>...

New Cells are Needed for Growth and Repair

The cells of your body <u>divide</u> to <u>produce more cells</u>, so your body can <u>grow</u> and <u>replace</u> damaged cells.
Cells <u>grow</u> and <u>divide</u> over and over again — this is called the <u>cell cycle</u>. Of course, cell division doesn't
just happen in humans — animals and plants do it too. There are <u>two main parts</u>:

First the cell physically grows and replicates its contents...

The period of <u>cell growth</u> and <u>replication of its contents</u> is divided up into <u>three</u> separate growth stages.
These are called <u>G_1</u>, <u>S</u> and <u>G_2</u>:

Here's how the <u>DNA</u> is <u>replicated</u> during '<u>S</u>' (<u>synthesis</u>):

MITOSIS
(see below)
the cycle starts
and ends here

GAP PHASE 2
cell keeps growing
and proteins needed
for cell division
are made

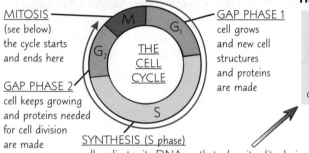

THE CELL CYCLE

GAP PHASE 1
cell grows
and new cell
structures
and proteins
are made

SYNTHESIS (S phase)
cell replicates its DNA, so that when it splits during
mitosis the two new cells will contain identical DNA

Molecule of DNA splits.

Bases on free-floating nucleotides pair up with matching bases on the DNA.

Cross links form between the new nucleotide bases (pink) and the old DNA bases (green), and the new nucleotides join together. So two new DNA molecules identical to the original one are formed.

See page 14 to remind yourself of the structure of DNA.

...then it splits into two by Mitosis

<u>Mitosis</u> is when a cell reproduces itself <u>by splitting</u> to form <u>two identical offspring</u>.

The cell has <u>two copies</u> of its DNA all spread out in <u>long strings</u>.

Before the cell <u>divides</u>, the DNA forms <u>X-shaped</u> chromosomes. Each 'arm' of a chromosome is an <u>exact copy</u> of the other.

Chromosomes are long lengths of coiled DNA — see page 49.

The left arm has the same DNA as the right arm of the chromosome.

The chromosomes then <u>line up</u> at the centre of the cell and <u>cell fibres</u> pull them apart. The <u>two arms</u> of each chromosome go to <u>opposite ends</u> of the cell.

<u>Membranes</u> form around each of the sets of chromosomes. These become the <u>nuclei</u> of the two new cells.

Lastly, the <u>cytoplasm</u> divides.

You now have <u>two new cells</u> containing exactly the same DNA — they're <u>genetically identical</u> to <u>each other</u> and to the <u>parent cell</u>.

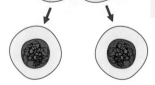

A cell's favourite computer game — divide and conquer...

This can seem tricky at first. But don't worry — just go through it slowly, one step at a time and it'll soon sink in.

Q1   Explain why a cell's DNA is replicated during the cell cycle.   [1 mark]

Q2   What is mitosis?   [1 mark]

Cell Differentiation and Stem Cells

Multicellular organisms have lots of cells — most of these cells are specialised to do a particular job...

Most Cells are Specialised for a Specific Job

1) Differentiation is the process by which a cell changes to become specialised for its job.

2) In most animal cells, the ability to differentiate is lost at an early stage, but lots of plant cells don't ever lose this ability.

3) Having specialised cells is important — it allows organisms to work more efficiently.

4) Most cells are specialised to carry out a particular job. For example:

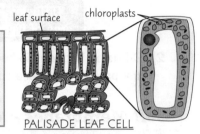

leaf surface   chloroplasts

PALISADE LEAF CELLS Palisade leaf cells do most of the photosynthesis in plants, so they are packed with chloroplasts (see p.11). Their tall shape means they have a lot of surface area exposed down the side for absorbing CO_2 from the air in the leaf, and their thin shape means that you can fit loads of them in at the top of a leaf, so they're nearer the light.

PALISADE LEAF CELL

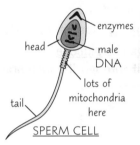

head   enzymes   male DNA   lots of mitochondria here   tail

SPERM CELL

SPERM The function of sperm is basically to get the male DNA to the female DNA during reproduction (see page 51). Sperm have long tails and streamlined heads to help them swim, they contain lots of mitochondria to provide them with energy, and they have enzymes in their heads to digest through the egg cell membrane.

5) In multicellular organisms, specialised cells are grouped together to form tissues — groups of cells working together to perform a particular function. Different tissues work together to form organs. Different organs make up an organ system.

Stem Cells can Differentiate into Different Types of Cells

1) Stem cells are undifferentiated. Depending on what instructions they're given, they can divide by mitosis to become new cells, which then differentiate.

2) Embryonic stem cells are found in early human embryos. They have the potential to turn into any kind of cell at all. This makes sense if you think about it — all the different types of cell found in a human being have to come from those few cells in the early embryo.

3) This means stem cells are really important for the growth and development of organisms.

4) Adults also have stem cells, but they're only found in certain places, like bone marrow. These aren't as versatile as embryonic stem cells — they can't turn into any cell type at all, only certain ones from the tissue they originally came from.

5) In animals, adult stem cells are used to replace damaged cells, e.g. to make new skin or blood cells.

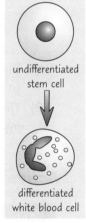

undifferentiated stem cell

differentiated white blood cell

Meristems Contain Plant Stem Cells

1) In plants, the only cells that divide by mitosis are found in plant tissues called meristems.

2) Meristem tissue is found in the areas of a plant that are growing — such as the roots and shoots.

3) Meristems produce unspecialised cells that are able to divide and form any cell type in the plant — they act like embryonic stem cells. But unlike human stem cells, these cells can divide to generate any type of cell for as long as the plant lives.

4) The unspecialised cells can become specialised and form tissues like xylem and phloem (see page 34).

Cheery cells, those merry-stems...

Turns out stem cells are pretty nifty. Now, let's see if you're specialised to answer this question...

Q1   What is differentiation?   [1 mark]

Diffusion and Active Transport

Substances need to move <u>in</u> and <u>out</u> of cells, through the <u>cell membrane</u>. <u>Diffusion</u> and <u>active transport</u> are <u>two</u> of the ways that this can happen. There's also <u>osmosis too</u> — see the next page.

Diffusion is the Movement of Particles from Higher to Lower Concentration

1) <u>Diffusion</u> is simple. It's just the <u>gradual movement</u> of particles from places where there are <u>lots</u> of them to places where there are <u>fewer</u> of them. That's all it is — just the <u>natural tendency</u> for stuff to <u>spread out</u>. Here's the fancy <u>definition</u>:

> Diffusion is the <u>net (overall) movement</u> of <u>particles</u> from an area of <u>higher concentration</u> to an area of <u>lower concentration</u>.

If something moves from an area of higher concentration to an area of lower concentration it is said to have moved down its concentration gradient.

2) Diffusion happens in both <u>liquids</u> and <u>gases</u> — that's because the particles in these substances are free to <u>move about</u> randomly.

Cell Membranes are Pretty Clever

1) They're clever because they <u>hold</u> the cell together <u>but</u> they let stuff <u>in and out</u> as well.

2) Substances can move in and out of cells by <u>diffusion</u>, <u>active transport</u> and <u>osmosis</u> (see next page).

3) Only very <u>small</u> molecules can <u>diffuse</u> through cell membranes though — things like <u>glucose</u>, <u>amino acids</u>, <u>water</u> and <u>oxygen</u>. Big molecules like <u>starch</u> and <u>proteins</u> can't fit through the membrane.

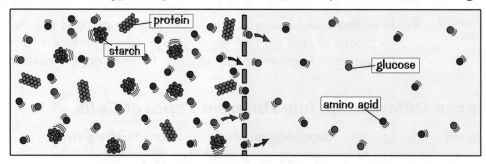

1) Particles move through the cell membrane from where there's a <u>higher concentration</u> (more of them) to where there's a <u>lower concentration</u> (not such a lot of them).

2) They're only moving about <u>randomly</u> of course, so they go <u>both</u> ways — but if there are a lot <u>more</u> particles on one side of the membrane, there's a <u>net</u> (overall) movement <u>from</u> that side.

Active Transport is the Opposite of Diffusion

> <u>Active transport</u> is the <u>movement of particles</u> across a membrane against a concentration gradient (i.e. from an area of <u>lower</u> to an area of <u>higher concentration</u>) <u>using ATP</u> released during respiration.

Here's an example of active transport at work in the <u>digestive system</u>:

1) When there's a <u>higher concentration</u> of nutrients in the gut they <u>diffuse naturally</u> into the blood.

2) <u>BUT</u> — sometimes there's a <u>lower concentration</u> of nutrients in the gut than in the blood.

3) Active transport allows nutrients to be taken into the blood, despite the fact that the <u>concentration gradient</u> is the wrong way. This is essential to stop us starving. But active transport needs <u>ATP</u> from <u>respiration</u> (see p. 18) to make it work.

diffusion

active transport

<u>Plants</u> use active transport to obtain the <u>minerals</u> they need from the soil (see p.30).

Revision by diffusion — you wish...

Hopefully there'll have been a net movement of information from this page into your brain...

Q1   What is: a) diffusion   b) active transport?   [3 marks]

Osmosis

If you've got your head round <u>diffusion</u>, osmosis will be a <u>breeze</u>. If not, have a read of the previous page...

Osmosis is a Special Case of Diffusion, That's All

> <u>Osmosis</u> is the <u>net movement of water molecules</u> across a <u>partially permeable membrane</u> from a region of <u>higher water concentration</u> to a region of <u>lower water concentration</u>.

1) A <u>partially permeable</u> membrane is just one with very small holes in it. Only tiny <u>molecules</u> (like <u>water</u>) can pass through them, and bigger molecules (e.g. <u>sucrose</u>) can't. A <u>cell membrane</u> is a <u>partially permeable</u> membrane.

2) The water molecules actually pass <u>both ways</u> through the membrane during osmosis. This happens because water molecules <u>move about randomly</u> all the time.

3) But because there are <u>more</u> water molecules on one side than on the other, there's a steady <u>net flow</u> of water into the region with <u>fewer</u> water molecules, e.g. into the <u>sucrose</u> solution.

4) This means the <u>sucrose</u> solution gets more <u>dilute</u>. The water acts like it's trying to <u>even up</u> the concentration either side of the membrane.

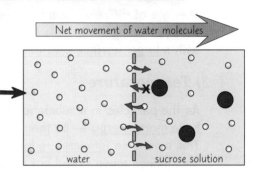

Net movement of water molecules

water   sucrose solution

I'm telling you, I've got great potential...

Water Potential Tells You How Concentrated a Solution is

1) You can talk about osmosis in terms of <u>water potential</u> — <u>water potential</u> is the <u>potential</u> (likelihood) of <u>water molecules</u> to diffuse <u>out of</u> or <u>into</u> a solution.

2) If a solution has a <u>high</u> water potential, then it has a <u>high concentration</u> of water molecules. If it has a <u>low</u> water potential, then it has a <u>low concentration</u> of water molecules.

3) So, you can say that <u>osmosis</u> is the <u>diffusion</u> of <u>water molecules</u> across a <u>partially permeable membrane</u> down a <u>water potential gradient</u> (i.e. from an area of <u>higher water potential</u> to an area of <u>lower water potential</u>).

> Pure water has the highest water potential. All solutions have a lower water potential than pure water.

Plants Are Supported by Turgid Cells

1) Watering a plant <u>increases</u> the <u>water potential</u> of the soil around it. This means that all the plant cells draw water in by <u>osmosis</u> until they become <u>turgid</u> (plump and swollen). The contents of the cell push against the cell wall — this is called <u>turgor pressure</u>. Turgor pressure helps <u>support</u> the plant tissues.

2) If there's no water in the soil, a plant starts to <u>wilt</u> (droop). This is because the cells become <u>flaccid</u> — they start to lose water. The plant doesn't totally lose its shape though, because the <u>inelastic cell wall</u> keeps things in position. It just droops a bit.

3) <u>Animal cells</u> don't have <u>cell walls</u> so they're <u>more bothered</u> by their <u>surroundings</u> — e.g. cells can <u>burst</u> if they're surrounded by a solution with a <u>higher water potential</u> than them.

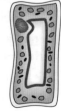

Turgid Cell   Flaccid Cell

Try saying osmosis backwards — it's not that fun, or educational...

Osmosis is why it's bad to drink sea water. The high salt content means you end up with a much lower water concentration in your blood and tissue fluid than in your cells. Lots of water moves out of your cells by osmosis, which makes them shrivel and die. So next time you're stranded at sea, remember this page...

Q1   Define osmosis.   [1 mark]

Q2   A piece of carrot is placed in a solution of lower water potential than its cells.
      Suggest what will happen to the piece of carrot. Explain your answer.   [2 marks]

Exchanging Substances

Now you know about how <u>substances</u> move, you need to know <u>how</u> they get to <u>where they're needed</u>...

Three Main Factors Affect The Movement of Substances

The <u>rates</u> of diffusion, osmosis and active transport <u>vary</u> — they're affected by these <u>three factors</u>:

1) Surface Area to Volume Ratio

The <u>rate</u> of diffusion, osmosis and active transport is <u>higher</u> in cells (or cubes) with a <u>larger surface area to volume ratio</u>.

2) Temperature

As the particles in a substance get <u>warmer</u> they have <u>more energy</u> — so they <u>move faster</u>. This means as <u>temperature increases</u>, substances move in and out of cells <u>faster</u>.

3) Concentration Gradient

Substances move in and out of a cell <u>faster</u> if there's a <u>big difference in concentration</u> between the inside and outside of the cell. If there are <u>lots more</u> particles on one side, there are more there to <u>move across</u>.

EXAMPLE:

Calculate the surface area to volume ratio of the cubes on the right.

Surface area (cm^2)	2 x 2 x 6 = 24	3 x 3 x 6 = 54
Volume (cm^3)	2 x 2 x 2 = 8	3 x 3 x 3 = 27
Surface area to volume ratio	24 : 8 = <u>3 : 1</u>	54 : 27 = <u>2 : 1</u>

The smaller cube has a larger surface area to volume ratio. This means substances would move into and out of this cube faster.

You might also see ratios written as fractions, e.g. 2/1, or as a single number, e.g. 54 ÷ 27 = 2 cm^{-1}.

This only increases the rate of diffusion and osmosis — concentration gradients don't affect the rate of active transport.

Exchanging Substances is Trickier in Multicellular Organisms

1) An organism needs to <u>supply</u> all its <u>cells</u> with the substances (e.g. glucose, oxygen, water, etc.) it needs to live (e.g. for processes like respiration and photosynthesis). It also needs to <u>get rid of waste products</u>. E.g:

> 1) Proteins can't be <u>stored</u> by the body — so any <u>excess amino acids</u> are converted in the <u>liver</u> into <u>fats</u> and <u>carbohydrates</u>, which can be stored.
>
> 2) <u>Urea</u> is produced as a <u>waste product</u> from the reactions.
>
> 3) Urea is <u>poisonous</u> so it needs to be <u>removed</u> from the body.

Urea is filtered out of the blood by the kidneys and removed from the body in the urine.

2) <u>Single-celled</u> organisms exchange substances differently to <u>multicellular</u> organisms. As they're only one cell big, substances can <u>diffuse straight into</u> and <u>out of</u> single-celled organisms <u>across</u> the <u>cell membrane</u>. Diffusion is <u>quite quick</u> because:

- Substances only have to <u>travel</u> a <u>short distance</u>.
- Single-celled organisms have a <u>relatively large</u> surface area to volume ratio — this means they're able to exchange <u>enough substances</u> across their cell membrane to supply the volume of the cell.

3) In <u>multicellular organisms</u> it is more <u>difficult</u> to <u>exchange substances</u>. Diffusion across the outer membrane is <u>too slow</u> because:

- Some cells are <u>deep inside</u> the organism — it's a <u>long way</u> from them to the <u>outside environment</u>.
- <u>Larger organisms</u> have a <u>low surface area to volume ratio</u> — it's difficult to exchange enough substances to <u>supply</u> a <u>large volume of organism</u> through a relatively <u>small outer surface</u>.

4) So instead of exchanging substances through their outer membrane, multicellular organisms need <u>specialised exchange organs</u>, each with a <u>specialised exchange surface</u> — see next page.

5) They also need <u>transport systems</u> to <u>carry materials</u> from the <u>exchange organs</u> to the body cells, and to <u>remove waste products</u>. In <u>animals</u>, the transport system is the <u>circulatory system</u> (see p.31). In <u>plants</u>, it's the <u>xylem</u> and <u>phloem vessels</u> (see p.34).

If you're bored, work out the surface area : volume of a loved one...

Time to exchange any useless facts stored in your brain with the information on this page. Then try this question...

Q1   Calculate the surface area : volume ratio of a cube with sides measuring 5 cm.   [1 mark]

Exchange Surfaces

The next couple of pages are all about how <u>exchange surfaces</u> found in different <u>multicellular organisms</u> are <u>adapted</u> so that substances can move through them <u>effectively</u>. It's exciting stuff, I promise you...

Exchange Surfaces have Adaptations to Maximise Exchange

The exchange surfaces in <u>specialised exchange organs</u> are <u>adapted</u> to maximise effectiveness:

- They are <u>thin</u>, so substances only have a <u>short distance</u> to <u>travel</u>.
- They have a <u>large surface area</u>, so <u>lots</u> of a substance can <u>move</u> at once.
- Exchange surfaces in <u>animals</u> have <u>lots of blood vessels</u>, to get stuff into and out of the blood quickly.
- <u>Gas exchange surfaces</u> in animals (e.g. alveoli, see below) are often <u>ventilated</u> too — air moves in and out.

For information about why exchange surfaces are needed see previous page.

Here are a few <u>examples</u> of exchange surfaces found in <u>multicellular organisms</u>. First up, the <u>alveoli</u>...

Gas Exchange Happens in the Lungs

1) The job of the lungs is to transfer <u>oxygen</u> to the <u>blood</u> and to remove <u>waste carbon dioxide</u> from it.

2) To do this the lungs contain millions of little air sacs called <u>alveoli</u> where <u>gas exchange</u> takes place.

3) The alveoli are specialised to maximise the <u>diffusion</u> of <u>oxygen</u> (O_2) and <u>carbon dioxide</u> (CO_2). They have:

- An <u>enormous</u> surface area (about 75 m² in humans).
- Very <u>thin walls</u>.
- A <u>moist lining</u> for dissolving gases.
- A <u>good blood supply</u>.

4) The <u>blood</u> passing next to the alveoli has just <u>returned</u> to the <u>lungs</u> from the rest of the body via the heart (see p.31), so it contains <u>lots of CO_2</u> and <u>very little oxygen</u>.

5) <u>CO_2</u> diffuses <u>out</u> of the <u>blood</u> (higher concentration) <u>into the alveolus</u> (lower concentration) to be breathed out.

6) <u>Oxygen</u> diffuses <u>out</u> of the <u>alveolus</u> (higher concentration) <u>into the blood</u> (lower concentration).

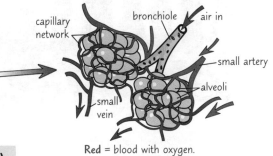

capillary network
bronchiole — air in
small artery
alveoli
small vein

Red = blood with oxygen.
Blue = blood with carbon dioxide.

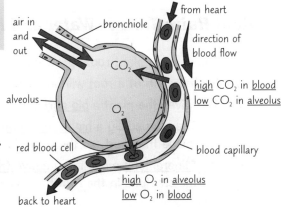

air in and out
bronchiole
from heart
direction of blood flow
CO_2
high CO_2 in <u>blood</u>
low CO_2 in <u>alveolus</u>
alveolus
O_2
red blood cell
blood capillary
high O_2 in <u>alveolus</u>
low O_2 in <u>blood</u>
back to heart

The Villi Provide a Really Big Surface Area

1) The <u>small intestine</u> is where <u>dissolved food molecules</u> are <u>absorbed</u> out of the digestive system and into the <u>blood</u>.

2) The inside of the <u>small intestine</u> is covered in millions and millions of tiny little projections called <u>villi</u>.

3) They increase the surface area in a big way so that dissolved food molecules are <u>absorbed</u> much more quickly into the <u>blood</u>. They have:

- A <u>single</u> layer of surface cells.
- A very good <u>blood supply</u> to assist <u>quick absorption</u>.

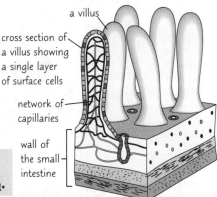

a villus
cross section of a villus showing a single layer of surface cells
network of capillaries
wall of the small intestine

Al Veoli — the Italian gas man...

Don't turn over 'til you've learnt exactly how these specialised surfaces help to maximise exchange.

Q1   Explain why it is beneficial for an exchange surface to be just one cell thick.   [1 mark]

More on Exchange Surfaces

All the stuff about <u>maximising the exchange</u> of substances from the previous page applies to <u>plants</u> too...

Leaves are Adapted for Efficient Gas Exchange

When plants <u>photosynthesise</u> they <u>use up CO$_2$</u> from the atmosphere and <u>produce oxygen</u> as a waste product. When plants <u>respire</u> they <u>use up oxygen</u> and <u>produce CO$_2$</u> as a waste product. So there are lots of gases moving to and fro in plants, and this movement happens by <u>diffusion</u>.

E.g. when the plant is photosynthesising it uses up lots of <u>CO$_2$</u>, so there's hardly any inside the leaf. This makes <u>more</u> CO$_2$ move into the leaf by <u>diffusion</u> (from an area of <u>higher</u> concentration to an area of <u>lower</u> concentration).

Leaves are <u>specialised</u> to maximise the diffusion of <u>O$_2$</u> and <u>CO$_2$</u>:

1) Leaves are <u>broad</u>, so there's a <u>large surface area</u> for <u>diffusion</u>.

2) They're also <u>thin</u>, which means <u>gases</u> only have to travel a <u>short distance</u>.

There's more about respiration on p.18-19 and more about photosynthesis on p.21-22.

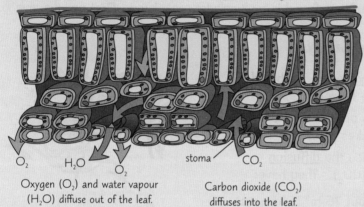

Oxygen (O$_2$) and water vapour (H$_2$O) diffuse out of the leaf.

Carbon dioxide (CO$_2$) diffuses into the leaf.

3) There are <u>air spaces</u> inside the leaf. This lets gases like CO$_2$ and O$_2$ move easily between cells. It also increases the surface area for <u>gas exchange</u>.

4) The lower surface is full of little holes called <u>stomata</u> (see p.35). They're there to let gases like <u>CO$_2$</u> and <u>O$_2$</u> diffuse in and out. They also allow <u>water</u> to escape — which is known as <u>transpiration</u> (see p.34).

Root Hairs Take in Water and Mineral Ions

1) The cells on plant roots grow into long 'hairs' which stick out into the soil.

2) Each branch of a root will be covered in <u>millions</u> of these microscopic hairs.

3) This gives the plant a <u>big surface area</u> for absorbing <u>water</u> and <u>mineral ions</u> from the soil:

   • There's usually a <u>higher concentration</u> of water in the soil than there is inside the plant, so the water is drawn into the root hair cell by <u>osmosis</u>.

   • <u>Mineral ions</u> move in by <u>active transport</u>, since the <u>concentration</u> of mineral ions in the root hair cells is usually <u>higher</u> than in the soil.

Molecules can only cross a membrane when they're right next to it, so a large surface area means loads more molecules are close to the membrane.

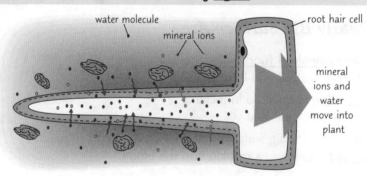

water molecule

mineral ions

root hair cell

mineral ions and water move into plant

Thirsty? Go dip your hair in your drink...

Living organisms are really well adapted for getting the substances they need to their cells.
Now that you've seen loads of examples of how exchange surfaces are adapted, these questions should be a breeze...

Q1   Give three ways that leaves are specialised to maximise the diffusion of O$_2$ and CO$_2$.   [3 marks]

Q2   How are plant roots adapted to be able to absorb lots of water and mineral ions from the soil?   [2 marks]

The Circulatory System

As you saw on page 28, multicellular organisms need transport systems to move substances around effectively. In humans, it's the job of the circulatory system. My heart's all of a flutter just thinking about it...

The DOUBLE Circulatory System, Actually

The circulatory system is made up of the heart, blood vessels and blood.
Humans have a double circulatory system — two circuits joined together:

1) In the first one, the heart pumps deoxygenated blood (blood without oxygen) to the gas exchange surfaces in the lungs to take in oxygen. The oxygenated blood then returns to the heart.

2) In the second one, the heart pumps oxygenated blood around all the other organs of the body. The blood gives up its oxygen at the body cells (see page 33) and the deoxygenated blood returns to the heart to be pumped out to the lungs again.

3) Not all animals have a double circulatory system — fish don't, for example.

4) There are advantages to mammals having a double circulatory system though:

- Returning the blood to the heart after it's picked up oxygen at the lungs means it can be pumped out around the body at a much higher pressure.

- This increases the rate of blood flow to the tissues (i.e. blood can be pumped around the body much faster), so more oxygen can be delivered to the cells.

- This is important for mammals because they use up a lot of oxygen maintaining their body temperature.

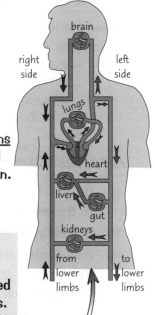

The diagram shows the right and left side of the person in the diagram, not your right and left as you look at them.

The Heart Pumps Blood Around The Body

1) The heart is a pumping organ that keeps the blood flowing around the body.

2) The heart has valves to make sure that blood flows in the right direction. When the ventricles contract, the valves to the atria close and the valves to the blood vessels open. This prevents backflow (when the blood flows backwards).

Atria is plural. Atrium is when there is just one.

3) This is how the heart uses its four chambers (right and left atria and ventricles) to pump blood around:

1) Blood flows into the two atria from the vena cava and the pulmonary vein.

2) The atria contract, pushing the blood into the ventricles.

3) The ventricles contract, forcing the blood into the pulmonary artery and the aorta, and out of the heart.

4) The blood then flows to the organs through arteries, and returns through veins (see next page).

5) The atria fill again and the whole cycle starts over.

The heart is made up of cardiac muscle. These muscle cells contain loads of mitochondria to provide the cells with ATP. They also need their own blood supply to deliver the nutrients and oxygen needed to keep the heart beating continually.

Blood is supplied to the heart by two coronary arteries, which branch from the base of the aorta (the biggest artery in the body).

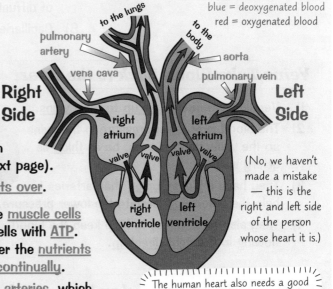

(No, we haven't made a mistake — this is the right and left side of the person whose heart it is.)

The human heart also needs a good blood supply to remove the carbon dioxide produced during respiration.

Okay — let's get to the heart of the matter...

Make sure you learn the names of the different parts of the heart and all the blood vessels that are attached to it.

Q1   Which chamber of the heart pumps deoxygenated blood to the lungs?   [1 mark]

The Blood Vessels

If you want to know more about the circulatory system you're in luck. Because here's a whole extra page.

Blood Vessels are Designed for Their Function

There are three main types of blood vessel:

1) **ARTERIES** — these carry the blood <u>away</u> from the heart.
2) **CAPILLARIES** — these are involved in the <u>exchange of materials</u> at the tissues.
3) **VEINS** — these carry the blood <u>to</u> the heart.

Arteries and veins <u>don't</u> lead straight into capillaries. <u>Arteries</u> branch into <u>arterioles</u>, which are much smaller than arteries. <u>Arterioles</u> then branch into <u>capillaries</u>. The <u>capillaries</u> connect to <u>venules</u>, which join together to form <u>veins</u>.

Arteries Carry Blood Under Pressure

1) The heart pumps the blood out at <u>high pressure</u> so the artery walls are <u>strong</u> and <u>elastic</u>.
2) The walls are <u>thick</u> compared to the size of the <u>lumen</u>.
3) They contain thick layers of <u>muscle</u> to make them <u>strong</u>, and <u>elastic fibres</u> to allow them to stretch and <u>spring back</u>.
4) Arteries branch into <u>arterioles</u>.

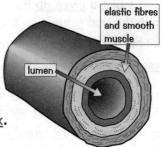

elastic fibres and smooth muscle

lumen

The lumen is just the hole down the middle — silly name.

Capillaries are Really Small

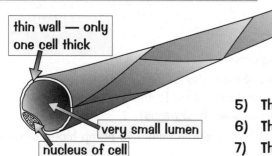

thin wall — only one cell thick

very small lumen

nucleus of cell

1) Arterioles branch into <u>capillaries</u>.
2) Capillaries are really <u>tiny</u> — too small to see.
3) <u>Networks of capillaries</u> in tissue are called <u>capillary beds</u>.
4) Capillaries carry the blood <u>really close</u> to <u>every cell</u> in the body to <u>exchange substances</u> with them.
5) They have <u>permeable</u> walls, so substances can <u>diffuse</u> in and out.
6) They supply <u>food</u> and <u>oxygen</u>, and take away <u>waste</u> like CO_2.
7) Their walls are usually <u>only one cell thick</u>. This <u>increases</u> the rate of diffusion by <u>decreasing</u> the <u>distance</u> over which it occurs.
8) Capillaries branch into <u>venules</u>.

Veins Take Blood Back to the Heart

1) Venules eventually <u>join up</u> to form <u>veins</u>.
2) The blood is at <u>lower pressure</u> in the veins so the walls don't need to be as <u>thick</u> as artery walls.
3) They have a <u>bigger lumen</u> than arteries to help the blood <u>flow</u> despite the lower pressure.
4) They also have <u>valves</u> to help keep the blood flowing in the <u>right direction</u>.

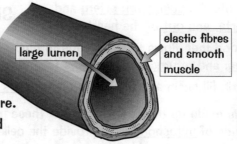

large lumen

elastic fibres and smooth muscle

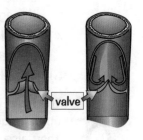

valve

Learn this page — don't struggle in vein...

Here's an interesting fact for you — your body contains about 60 000 miles of blood vessels. That's about six times the distance from London to Sydney in Australia. Of course, capillaries are really tiny, which is how such a massive amount of them can fit in your body — they can only be seen with a microscope.

Q1   Describe how veins are adapted to carry blood back to the heart.   [2 marks]

Q2   Explain how capillaries are adapted to their function.   [3 marks]

The Blood

Right, a tiny bit more about the <u>blood vessels</u> coming up first, then onto the <u>blood</u> itself...
(Hmmm — is it me, or is this starting to sound a tiny bit like a lecture for <u>vampires</u>...)

The Total Cross-Sectional Area of Vessels Affects Blood Flow

1) As the <u>total cross-sectional area</u> of blood vessels <u>increases</u>, the <u>mean velocity</u> of the blood flowing through the vessels <u>decreases</u> (i.e. blood flows more <u>slowly</u> through <u>capillaries</u> than veins or arteries).

2) Although <u>capillaries</u> are tiny there are so <u>many</u> of them that their <u>total cross-sectional area</u> is <u>huge</u>.

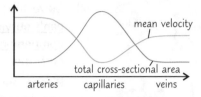

3) This means that blood flows <u>slowly</u> through <u>capillary beds</u>, which allows <u>more time</u> for the <u>exchange</u> of substances — it'd be no good if the blood just whizzed past the body cells.

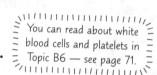

mean velocity

total cross-sectional area

arteries   capillaries   veins

4) The <u>mean pressure</u> of the blood is <u>highest</u> in the <u>arteries</u> because they're <u>closest</u> to the <u>heart</u> but the <u>larger total cross-sectional area</u> of the <u>capillaries</u> causes the <u>pressure</u> to <u>fall</u>.

Blood Acts as a Transport System

Blood consists of <u>plasma</u>, <u>platelets</u>, <u>red blood cells</u> and <u>white blood cells</u>. For now, all you need to know about is the <u>plasma</u> and the <u>red blood cells</u>...

You can read about white blood cells and platelets in Topic B6 — see page 71.

Plasma is the Liquid Bit of Blood

It's basically blood minus the blood cells. Plasma is a pale yellow liquid which <u>carries just about everything</u> that needs transporting around your body:

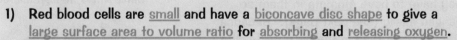

1) <u>Red blood cells</u> (see below), <u>white blood cells</u>, and <u>platelets</u>.
2) <u>Water</u>.
3) Digested <u>food products</u> like <u>glucose</u> and <u>amino acids</u> from the gut to all the body cells.
4) <u>Carbon dioxide</u> from the body cells to the lungs.
5) <u>Urea</u> from the liver to the kidneys (where it's removed in the urine).
6) <u>Hormones</u> — these act like chemical messengers (see p.39).
7) <u>Antibodies</u> — these are proteins involved in the body's immune response (see p.71).

Red Blood Cells Have the Job of Carrying Oxygen

Red blood cells transport <u>oxygen</u> from the <u>lungs</u> to <u>all</u> the cells in the body. The <u>structure</u> of a red blood cell is adapted to its <u>function</u>:

Biconcave means they look like they've been pressed in (they're concave) on both sides (see diagram below).

1) Red blood cells are <u>small</u> and have a <u>biconcave disc shape</u> to give a <u>large surface area to volume ratio</u> for <u>absorbing</u> and <u>releasing oxygen</u>.

2) They contain <u>haemoglobin</u>, which is what gives blood its <u>colour</u> — it contains a lot of <u>iron</u>. In the lungs, haemoglobin <u>combines with oxygen</u> to become <u>oxyhaemoglobin</u>. In body tissues the reverse happens to <u>release oxygen to the cells</u>.

3) Red blood cells <u>don't</u> have a <u>nucleus</u> — this frees up <u>space</u> for more haemoglobin, so they can carry more oxygen.

4) As they are <u>small</u> and very <u>flexible</u> they can easily pass through the <u>tiny capillaries</u>.

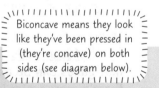

Blood's other function is to let you know you're bleeding...

Every single drop contains millions of red blood cells — all of them perfectly designed for carrying plenty of oxygen to where it's needed. Which right now is your brain, so you can get cracking with learning this page.

Q1   Describe three ways in which red blood cells are adapted to carry oxygen.   [3 marks]

Plant Transport Systems and Transpiration

Plants have <u>two</u> separate types of transport vessel — <u>xylem</u> and <u>phloem</u> — for transporting stuff around. <u>Both</u> types of vessel go to <u>every part</u> of the plant in a <u>continuous system</u>, but they're totally <u>separate</u>.

Phloem Tubes Transport Food

1) Made of <u>columns</u> of <u>living cells</u> called <u>sieve tube elements</u>. These have <u>perforated end-plates</u> to allow stuff to flow through.

2) Sieve tube elements have <u>no nucleus</u>. This means that they <u>can't survive</u> on their own, so each sieve tube element has a <u>companion cell</u>. These cells carry out the <u>living functions</u> for both themselves and their sieve cells.

3) Phloem vessels transport <u>food substances</u> (mainly <u>sugars</u>) both <u>up</u> and <u>down</u> the stem to growing and storage tissues. This movement of food substances around the plant is known as <u>translocation</u>.

Xylem Tubes Take Water UP

Like phloem, xylem cells don't contain any nuclei.

1) Made of <u>dead cells</u> joined end to end with <u>no</u> end walls between them and a hole (<u>lumen</u>) down the middle.

2) The <u>thick side walls</u> are made of <u>cellulose</u>. They're <u>strong</u> and <u>stiff</u>, which gives the plant <u>support</u>. The cell walls are also strengthened with a material called <u>lignin</u>.

3) They carry <u>water</u> and <u>minerals</u> from the <u>roots</u> up the shoot to the leaves in the <u>transpiration stream</u> (see below).

Water and minerals

Transpiration is the Loss of Water from the Plant

1) Transpiration is caused by the <u>evaporation</u> and <u>diffusion</u> of water from a plant's surface. Most transpiration happens at the <u>leaves</u>.

2) This evaporation and diffusion creates a slight <u>shortage</u> of water in the leaf, and so more water is drawn up from the rest of the plant through the <u>xylem vessels</u> to replace it.

3) This in turn means more water is drawn up from the <u>roots</u>, and so there's a constant <u>transpiration stream</u> of water through the plant.

Head back to page 30 to see how root hair cells are adapted for taking up water.

Transpiration is just a <u>side-effect</u> of the way leaves are adapted for <u>photosynthesis</u>. They have to have <u>stomata</u> in them so that gases can be exchanged easily (see next page). Because there's <u>more water inside</u> the plant than in the <u>air outside</u>, the water escapes from the leaves through the stomata by diffusion.

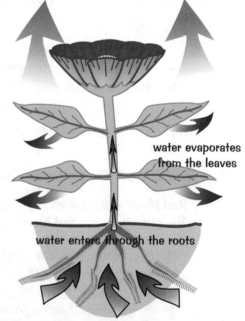

water evaporates from the leaves

water enters through the roots

The transpiration stream does have some <u>benefits</u> for the plants, however:

1) The constant stream of water from the ground helps to keep the plant <u>cool</u>.

2) It provides the plant with a constant supply of water for <u>photosynthesis</u>.

See page 27 for more on turgidity in plant cells.

3) The water creates <u>turgor pressure</u> in the plant cells, which helps <u>support</u> the plant and stops it wilting.

4) <u>Minerals</u> needed by the plant can be brought in from the soil along with the water.

Don't let revision stress you out — just go with the phloem...

Phloem goes up and down, whereas xylem just goes up. You could remember it as xy to the sky... it sort of rhymes.

Q1 Explain why there is a continuous upward flow of water in plants. [3 marks]

More on Transpiration

If you thought that stuff on <u>transpiration</u> was <u>interesting</u>, you're not gonna believe your luck — here's another page all about <u>water transport</u> in plants. I don't know about you, but I'm feeling pretty thirsty...

Transpiration Rate is Affected by Three Main Things

1) <u>AN INCREASE IN LIGHT INTENSITY</u> — the <u>brighter</u> the light, the <u>greater</u> the transpiration rate. Bright light <u>increases</u> the rate of <u>photosynthesis</u>, causing the <u>stomata</u> to <u>open</u> to let <u>CO_2</u> in. <u>Stomata</u> begin to <u>close</u> as it gets darker because photosynthesis can't happen in the dark. When the stomata are closed, <u>water can't escape</u>.

2) <u>AN INCREASE IN TEMPERATURE</u> — the <u>warmer</u> it is, the <u>faster</u> transpiration happens. When it's warm the water particles have <u>more energy</u> to evaporate and diffuse out of the stomata.

3) <u>AN INCREASE IN AIR MOVEMENT</u> — if there's <u>lots</u> of air movement (wind) around a leaf, transpiration happens <u>faster</u>. If the air around a leaf is very still, the water vapour just <u>surrounds the leaf</u> and doesn't move away. This means there's a <u>high concentration</u> of water particles outside the leaf as well as inside it, so <u>diffusion</u> doesn't happen as quickly. If it's windy, the water vapour is <u>swept away</u>, maintaining a <u>low concentration</u> of water in the air outside the leaf. Diffusion then happens quickly, from an area of higher concentration to an area of lower concentration.

Plants Need to Balance Water Loss with Water Uptake

Transpiration can help plants in some ways (see previous page), but if it hasn't rained for a while and you're <u>short of water</u> it's not a good idea to have it rushing out of your leaves. So plants have <u>adaptations</u> to help <u>reduce water loss</u> from their leaves:

Stomata is the plural of stoma.

1) Leaves usually have a <u>waxy cuticle</u> covering the <u>upper epidermis</u>. This helps make the upper surface of the leaf <u>waterproof</u>.

2) Most <u>stomata</u> are found on the <u>lower surface</u> of a leaf where it's <u>darker</u> and <u>cooler</u>. This helps slow down <u>diffusion</u> of water out of the leaf.

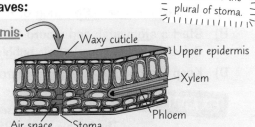

3) The <u>bigger</u> the stomata and the <u>more</u> stomata a leaf has, the more <u>water</u> the plant will <u>lose</u>. Plants in <u>hot climates</u> really need to conserve water, so they have <u>fewer</u> and <u>smaller</u> stomata on the underside of the leaf and <u>no</u> stomata on the upper epidermis.

Stomata Open and Close Automatically

Guard cells <u>turgid</u> — stoma <u>opens</u>

Guard cells <u>flaccid</u> — stoma <u>closes</u>

1) <u>Stomata</u> close <u>automatically</u> when supplies of water start to <u>dry up</u>.
2) The <u>guard cells</u> have a special kidney shape which opens and closes the <u>stomata</u> as the guard cells go <u>turgid</u> or <u>flaccid</u> (see p.27).
3) <u>Thin</u> outer walls and <u>thickened</u> inner walls make this opening and closing function work properly.
4) Open stomata allow gases in and out for <u>photosynthesis</u>.
5) They're <u>sensitive to light</u>, so they <u>open</u> during the <u>day</u> and <u>close</u> at <u>night</u>. This allows them to conserve water without losing out on photosynthesis.

I say stomaaarta, you say stomaaayta...

Here's an interesting fact — a biggish tree loses around 1000 litres of water from its leaves every day. That's about as much water as the average person drinks in a whole year, so the roots have to draw lots of water from the soil to replace it. No wonder the stomata close when the soil's dry or it's too dark.

Q1   Name the cells that control the size of stomata.   [1 mark]

Q2   Explain how low light intensity affects the rate of transpiration.   [2 marks]

Q3   Explain how temperature affects the rate of transpiration.   [2 marks]

Investigating Transpiration

One page. That's it — that's all that's left between you and the end of this section. You can do this.

A Potometer can be Used to Estimate Transpiration Rate

A potometer is a special piece of apparatus used to estimate transpiration rate. It actually measures water uptake by a plant, but it's assumed that water uptake by the plant is directly related to water loss from the leaves (transpiration). Here's how to use a potometer:

1) Cut a shoot underwater to prevent air from entering the xylem. Cut it at a slant to increase the surface area available for water uptake.

2) Assemble the potometer in water and insert the shoot under water, so no air can enter.

3) Remove the apparatus from the water but keep the end of the capillary tube submerged in a beaker of water.

4) Check that the apparatus is watertight and airtight.

5) Dry the leaves, allow time for the shoot to acclimatise and then shut the tap.

6) Remove the end of the capillary tube from the beaker of water until one air bubble has formed, then put the end of the tube back into the water.

7) Record the starting position of the air bubble.

8) Start a stopwatch and record the distance moved by the bubble per unit time, e.g. per hour. Calculating the speed of air bubble movement gives an estimate of the transpiration rate.

9) Keep the conditions constant throughout the experiment, e.g. the temperature and air humidity.

Setting up a potometer is tough — if there are air bubbles in the apparatus or the plant's xylem it will affect your results.

Potometers can be set up in different ways. You might see one in the exam that's a bit different to this one but they're all used to estimate transpiration rate.

reservoir of water

Tap is shut off during experiment.

As the plant takes up water, the air bubble moves along the scale.

Water moves this way.

capillary tube with a scale

Bubble moves this way.

Beaker of water.

EXAMPLE: A potometer was used to estimate the transpiration rate of a plant cutting. The bubble moved 25 mm in 10 minutes. Estimate the transpiration rate.

To estimate the rate of transpiration, divide the distance the bubble moved by the time taken.

$$\frac{\text{distance moved}}{\text{time taken}} = \frac{25}{10} = 2.5 \text{ mm per minute}$$

You Can See How Environmental Conditions Affect Transpiration Rates

You can use a potometer to estimate how different factors affect the transpiration rate. The set up above will be your control — you can vary an environmental condition (see below), run the experiment again and compare the results to the control to see how the change affected the transpiration rate.

1) Light intensity — You could use a lamp to increase the intensity of light that hits the plant — this should increase the transpiration rate. To decrease the light intensity, put the potometer in a cupboard (this should decrease the transpiration rate).

2) Temperature — You could increase or decrease the temperature by putting the potometer in a room that's warmer or colder than where you did the control experiment. An increase in temperature should increase the transpiration rate and a decrease in temperature should lower it.

3) Air movement — You could use a fan to increase the air movement around the plant — this should increase the transpiration rate.

Potometer — a surprisingly useless tool for measuring crockery...

You made it. Congratulations. One good way to remember the three factors that affect the rate of transpiration is to think about drying washing. A good day for drying is sunny, warm and windy. It's the same stuff. Fancy that.

Q1 Give two variables you should keep constant if investigating the effect of temperature on transpiration rate.

[2 marks]

Revision Questions for Topic B2

That's Topic B2 over and done with — now, let's see if you know your stem cells from your stomata...
- Try these questions and tick off each one when you get it right.
- When you've done all the questions under a heading and are completely happy with it, tick it off.

The Cell Cycle, Cell Differentiation and Stem Cells (p24-25) ☐

1) Briefly describe the stages involved in the cell cycle. ☑
2) Explain why the cells produced during mitosis are genetically identical. ☑
3) Give an example of a cell that is specialised to carry out a particular function. ☑
4) Give two differences between embryonic stem cells and adult stem cells in animals. ☑
5) Where are stem cells found in plants? ☑

Diffusion, Active Transport and Osmosis (p26-27) ☑

6) Give three substances that move across cell membranes by diffusion. ☑
7) Explain how active transport is different from diffusion. ☑
8) What is a partially permeable membrane? ☑
9) Liquid A and liquid B are separated by a partially permeable membrane. There is a net movement of water from liquid B into liquid A. Which liquid has the highest water potential? ☑

Exchanging and Transporting Substances (p28-30) ☑

10) Give three factors that affect the movement of substances. ☑
11) Explain why single-celled organisms don't require specialised exchange surfaces and transport systems to exchange substances. ☑
12) Give an example of a specialised exchange surface found in an animal and explain how it is adapted to maximise the exchange of substances. ☑
13) Give two substances that a plant takes in via its root hairs. ☑

The Circulatory System, Blood Vessels and Blood (p31-33) ☐

14) True or false? Humans have a single circulatory system. ☑
15) How many chambers does the human heart have? ☑
16) Is blood in the pulmonary artery oxygenated or deoxygenated? ☑
17) Through which vessel does blood leave the left ventricle of the heart? ☑
18) Which type of blood vessel carries blood at high pressure? ☑
19) What is the role of plasma? ☑
20) What is the role of red blood cells? ☑

Plant Transport Systems and Transpiration (p34-36) ☐

21) Explain what is meant by translocation. ☑
22) Which type of plant transport vessel contains sieve tube elements? ☑
23) What is carried by xylem tubes? ☑
24) Which type of plant transport vessel is made up of dead cells? ☑
25) Give three factors that affect the rate of transpiration. ☑
26) Where can most stomata be found? ☑
27) Draw a diagram showing how a potometer can be used to investigate the rate of transpiration. ☑

The Nervous System

The nervous system is what lets you react to what goes on around you, so you'd find life tough without it.

The Central Nervous System Coordinates a Response

1) The nervous system is made up of neurones (nerve cells), which go to all parts of the body.

2) The body has lots of sensory receptors, which can detect a change in your environment (a stimulus). Different sensory receptors detect different stimuli. For example, receptors in your eyes detect light, and receptors in your skin detect touch (pressure) and temperature change.

3) When a stimulus is detected by receptors, the information is sent as nervous (electrical) impulses along sensory neurones to the central nervous system (CNS).

4) The CNS consists of the brain and spinal cord.

5) The CNS coordinates the response (in other words, it decides what to do about the stimulus and tells something to do it).

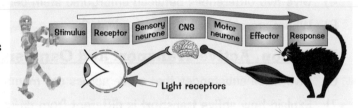

Stimulus → Receptor → Sensory neurone → CNS → Motor neurone → Effector → Response

Light receptors

6) The CNS sends information to an effector (muscle or gland) along a motor neurone. The effector then responds accordingly — e.g. a muscle may contract or a gland may secrete a hormone.

Neurones Transmit Information as Electrical Impulses

1) Electrical impulses are passed along the axon of a neurone.

2) Neurones have branched endings (dendrites) so they can connect with lots of other neurones.

3) Some axons are also surrounded by a fatty (myelin) sheath. This acts as an electrical insulator, speeding up the electrical impulse.

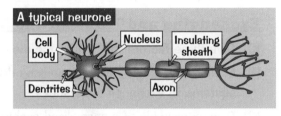

A typical neurone

Cell body | Nucleus | Insulating sheath | Dentrites | Axon

4) Neurones are long, which also speeds up the impulse (connecting with another neurone slows the impulse down, so one long neurone is much quicker than lots of short ones joined together).

5) The connection between two neurones is called a synapse. It's basically just a very tiny gap:

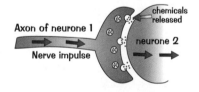

Axon of neurone 1
chemicals released
neurone 2
Nerve impulse

- The electrical impulse triggers the release of transmitter chemicals, which diffuse across the gap.
- These chemicals bind to receptor molecules in the membrane of the next neurone. This sets off a new electrical impulse.

Reflex Actions Stop You Injuring Yourself

1) Reflex actions are automatic (done without thinking) so they're even quicker than normal responses. The passage of information in a reflex (from receptor to effector) is called a reflex arc.

2) The conscious brain isn't involved in a reflex arc. The sensory neurone connects to a relay neurone in the spinal cord or in an unconscious part of the brain — which links directly to the right motor neurone, so no time's wasted thinking about the right response.

3) Reflex actions often have a protective role, e.g. snatching back your hand when you touch a burning hot plate happens almost before you realise you've done it.

Relay neurones just connect sensory neurones to motor neurones.

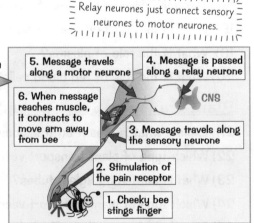

5. Message travels along a motor neurone
4. Message is passed along a relay neurone
6. When message reaches muscle, it contracts to move arm away from bee
CNS
3. Message travels along the sensory neurone
2. Stimulation of the pain receptor
1. Cheeky bee stings finger

Don't let the thought of exams play on your nerves...

Make sure you understand how the different parts of the nervous system work together to coordinate a response.

Q1   Name the two main parts of the central nervous system.   [2 marks]

Hormones and Negative Feedback Systems

The other way to <u>send information</u> around the body (apart from along neurones) is by using <u>hormones</u>.

Hormones are Chemical Messengers Sent in the Blood

1) Hormones are chemicals produced in various <u>glands</u> called <u>endocrine glands</u>. These glands make up your <u>endocrine system</u>.

2) Hormones are released directly into the <u>blood</u>. The blood then carries them to other parts of the body.

3) They travel all over the body but they only affect <u>particular cells</u> in particular places.

4) The affected cells are called <u>target cells</u> — they have the right <u>receptors</u> to respond to that hormone. An organ that contains target cells is called a <u>target organ</u>.

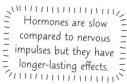
Hormones are slow compared to nervous impulses but they have longer-lasting effects.

Adrenaline Prepares you for 'Fight or Flight'

1) <u>Adrenaline</u> is a hormone released by the <u>adrenal glands</u> (which are located just above the kidneys).

2) Adrenaline prepares the body for '<u>fight or flight</u>' — in other words, <u>standing</u> your <u>ground</u> in the face of a <u>threat</u> (e.g. a predator) or bravely <u>running away</u>. It does this by activating processes that increase the supply of <u>oxygen and glucose</u> to cells. For example:

- Adrenaline <u>binds</u> to specific <u>receptors</u> in the <u>heart</u>. This causes the heart muscle to <u>contract</u> more frequently and with <u>more force</u>, so heart rate and blood pressure <u>increase</u>.

- This increases <u>blood flow</u> to the <u>muscles</u>, so the cells receive more <u>oxygen</u> and <u>glucose</u> for increased <u>respiration</u>.

- Adrenaline also binds to receptors in the <u>liver</u>. This causes the liver to <u>break down</u> its <u>glycogen</u> stores (see. p.43) to release <u>glucose</u>.

- This increases the <u>blood glucose level</u>, so there's more glucose in the blood to be transported to the cells.

3) When your brain detects a <u>stressful situation</u>, it sends <u>nervous impulses</u> to the <u>adrenal glands</u>, which respond by secreting <u>adrenaline</u>. This gets the body ready for <u>action</u>.

Hormone Release can be Affected by Negative Feedback

Your body can <u>control</u> the levels of hormones (and other substances) in the blood using <u>negative feedback systems</u>. When the body detects that the level of a substance has gone <u>above or below</u> the <u>normal level</u>, it <u>triggers a response</u> to bring the level <u>back to normal</u> again. Here's an example of just that:

Thyroxine Regulates Metabolism

Thyroxine is made in the thyroid gland from iodine and amino acids.

1) <u>Thyroxine</u> is a hormone released by the <u>thyroid gland</u> (found in the <u>neck</u>).

2) It plays an important role in regulating <u>metabolic rate</u> — the speed at which chemical reactions in the body occur. It's important for loads of processes in the body, such as <u>growth</u> and <u>protein synthesis</u>.

3) Thyroxine is released in response to <u>thyroid stimulating hormone</u> (<u>TSH</u>), which is released from the <u>pituitary gland</u>.

4) A <u>negative feedback system</u> keeps the amount of thyroxine in the blood at the right level — when the level of thyroxine in the blood is <u>higher than normal</u>, the secretion of <u>TSH</u> from the pituitary gland is <u>inhibited</u>. This reduces the amount of thyroxine released from the thyroid gland so the level in the blood <u>falls</u> back towards normal.

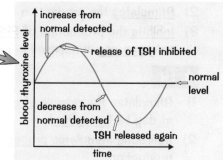

Negative feedback sucks, especially from your science teacher...

Negative feedback can be a bit difficult to get your head round at first — best give this page a good going over.

Q1   Explain how the endocrine system allows communication within the body.   [5 marks]

Hormones in Reproduction

You need to know about <u>sex hormones</u> and how some of them <u>interact</u> to control the <u>menstrual cycle</u>.

You Need to Know About These Sex Hormones

1) <u>Testosterone</u> — this is the <u>main male sex hormone</u>. It's produced in the <u>testes</u>. It stimulates <u>sperm production</u> and is important for the development of the male <u>reproductive system</u>.

2) <u>Oestrogen</u> — this is the <u>main female sex hormone</u>. It's produced in the <u>ovaries</u> (in the lower abdomen). It's involved in the <u>menstrual cycle</u> and promotes female <u>sexual characteristics</u>, e.g. breast development.

3) <u>Progesterone</u> — this is also produced by the <u>ovaries</u>. It helps to <u>support pregnancy</u> and is involved in the <u>menstrual cycle</u>.

4) <u>FSH (follicle-stimulating hormone)</u> and <u>LH (luteinising hormone)</u> — these hormones are released from the <u>pituitary gland</u> in the brain. They help to control the <u>menstrual cycle</u>.

The Menstrual Cycle Has Four Stages

The menstrual cycle is the <u>monthly sequence of events</u> in which the female body releases an <u>egg</u> and prepares the <u>uterus</u> (womb) in case it receives a <u>fertilised egg</u>. This is what happens at <u>each stage</u>:

<u>Stage 1</u> <u>Day 1 is when menstruation starts</u>. The uterus lining breaks down and is released.

<u>Stage 2</u> <u>The lining of the uterus builds up again</u>, from day 4 to day 14, into a thick spongy layer full of blood vessels ready to receive a fertilised egg.

<u>Stage 3</u> <u>An egg develops and is released</u> from an ovary (<u>ovulation</u>) at about day 14.

<u>Stage 4</u> <u>The lining is then maintained</u> for about 14 days, until day 28. If no fertilised egg has implanted into the uterus wall by day 28, the spongy lining starts to break down again and the whole cycle starts over.

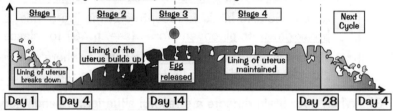

The Menstrual Cycle is Controlled by Four Hormones

1. FSH

1) Causes an <u>egg to mature</u> in one of the ovaries.

2) <u>Stimulates</u> the <u>ovaries</u> to produce <u>oestrogen</u>.

2. Oestrogen

1) Causes the lining of the uterus to <u>thicken</u> and <u>grow</u>.

2) <u>Stimulates</u> the production of <u>LH</u>.

3) <u>Inhibits</u> the production of <u>FSH</u> so that only <u>one egg</u> is released in each cycle.

3. LH

1) Stimulates the <u>release of an egg</u> at day 14 (<u>ovulation</u>).

2) Indirectly <u>stimulates progesterone</u> production.

4. Progesterone

1) <u>Maintains</u> the lining of the uterus. When the level of progesterone <u>falls</u> and there's a <u>low oestrogen level</u>, the lining <u>breaks down</u>.

2) <u>Inhibits</u> the production of <u>FSH</u> and <u>LH</u>.

3) A <u>low</u> progesterone level allows <u>FSH</u> to <u>increase</u>... and then the whole cycle starts again.

If a fertilised egg implants in the uterus (i.e. the woman becomes pregnant) then the progesterone level will stay high to maintain the uterus lining during pregnancy.

What do you call a fish with no eye — FSH...

OK, this stuff is pretty tricky. Try scribbling down everything on the page until you can get it all without peeking.

Q1   Explain the role of LH in the menstrual cycle.   [2 marks]

Topic B3 — Organism Level Systems

Hormones for Fertility and Contraception

Hormones play a big role in <u>reproduction</u>. No surprise then that hormones are used to help <u>infertile</u> women <u>have babies</u> and to help <u>fertile</u> women <u>not have babies</u>. What a topsy-turvy world we live in.

Hormones can be Used to Treat Infertility

If a person is <u>infertile</u>, it means they <u>can't reproduce naturally</u>. Infertility can now be <u>treated</u> due to developments in <u>modern reproductive technologies</u>, many of which involve <u>hormones</u>.

Hormones are Used to Promote Natural Pregnancy...

1) Some women have levels of <u>FSH</u> (see previous page) that are <u>too low</u> to cause their <u>eggs to mature</u>. This means that <u>no ovulation</u> takes place (<u>no eggs</u> are <u>released</u>) and the women <u>can't get pregnant</u>.

2) The hormones <u>FSH</u> and <u>LH</u> can be injected by these women to stimulate <u>ovulation</u>.

...and They Play a Role in IVF

1) <u>IVF</u> ("*in vitro* fertilisation") involves collecting <u>eggs</u> from the woman's ovaries and fertilising them in a <u>lab</u> using the man's <u>sperm</u>. These are then grown into <u>embryos</u>.

2) Once the embryos are <u>tiny balls of cells</u>, one or two of them are <u>transferred</u> to the woman's uterus to improve the chance of <u>pregnancy</u>.

3) <u>FSH</u> and <u>LH</u> are given before egg collection to <u>stimulate egg production</u> (so more than one egg can be collected).

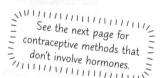

See the next page for contraceptive methods that don't involve hormones.

Hormones can be Used as Contraceptives

Contraceptives are used to <u>prevent pregnancy</u>. Some contraceptive methods involve <u>hormones</u>:

Contraceptive method	Hormone(s) involved	How it works
<u>Injection</u> — effective for up to 3 months.	Progesterone	• Stimulates the production of <u>thick cervical mucus</u> (at the entrance to the uterus) making it less likely that any sperm will get through and reach an egg. • <u>Thins the lining of the uterus</u> to reduce the chance of a fertilised egg <u>implanting</u>. • <u>Prevents ovulation</u>* by inhibiting the production of <u>FSH</u> and <u>LH</u> (see previous page). *not true for all types of mini-pill
<u>Implant</u> — inserted beneath the skin of the arm. Effective for 3 years.		
<u>Intrauterine system (IUS)</u> — a T-shaped piece of plastic inserted into the uterus. Effective for 3-5 years.		
<u>Mini-pill</u> (aka progesterone-only pill) — has to be taken every day.		
<u>Combined pill</u> — taken in a '21 day pill, 7 days no pill' cycle.	Progesterone and oestrogen	All of the effects of progesterone listed above, plus oestrogen also <u>prevents ovulation</u> by inhibiting FSH.
<u>Patch</u> — worn on the skin in a 4-week cycle (replaced once a week for 3 weeks, then no patch worn for a week).		

The mini-pill and the combined pill are 'oral contraceptives'.

If <u>used correctly</u> (e.g. pills taken on time) all of these contraceptive methods are <u>more than 99% effective</u>.

IVF... FSH... IUS... LH... — I feel like I'm at the opticians...

Hormones can be used to manipulate the menstrual cycle so that the reproductive system does what we want it to do, when we want it to do it. Great for both increasing and decreasing the chance of pregnancy.

Q1   Explain how hormones may be used to promote a natural pregnancy in an infertile woman.   [3 marks]

More on Contraception

There are ways to prevent pregnancy that don't include the use of hormones. Now, as a warning, this page does include themes of a sexual nature from the outset. You might not want to read it aloud to your parents.

There are Plenty of Non-Hormonal Contraceptive Methods

1) Barrier methods — these try to stop the egg and sperm meeting. For example:

   The figures given here for effectiveness assume that the methods are used properly.

   - Condom (98% effective) — worn over the penis during intercourse to prevent sperm entering the vagina.
   - Female condom (95% effective) — worn inside the vagina during intercourse.
   - Diaphragm (92-96% effective) — fits over the cervix (opening of the uterus) to stop sperm from meeting the egg. Has to be fitted by a GP/nurse the first time it's used and has to be used with a spermicide (a chemical that kills sperm).

2) Intrauterine devices (IUDs) — T-shaped devices that contain copper. They're inserted into the uterus and prevent sperm from surviving. They also alter the lining of the womb so that fertilised eggs can't implant. They're more than 99% effective and can be kept in for up to ten years.

3) 'Natural' methods — these don't use any bits and bobs like all the other methods. They refer to basically just not having sexual intercourse when the woman is most fertile (the period around ovulation) or 'withdrawal' (the man pulling the penis out before ejaculation). These methods are the least effective at preventing pregnancy as they rely on getting the timing exactly right.

4) Sterilisation — involves a surgical procedure to cut or tie tubes in the reproductive system. In women, the procedure means eggs are prevented from travelling from the ovaries to the uterus. In men, it prevents sperm from being ejaculated. The methods are over 99% effective.

There are Pros and Cons to All Forms of Contraception

In the exam you may have to evaluate hormonal (see previous page) and non-hormonal methods of contraception. Here are some things to think about:

1) Side-effects — hormonal methods can have unpleasant side-effects, e.g. heavy or irregular periods, acne, headaches, mood changes.

2) Possibility of 'doing it wrong' — barrier methods and 'natural' methods have to be done properly each time a couple have intercourse. If, for example, a condom splits or a man doesn't withdraw soon enough, then the methods won't work. The same is true with some hormonal methods, e.g. if a woman doesn't take her pills correctly or replace her patch at the right time, the methods won't work properly.

   I've got this barrier thing sorted...

3) Medical input — many methods involve at least one trip to a nurse or doctor (e.g. to get a prescription for pills or to have a device inserted). Although these methods tend to be more effective than barrier or 'natural' methods, people may feel uncomfortable about the procedures involved.

4) Length of action — long-lasting methods (i.e. those that last several months or years) may be preferable over having to think about contraception every day or every time intercourse is on the cards.

5) Sexually transmitted infections (STIs) — these are infections that are passed from person to person during sexual intercourse. The only method of contraception that can protect against them is condoms (male or female types).

The winner of best contraceptive ever — just not doing it...

By now you should be pretty clued up on the different methods of contraception. Whether hormonal or non-hormonal, no method is guaranteed to be 100% effective and each method has its own pros and cons.

Q1 Give one reason why a woman may prefer to use a diaphragm rather than an oral contraceptive. [1 mark]

Q2 Give two advantages of using an intrauterine device (IUD) as a contraceptive method rather than male condoms. [2 marks]

Controlling Blood Sugar Level

It's important to maintain a <u>constant internal environment</u>, e.g. <u>blood sugar levels</u> need to be kept <u>constant</u>.

Insulin and Glucagon Control Blood Sugar Level

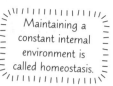

Maintaining a constant internal environment is called homeostasis.

1) Conditions in your body need to be kept <u>steady</u> — this is really important so that all the <u>metabolic reactions</u> vital for keeping you alive can <u>continue</u> at an <u>appropriate rate</u>. It can be <u>dangerous</u> for your <u>health</u> if conditions <u>vary too much</u> from normal levels.

2) To maintain a constant internal environment, your body needs to respond to both <u>internal</u> and <u>external</u> changes whilst balancing <u>inputs</u> (stuff going into your body) with <u>outputs</u> (stuff leaving).

3) For example, the <u>level of glucose</u> in the <u>blood</u> must be kept <u>steady</u>.

- Eating foods containing <u>carbohydrate</u> puts <u>glucose</u> into the <u>blood</u> from the <u>small intestine</u>. The normal <u>metabolism</u> of cells <u>removes glucose</u> from the blood — during vigorous exercise <u>even more</u> is removed.

- <u>Excess</u> glucose can be stored as <u>glycogen</u> in the <u>liver</u> and in the <u>muscles</u>. When these stores are <u>full</u> then the excess glucose is stored as <u>lipid</u> (fat) in the tissues.

- The <u>pancreas monitors</u> and <u>controls</u> blood sugar level, using the hormones <u>insulin</u> and <u>glucagon</u>:

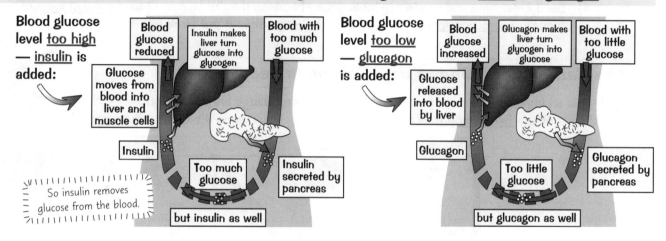

Blood glucose level <u>too high</u> — <u>insulin</u> is added:

Glucose moves from blood into liver and muscle cells

Blood glucose reduced

Insulin makes liver turn glucose into glycogen

Blood with too much glucose

Insulin

Too much glucose

Insulin secreted by pancreas

but insulin as well

So insulin removes glucose from the blood.

Blood glucose level <u>too low</u> — <u>glucagon</u> is added:

Glucose released into blood by liver

Blood glucose increased

Glucagon makes liver turn glycogen into glucose

Blood with too little glucose

Glucagon

Too little glucose

Glucagon secreted by pancreas

but glucagon as well

Having Diabetes Means You Can't Control Your Blood Sugar Level

<u>Diabetes</u> is a condition that affects your ability to <u>control</u> your blood sugar level. There are <u>two types</u>:

TYPE 1

<u>Type 1 diabetes</u> is where the <u>pancreas</u> produces little or no <u>insulin</u>. The result is that a person's blood glucose level can rise to a level that can <u>kill them</u>. People with type 1 diabetes need <u>insulin therapy</u>. This usually involves <u>injecting insulin</u> into the blood several times a day (often at mealtimes). This makes sure that glucose is <u>removed</u> from the blood quickly once food has been <u>digested</u>. This stops the level of glucose in the blood from getting too high and is a <u>very effective treatment</u>. The amount of insulin needed depends on the person's <u>diet</u> and how <u>active</u> they are. As well as insulin therapy, people with type 1 diabetes need to think about <u>limiting</u> their <u>intake</u> of food rich in <u>simple carbohydrates</u>, e.g. sugars (which cause the blood glucose to rise rapidly) and taking <u>regular exercise</u> (which helps to <u>remove excess glucose</u> from the blood).

TYPE 2

<u>Type 2 diabetes</u> is where a person becomes <u>resistant to insulin</u> (their body's cells <u>don't respond</u> properly to the hormone). This can also cause blood sugar level to rise to a dangerous level. Being <u>overweight</u> can <u>increase</u> your chance of <u>developing</u> type 2 diabetes, as <u>obesity</u> is a major <u>risk factor</u> in the development of the disease (see page 76). Type 2 diabetes can be controlled by eating a <u>healthy diet</u>, <u>exercising regularly</u> and <u>losing weight</u> if necessary. There are also some <u>drugs</u> available which <u>improve</u> the way that the body's cells <u>respond</u> to insulin.

And people used to think the pancreas was just a cushion... (true)

This stuff can seem a bit confusing at first, but if you learn those two diagrams, it'll all start to get a lot easier.

Q1   Describe how the production of insulin differs between type 1 and type 2 diabetes.   [2 marks]

The Carbon Cycle

Carbon flows through the Earth's ecosystems in the carbon cycle. The beauty of the carbon cycle is that carbon is recycled — it's used by organisms but then ends up back in the atmosphere again. Splendid.

Materials are Constantly Recycled in an Ecosystem

1) An ecosystem is all the organisms living in an area, as well as all the non-living conditions, e.g. soil quality, availability of water, temperature.

There's more on biotic and abiotic factors on page 46.

2) Materials are recycled through both the living (biotic) and non-living (abiotic) components of ecosystems:

> 1) Living things are made of elements they take from the environment. For example, plants take in carbon, hydrogen, oxygen, nitrogen, etc.
>
> 2) They turn these elements into the complex compounds (carbohydrates, proteins and fats) that make up living organisms. These are taken in by animals when they eat the plants.
>
> 3) The elements are recycled — they return to the environment (e.g. soil or air) through waste products or when organisms die, ready to be used by new plants and put back into the food chain.
>
> 4) Dead organisms and waste products decay because they're broken down by decomposers (usually microorganisms) — that's how the elements get put back into the soil.

The Carbon Cycle Shows How Carbon is Recycled

Carbon is an important element in the materials that living things are made from. But there's only a fixed amount of carbon in the world. This means it's constantly recycled:

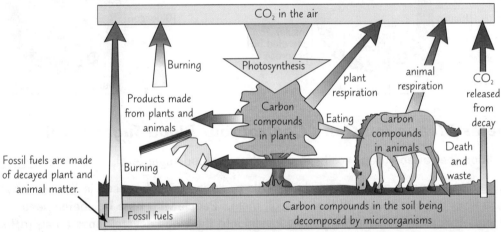

CO_2 = carbon dioxide

This diagram isn't half as bad as it looks. Learn these important points:

1) There's only one arrow going down from CO_2 in the air. The whole thing is 'powered' by photosynthesis. Green plants use the carbon from CO_2 in the air to make carbohydrates, fats and proteins.

2) Eating passes the carbon compounds in the plant along to animals that eat them.

3) Both plant and animal respiration while the organisms are alive releases CO_2 back into the air.

4) Plants and animals eventually die and decompose, or are killed and turned into useful products.

5) When plants and animals decompose they're broken down by microorganisms, such as bacteria and fungi. These decomposers release CO_2 back into the air by respiration, as they break down the material.

6) Some useful plant and animal products, e.g. wood and fossil fuels, are burned (combustion). This also releases CO_2 back into the air.

7) Decomposition of materials means that habitats can be maintained for the organisms that live there, e.g. nutrients are returned to the soil and waste material, such as dead leaves, doesn't just pile up.

Carbon cycle — isn't that what Wiggo rides...

Carbon atoms are very important — they're found in plants, animals, your petrol tank and on your burnt toast.

Q1　　Suggest two reasons why chopping down trees can increase the concentration of CO_2 in the air.　[2 marks]

The Nitrogen Cycle and the Water Cycle

Just like carbon, nitrogen and water are constantly being <u>recycled</u>. It's amazing really — the nitrogen in your proteins might once have been in the <u>air</u>. And before that in a <u>plant</u>. Or even in some <u>horse wee</u>. Nice.

Nitrogen is Recycled in the Nitrogen Cycle...

1) The <u>atmosphere</u> contains <u>78% nitrogen gas</u>, N_2. This is <u>very unreactive</u> and so it can't be used <u>directly</u> by plants or animals. <u>Nitrogen</u> is <u>needed</u> for making <u>proteins</u> for growth, so living organisms have to get it somehow.

2) Plants get their nitrogen from the <u>soil</u>, so nitrogen in the air has to be turned into <u>nitrates</u> before plants can use it. <u>Nitrogen compounds</u> are then passed along <u>food chains</u> as animals eat plants (and each other).

3) <u>Decomposers</u> (bacteria and fungi in the soil) break down <u>proteins</u> in rotting plants and animals, and <u>urea</u> in animal waste, into <u>ammonia</u>, which goes on to form <u>ammonium ions</u>. This returns the nitrogen compounds to the soil — so the nitrogen in these organisms is <u>recycled</u>.

4) <u>Nitrogen fixation</u> is the process of turning N_2 <u>from the air</u> into <u>nitrogen compounds</u> in the soil which <u>plants can use</u>.
There are <u>two main ways</u> that this happens:
   a) <u>Lightning</u> — there's so much <u>energy</u> in a bolt of lightning that it's enough to make nitrogen <u>react with oxygen</u> in the air to give nitrates.
   b) <u>Nitrogen-fixing bacteria</u> in roots and soil (see below).

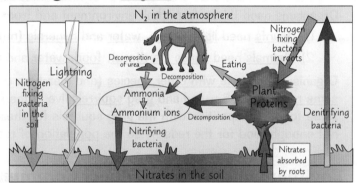

5) There are <u>four</u> different types of <u>bacteria</u> involved in the nitrogen cycle:
   a) <u>DECOMPOSERS</u> — decompose <u>proteins</u> and <u>urea</u> and turn them into <u>ammonia</u>, which goes on to form <u>ammonium ions</u>.
   b) <u>NITRIFYING BACTERIA</u> — turn <u>ammonium ions</u> in decaying matter into <u>nitrates</u>.
   c) <u>NITROGEN-FIXING BACTERIA</u> — turn <u>atmospheric N_2</u> into <u>nitrogen compounds</u> that plants can use.
   d) <u>DENITRIFYING BACTERIA</u> — turn <u>nitrates</u> back into <u>N_2 gas</u>. This is of no benefit to living organisms. Denitrifying bacteria are often found in <u>waterlogged soils</u>.

6) Some <u>nitrogen-fixing bacteria</u> live in the <u>soil</u>. Others live in <u>nodules</u> on the roots of <u>legume plants</u> (e.g. peas and beans). This is why legume plants are so good at putting nitrogen <u>back into the soil</u>. The plants have a <u>mutualistic relationship</u> (see page 47) with the bacteria — the bacteria get <u>food</u> (sugars) from the plant, and the plant gets <u>nitrogen compounds</u> from the bacteria to make into <u>proteins</u>. So the relationship benefits <u>both</u> of them.

...and Water is Recycled in the Water Cycle

1) The <u>Sun</u> makes water <u>evaporate</u> from the land and sea, turning it into <u>water vapour</u>. Water also evaporates from plants via <u>transpiration</u> (see p.34).

2) The warm water vapour is <u>carried upwards</u> (as warm air rises). When it gets higher up it <u>cools</u> and <u>condenses</u> to form <u>clouds</u>.

3) Water falls from the clouds as <u>precipitation</u> (usually rain, but sometimes snow or hail) and is <u>returned</u> to the land and sea.

4) The <u>flow</u> of <u>fresh water</u> through the water cycle allows <u>nutrients</u> to be <u>transported</u> to different ecosystems.

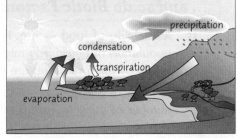

It's the cyyyycle, the cyycle of liiiiife...

Bacteria do all the hard work in the nitrogen cycle. Aided by a bolt or two of lightning. Naturally. And who knew rain could be so useful. Getting soaked on the way to school is a small price to pay for all that lovely fresh water...

Q1   Describe how the nitrogen compounds in dead leaves are turned into nitrates in the soil.   [2 marks]

Ecosystems and Interactions Between Organisms

It's tough in the wild — there's always <u>competition</u> for <u>food</u> and other resources. So if the environment <u>changes</u>, e.g. there's <u>not enough food</u> or it's <u>too hot</u>, it can be the last straw for some organisms...

Ecosystems are Organised into Different Levels

Ecosystems have <u>different levels</u> of <u>organisation</u>:

1) <u>Individual</u> — A <u>single</u> organism.
2) <u>Population</u> — <u>All</u> the organisms of <u>one species</u> in a <u>habitat</u>.
3) <u>Community</u> — All the organisms (<u>different species</u>) living in a habitat.
4) <u>Ecosystem</u> — A community of <u>organisms</u> along with all the <u>non-living</u> (<u>abiotic</u>) <u>conditions</u> (see below).

> A habitat is the place where an organism lives, e.g. a rocky shore or a field.

> A species is a group of similar organisms that can reproduce to give fertile offspring.

Organisms Compete for Resources to Survive

Organisms need things from their <u>environment</u> and from <u>other organisms</u> in order to <u>survive</u> and <u>reproduce</u>:

1) <u>Plants</u> need <u>light</u>, <u>space</u>, <u>water</u> and <u>minerals (nutrients)</u> from the soil.
2) <u>Animals</u> need <u>space (territory)</u>, <u>food</u>, <u>water</u> and <u>mates</u>.

Organisms <u>compete with other species</u> (and members of their own species) for the <u>same resources</u>. E.g. red and grey <u>squirrels</u> live in the same habitat and eat the same food. Competition with the grey squirrels for these resources means there's not enough food for the reds — so the <u>population</u> of red squirrels is <u>decreasing</u>.

Environmental Changes Affect Communities in Different Ways

The <u>environment</u> in which plants and animals live <u>changes all the time</u>. These changes are caused by <u>abiotic</u> (non-living) and <u>biotic</u> (living) factors and affect communities in different ways — for some species <u>population size</u> may <u>increase</u>, for others it may <u>decrease</u>, or the <u>distribution</u> of populations (where they live) may change. Here are some <u>examples</u> of the effects of <u>abiotic</u> and <u>biotic</u> factors:

Abiotic Factors Affect Communities...

1) <u>Temperature</u> — e.g. the distribution of <u>bird species</u> in Germany is changing because of a rise in average temperature. For instance, the <u>European Bee-Eater bird</u> is a <u>Mediterranean</u> species but it's now present in parts of <u>Germany</u>.

2) <u>Moisture level</u> — e.g. <u>daisies</u> grow best in soils that are <u>slightly damp</u>. If the soil becomes <u>waterlogged</u> or <u>too dry</u>, the population of daisies will <u>decrease</u>.

3) <u>Light intensity</u> — e.g. as trees grow and provide more <u>shade</u>, <u>grasses</u> may be replaced by e.g. <u>fungi</u>, <u>mosses</u> etc., which are better able to <u>cope</u> with the <u>low light intensity</u>.

4) <u>pH</u> of the <u>soil</u> — e.g. most species of <u>heather</u> grow best in <u>acidic</u> soils. If the pH of the soil becomes too <u>alkaline</u>, the heather population will <u>decrease</u>.

... and so do Biotic Factors

1) Availability of <u>food</u> — e.g. if there's a <u>bumper year</u> for <u>berries</u>, then the population of <u>blackbirds</u> might <u>increase</u> because there will be <u>enough food</u> for all of them, so they are more likely to <u>survive</u> and <u>reproduce</u>.

2) Number of <u>predators</u> — e.g. if the <u>number of lions</u> (predator) <u>decreases</u> then the number of <u>gazelles</u> (prey) might <u>increase</u> because <u>fewer</u> of them will be <u>eaten</u> by the lions.

> See next page for more on predator-prey relationships.

Revision — an abiotic factor causing stress in my community...

Organisms like everything to be just right — temperature, light, food... I'd never get away with being that fussy.

Q1   What is meant by the term 'community' in the organisation of an ecosystem?   [1 mark]

Q2   Give two abiotic factors that could affect the community in an ecosystem.   [2 marks]

More on Interactions Between Organisms

The <u>organisms</u> in an ecosystem are always <u>interacting</u> — well, if you can call <u>eating one another</u> interacting...
However, some organisms take interaction to a whole new level and become <u>totally dependent</u> on one another.

Populations of Prey and Predators Go in Cycles

In a community containing <u>prey</u> and <u>predators</u> (as most of them do of course):

1) The <u>population</u> of any species is usually <u>limited</u> by the amount of <u>food</u> available.

2) If the population of the <u>prey</u> increases, then so will the population of the <u>predators</u>.

3) However as the population of predators <u>increases</u>, the number of prey will <u>decrease</u>.

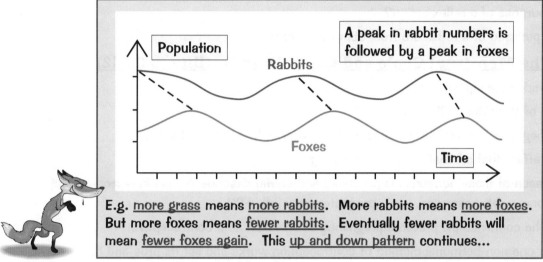

E.g. <u>more grass</u> means <u>more rabbits</u>. More rabbits means <u>more foxes</u>.
But more foxes means <u>fewer rabbits</u>. Eventually fewer rabbits will
mean <u>fewer foxes again</u>. This <u>up and down pattern</u> continues...

4) Predator-prey cycles are always <u>out of phase</u> with each other. This is because it <u>takes a while</u> for
one population to <u>respond</u> to changes in the other population. E.g. when the number of rabbits goes
up, the number of foxes doesn't increase immediately because it takes time for them to reproduce.

5) Predator-prey cycles show how <u>interdependent</u> (affected by one another) populations are.

Parasitic and Mutualistic Relationships are Other Types of Interdependence

Some organisms <u>depend</u> entirely on <u>other species</u> to survive. So <u>where</u> an organism lives and its
<u>abundance</u> (population size) is often influenced by the <u>distribution</u> and <u>abundance</u> of these species.

1) <u>PARASITES</u> live off a host. They <u>take</u> what they need to survive, <u>without</u> giving anything <u>back</u>.
This often <u>harms</u> the host — which makes it a win-lose situation.

- <u>Tapeworms</u> absorb lots of <u>nutrients</u> from the host, causing them to suffer from <u>malnutrition</u>.
- <u>Fleas</u> are parasites. Dogs gain nothing from having fleas (unless you count hundreds of bites).

2) <u>MUTUALISM</u> is a relationship where <u>both</u> organisms benefit — so it's a win-win relationship.

- <u>Clownfish</u> live among the <u>poisonous</u> tentacles of <u>sea anemones</u>. They are the only fish
that can <u>survive</u> the toxins, so they are <u>protected</u> from their <u>predators</u>. In return, the
clownfish help <u>protect</u> the anemones by <u>eating</u> the <u>parasites</u> that could cause them <u>harm</u>.
- Lots of plants are <u>pollinated</u> by insects, allowing them to <u>reproduce</u>.
In return, the insects get a sip of sweet, <u>sugary nectar</u>.

My sister's a parasite — she takes my shoes, my dresses...

In summary, everything affects everything else. But, it's probably best if you learn the proper terms for the exams.

Q1   A cow's stomach is an ideal environment for some types of microorganisms.
       Without these microorganisms, cows are unable to digest grass fully.
       What type of interdependence is this an example of? Explain your answer.   [2 marks]

Revision Questions for Topics B3 and B4

Right, now it's time to find out how much you really know about the last two topics...
- Try these questions and tick off each one when you get it right.
- When you've done all the questions under a heading and are completely happy with it, tick it off.

The Nervous System (p.38) ☑

1) Describe the role of sensory neurones. ☑
2) Give an example of an effector. ☑
3) Draw a diagram of a typical neurone and label all the parts. ☑
4) What is the purpose of a reflex action? ☑
5) Describe the pathway of a reflex arc from stimulus to response. ☑

Hormones, The Menstrual Cycle and Controlling Fertility (p.39-42) ☑

6) What is the endocrine system? ☑
7) Give one role of thyroxine in the body. ☑
8) Explain how negative feedback helps to control the level of thyroxine in the blood. ☑
9) Describe the effect that adrenaline has on the body. ☑
10) State where each of these hormones is produced and briefly describe its role in reproduction:
    a) testosterone, b) oestrogen, c) progesterone, d) FSH. ☑
11) Explain how the combined pill prevents pregnancy when taken as a contraceptive. ☑
12) Describe how one non-hormonal method of contraception works and list its pros and cons. ☑

Controlling Blood Sugar Level (p.43) ☑

13) Why is it important to maintain steady conditions in the body? ☑
14) Describe the roles of insulin and glucagon in controlling a person's blood sugar level. ☑
15) Explain how type 1 and type 2 diabetes can be treated. ☑

Nutrient Cycles and the Water Cycle (p.44-45) ☑

16) How does carbon in the atmosphere enter food chains? ☑
17) What is the role of microorganisms in the carbon cycle? ☑
18) What is the role of nitrogen-fixing bacteria in the nitrogen cycle? ☑
19) Which microorganisms turn nitrates into N_2 gas? ☑
20) List the four main processes in the water cycle. ☑

Ecosystems and Interactions Between Organisms (p.46-47) ☑

21) What is meant by the term 'population' in the organisation of ecosystems? ☑
22) Give two resources that plants compete for in ecosystems. ☑
23) Suggest how light intensity might affect a community. ☑
24) Give two biotic factors that affect communities in ecosystems. ☑
25) Explain why the populations of predators and prey often change in cycles. ☑
26) What is a parasitic relationship? ☑

Genes and Variation

You may remember the <u>structure of DNA</u> from page 14. Well, now you get to learn why DNA is so <u>important</u>...

Chromosomes Are Really Long Molecules of DNA

1) The <u>genome</u> is the <u>entire genetic material</u> of an organism.
2) The genetic material is stored in the nucleus and is arranged into <u>chromosomes</u>.
3) Each chromosome is <u>one</u> very long <u>molecule of DNA</u> that's <u>coiled up</u>.

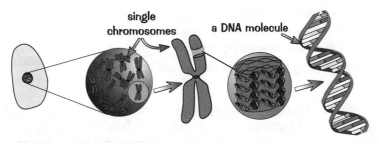

single chromosomes   a DNA molecule

4) A <u>gene</u> is a <u>short length</u> of a chromosome.
5) Genes determine the production of <u>proteins</u>. The <u>sequence of bases</u> (see page 14) in the gene determines the <u>type</u> of protein which is produced. The production of different proteins <u>controls</u> the development of different <u>characteristics</u>, e.g. dimples, and how an organism <u>functions</u>.
6) Genes can exist in <u>different versions</u>. Each version gives a different form of a <u>characteristic</u>, like blue or brown eyes. The different versions of the same gene are called <u>alleles</u> or <u>variants</u> (see next page).

Organisms of the Same Species Have Differences

1) Different species look... well... different — my dog definitely doesn't look like a daisy.
2) But even organisms of the <u>same species</u> will usually look at least <u>slightly</u> different — e.g. in a room full of people you'll see different <u>colour hair</u>, individually <u>shaped noses</u>, a variety of <u>heights</u>, etc.
3) These differences are called the <u>variation</u> within a species.
4) Variation can be <u>genetic</u> — this means it's caused by differences in <u>genotype</u>. Genotype is all of the <u>genes</u> and <u>alleles</u> that an organism has. An organism's genotype affects its <u>phenotype</u> — the <u>characteristics</u> that it <u>displays</u>.
5) An organism's genes are <u>inherited</u> (passed down) from its parents (see page 51).
6) It's <u>not only</u> genotype that can affect an organism's <u>phenotype</u> though — interactions with its <u>environment</u> (conditions in which it lives) can also influence phenotype. For example, a plant grown on a nice sunny windowsill could grow <u>luscious</u> and <u>green</u>. The same plant grown in darkness would grow <u>tall</u> and <u>spindly</u> and its leaves would turn <u>yellow</u> — these are <u>environmental variations</u>.
7) Most variation in phenotype is determined by a <u>mixture</u> of <u>genetic</u> and <u>environmental</u> factors. For example, the <u>maximum height</u> that an animal or plant could grow to is determined by its <u>genes</u>. But whether it actually grows that tall depends on its <u>environment</u> (e.g. how much food it gets).

Environmental variation — pretty much sums up British weather...

It's dead important that you understand this page — it'll help everything else in this topic make much more sense.

Q1   Explain how your height is influenced by both your genome and the environment.   [2 marks]

More on Variation and Genetic Variants

You saw on the previous page that organisms show variation, largely due to differences in their DNA. These genetic differences come about partly due to sexual reproduction (see next page) and partly due to mutations.

Variation can be Continuous or Discontinuous

Continuous variation is when the individuals in a population vary within a range — there are no distinct categories, e.g. humans can be any height within a range, not just tall or short. Other examples include an organism's mass, and the number of leaves on a tree. Characteristics that are influenced by more than one gene or that are influenced by both genetic and environmental factors usually show continuous variation.

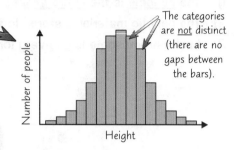
The categories are not distinct (there are no gaps between the bars).

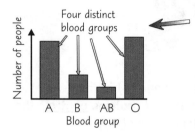
Four distinct blood groups

Discontinuous variation is when there are two or more distinct categories — each individual falls into only one of these categories, there are no intermediates. For example, humans can only be blood group A, B, AB or O. Characteristics that are only influenced by one gene and that aren't influenced by the environment are likely to show discontinuous variation.

Mutations are Changes to the Genome

1) Occasionally, a gene may mutate. A mutation is a rare, random change in an organism's DNA that can be inherited.

2) Mutations mean that the sequence of DNA bases in the gene is changed, which produces a genetic variant (a different form of the gene).

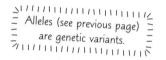
Alleles (see previous page) are genetic variants.

3) As the sequence of DNA bases in a gene codes for the sequence of amino acids that make up a protein, gene mutations sometimes lead to changes in the protein that it codes for.

4) Most genetic variants have very little or no effect on the protein the gene codes for. Some will change it to such a small extent that its function is unaffected. This means that most mutations have no effect on an organism's phenotype.

5) Some variants have a small influence on the organism's phenotype — they alter the individual's characteristics but only slightly. For example:

> Some characteristics, e.g. eye colour, are controlled by more than one gene. A mutation in one of the genes may change the eye colour a bit, but the difference might not be huge.

Well, I s'pose it's time for some new jeans.

6) Very occasionally, variants can have such a dramatic effect that they determine phenotype. For example:

> The genetic disorder, cystic fibrosis, can be caused by the deletion of just three bases but it has a huge effect on phenotype. The gene codes for a protein that controls the movement of salt and water into and out of cells. However, the protein produced by the mutated gene doesn't work properly. This leads to excess mucus production in the lungs and digestive system, which can make it difficult to breathe and to digest food.

I was hoping for the 'grow wings' mutation — I'm still waiting...

Mutations might sound alarming but remember, most are tiny changes that you don't even notice. And mutations introduce variation, and variation can be good (see p.55) so chin up and learn this page.

Q1   Explain why a gene mutation may affect the phenotype of an organism.   [3 marks]

Sexual Reproduction and Meiosis

If you've ever wondered why you look <u>a bit like</u> your <u>mum</u> and <u>a bit like</u> your <u>dad</u> but <u>not exactly like</u> your <u>brothers</u> and <u>sisters</u> (unless you're an identical twin), then today's your lucky day...

Sexual Reproduction Produces Genetically Different Cells

1) <u>Sexual reproduction</u> is where genetic information from <u>two</u> organisms (a <u>father</u> and a <u>mother</u>) is combined to produce offspring which are <u>genetically different</u> to either parent.

2) In <u>sexual reproduction</u>, the mother and father produce <u>gametes</u> — in animals these are <u>sperm</u> and <u>egg cells</u>.

3) Gametes only contain <u>half the number</u> of <u>chromosomes</u> of normal cells — they are <u>haploid</u>. <u>Normal cells</u> (with the full number of chromosomes) are called <u>diploid</u>.

4) At <u>fertilisation</u>, a male gamete <u>fuses</u> with a female gamete to produce a <u>fertilised egg</u>. The fertilised egg ends up with the <u>full set</u> of chromosomes (so it is diploid).

5) The fertilised egg then undergoes <u>cell division</u> (by mitosis — see p.24) and develops into an <u>embryo</u>.

6) The embryo <u>inherits characteristics</u> from <u>both parents</u> as it's received a <u>mixture of chromosomes</u> (and therefore <u>genes</u>) from its mum and its dad.

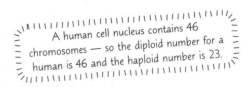

A human cell nucleus contains 46 chromosomes — so the diploid number for a human is 46 and the haploid number is 23.

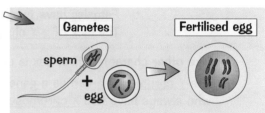

Gametes   Fertilised egg

sperm   +   egg

Gametes are Produced by Meiosis

Meiosis is a type of <u>cell division</u>. It's different to mitosis because it <u>doesn't produce identical cells</u>. In humans, meiosis <u>only</u> happens in the <u>reproductive organs</u> (ovaries and testes).

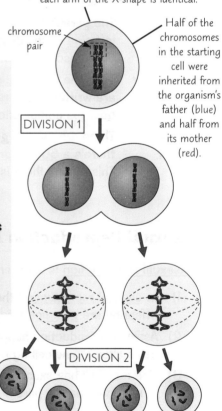

This cell has duplicated each chromosome — each arm of the X-shape is identical.

chromosome pair

Half of the chromosomes in the starting cell were inherited from the organism's father (blue) and half from its mother (red).

DIVISION 1

DIVISION 2

Division 1

1) Before the cell starts to divide, it <u>duplicates</u> its <u>DNA</u> (so there's enough for each new cell). One arm of each X-shaped chromosome is an <u>exact copy</u> of the other arm.

2) In the <u>first division</u> in meiosis (there are two divisions) the chromosomes <u>line up</u> in pairs in the centre of the cell. One chromosome in each pair came from the organism's mother and one came from its father.

3) The <u>pairs</u> are then <u>pulled apart</u>, so each new cell only has one copy of each chromosome. <u>Some</u> of the father's chromosomes and <u>some</u> of the mother's chromosomes go into each new cell.

4) Each new cell will have a <u>mixture</u> of the mother's and father's chromosomes. Mixing up the genes like this is <u>really important</u> — it creates <u>genetic variation</u> in the offspring.

Division 2

5) In the <u>second division</u> the chromosomes <u>line up</u> again in the centre of the cell. It's a lot like mitosis. The <u>arms</u> of the chromosomes are <u>pulled apart</u>.

6) You get <u>four haploid gametes</u> — each only has a <u>single set</u> of chromosomes. The gametes are all <u>genetically different</u>.

Now that I have your undivided attention...

Remember — in humans, meiosis only occurs in the reproductive organs, when gametes are made.

Q1   Explain why gametes need to be haploid.   [2 marks]

Q2   How does meiosis introduce genetic variation?   [2 marks]

Sex Determination and Asexual Reproduction

The previous page talks about how the chromosomes you inherit from your parents can determine your characteristics. Well this page is about how the chromosomes that you inherit determine what sex you are. There's also a wee bit on asexual reproduction, just to spice things up a bit...

Your Chromosomes Control Whether You're Male or Female

1) As you saw on the previous page, during sexual reproduction, the male gamete fuses with the female gamete during fertilisation and the resulting cell has two copies of every chromosome.

2) There are 23 pairs of chromosomes in every human body cell. The 23rd pair are labelled XY. These are sex chromosomes — they decide whether you turn out male or female.

- Males have an X and a Y chromosome: XY
  The Y chromosome causes male characteristics.

- Females have two X chromosomes: XX
  The lack of a Y chromosome causes female characteristics.

3) Like other characteristics, sex is determined by a gene.

4) The Y chromosome carries a gene which makes an embryo develop into a male as it grows. Females, who always have two X chromosomes, don't have this gene and so they develop in a different way.

1) You can draw a genetic diagram to show the probability of a child being a boy or a girl. These diagrams are explained on the next page.

2) Genetic diagrams are often used to show the inheritance of individual alleles, but here one is being used to show how whole sex chromosomes are inherited. Here's how it works:

- The parents' gametes are written along the top and on the left side of the diagram. The male parent has an X and a Y chromosome and the female parent has two X chromosomes.

- Then the combinations of the alleles from both parents are written in the relevant box in the table, to give all the possible combinations in the offspring.

- There are two XX genotypes and two XY genotypes, so there's a 50% chance of having either a boy or a girl. This means there is a 50:50 ratio of boys to girls.

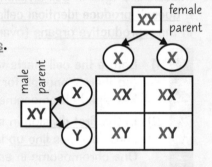

Asexual Reproduction Involves Mitosis

Asexual reproduction is another form of reproduction — it's different to sexual reproduction in several ways:

1) In asexual reproduction there's only one parent so the offspring are genetically identical to that parent.

2) Asexual reproduction happens by mitosis — an ordinary cell makes a new cell by dividing in two (see p.24).

3) The new cell has exactly the same genetic information (i.e. genes) as the parent cell — it's called a clone.

A handsome bunch — even if I do say so myself...

Bacteria, some plants and some animals reproduce asexually.

Have you got the Y-factor...

Who'd have thought that swapping an X chromosome for a Y could make such a massive difference — I thought my brother was a new species. Learn the diagram for sex determination, then it's biscuit time.

Q1   Draw a genetic diagram showing that there's an equal chance of a baby being a boy or a girl.   [2 marks]

Topic B5 — Genes, Inheritance and Selection

Genetic Diagrams

This page is about how <u>characteristics</u> are <u>inherited</u> — it involves drawing little <u>diagrams</u> too, which is (a bit) fun.

Alleles are Different Versions of the Same Gene

1) Most of the time you have <u>two copies</u> of each gene (i.e. <u>two alleles</u>, see p.49) — one from each parent.

2) If the alleles are different, you have <u>instructions</u> for <u>two different versions</u> of a characteristic (e.g. freckles or no freckles) but you only <u>show one version</u> of the two (e.g. freckles). The version of the characteristic that appears is caused by the <u>dominant allele</u>. The other allele is said to be <u>recessive</u>. The characteristic caused by the recessive allele only appears if <u>both alleles</u> are recessive.

3) In genetic diagrams, <u>letters</u> are used to represent <u>genes</u>. <u>Dominant alleles</u> are always shown with a <u>capital letter</u> (e.g. 'C') and <u>recessive alleles</u> with a <u>small letter</u> (e.g. 'c').

4) If you're <u>homozygous</u> for a trait you have <u>two alleles the same</u> for that particular gene, e.g. CC or cc. If you're <u>heterozygous</u> for a trait you have <u>two different alleles</u> for that particular gene, e.g. Cc.

5) Remember, an organism's <u>genotype</u> is the genes and alleles it has and its <u>phenotype</u> is the characteristics that it displays.

Characteristics can also be called 'phenotypic features'.

Genetic Diagrams show the Possible Alleles in the Offspring

Some characteristics are controlled by a <u>single gene</u>, e.g. blood group — this is called <u>single gene inheritance</u>. Genetic diagrams help to <u>predict the phenotype</u> of the <u>offspring</u> when you know the <u>genotype</u> of the <u>parents</u>.

Imagine you're cross-breeding <u>hamsters</u>, and that some have a <u>boring</u> disposition while others have superpowers. And suppose you know that the behaviour is due to <u>one gene</u>...

Let's say that the allele which causes the superpowers is <u>recessive</u> — so use a '<u>b</u>'. And boring behaviour is due to a <u>dominant allele</u> — call it '<u>B</u>'.

1) A <u>superpowered</u> hamster <u>must</u> have the <u>genotype bb</u> (i.e. it must be homozygous for this trait).

2) However, a <u>boring hamster</u> could have <u>two</u> possible genotypes — BB (homozygous) or Bb (heterozygous), because the dominant allele (B) <u>overrules</u> the recessive one (b).

3) Here's what happens if you breed from two <u>heterozygous</u> hamsters:

Parents' <u>phenotypes</u>: boring boring
Parents' <u>genotypes</u>: Bb Bb
Gametes' <u>genotypes</u>: B b B b
Offsprings' <u>genotypes</u>: BB Bb Bb bb
Offsprings' <u>phenotypes</u>: boring boring boring <u>superpowered!</u>

There's a <u>75% chance</u> of having a boring hamster, and a <u>25% chance</u> of a superpowered one. To put that another way... you'd expect a <u>3:1 ratio</u> of boring:superpowered hamsters. Or another way... out of 100 hamsters, the <u>proportion</u> of them you'd expect to be superpowered would be 25.

4) If you breed <u>two homozygous</u> hamsters there's only <u>one possible offspring</u> you can end up with. E.g. breeding BB and bb hamsters can only give offspring with a <u>Bb</u> genotype — and they'd all have a <u>boring</u> phenotype.

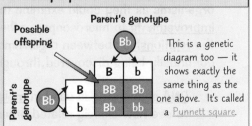

This is a genetic diagram too — it shows exactly the same thing as the one above. It's called a <u>Punnett square</u>.

However, it's not always quite this simple — <u>most</u> characteristics are actually controlled by <u>multiple genes</u>, e.g. height. (You don't need to be able to draw the genetic diagrams for these though.)

Your meanotype determines how nice you are to your sibling...

At first glance this stuff can look quite confusing, but the more you go over it, the more it makes sense.

Q1   People with albinism lack pigment in their skin and eyes, and can appear pale-skinned and white-haired. The gene for albinism (a) is recessive. A heterozygous man has a baby with a woman with albinism.
a) Draw a genetic diagram for the cross. b) What is the chance that the baby will have albinism? [3 marks]

Classification

It seems to be a basic human urge to want to classify things — that's the case in biology anyway...

Classification is Organising Living Organisms into Groups

1) Looking at the similarities and differences between organisms allows us to classify them into groups.

2) Scientists have been doing this for thousands of years but the way in which organisms are classified has changed over time.

3) There are two different classification systems you need to know about, artificial and natural.

Artificial Classification Systems Use Observable Features

1) Early classification systems only used observable features (things you can see) to place organisms into groups, e.g. whether they lay eggs, can fly or can cook a mean chilli... This system of putting organisms into groups is known as an artificial classification system.

2) Artificial classification systems are still used to make keys so that scientists can easily identify and group organisms (see page 60) but they're no longer seen as the best way to classify organisms.

Natural Classification Systems use Evolutionary Relationships

1) As people began to understand more about evolution, evolutionary relationships became much more important when classifying organisms.

2) Natural classification systems use information about organisms' common ancestors and about their common structural features to sort organisms. For example, even though bats and humans have many differences, the bone structure of a bat wing is similar to that of a human hand, so in a natural classification system, bats and humans are grouped together.

3) In natural classification systems, living things are divided into five kingdoms (e.g. the plant kingdom, the animal kingdom).

4) The kingdoms are then subdivided into smaller and smaller groups — phylum, class, order, family, genus, species.

5) The hierarchy ends with species — the groups that contain only one type of organism (e.g. humans, dogs, *E. coli*). A species is defined as a group of similar organisms that are able to reproduce to give fertile offspring.

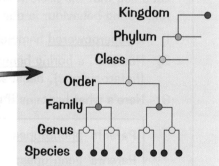

Developments in Biology Lead to Improvements in Classification

As technology improves, scientists are able to learn more and more about organisms and how they're related to each other. Many years ago, the invention of the microscope helped scientists to classify organisms as they could examine the structure of organisms in more detail. Nowadays, as well as improvements to microscopes, other new technologies are resulting in new discoveries being made and the relationships between organisms being clarified. For example, new evolutionary relationships are continually being discovered through molecular phylogenetics.

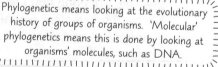
Phylogenetics means looking at the evolutionary history of groups of organisms. 'Molecular' phylogenetics means this is done by looking at organisms' molecules, such as DNA.

- DNA sequencing is used in molecular phylogenetics to see how closely related organisms are.

- DNA sequencing is a technique that compares the sequence of DNA bases for different species (see page 14). The more similar the DNA sequence between species, the more closely related they are. E.g. the base sequence for human and chimpanzee DNA is about 94% the same.

My brother's been reclassified — he's back with the apes...

As new techniques enable us to study organisms at the level of their genes, our classification systems get better.

Q1   Describe the main difference between an artificial and a natural classification system.   [2 marks]

Topic B5 — Genes, Inheritance and Selection

Evolution and Natural Selection

The <u>theory of evolution</u> states that one of your (probably very distant) ancestors was a <u>blob</u> in a swamp somewhere. Something like that, anyway. It's probably best to <u>read on</u> for more details...

Natural Selection Increases Advantageous Phenotypes

1) Populations of species usually show a lot of <u>genetic variation</u> — this means that there's a big <u>mix</u> of gene <u>variants</u> (alleles) present in the population.

2) Variants arise when <u>DNA randomly mutates</u> (see page 50).

3) The <u>resources</u> living things need to survive are <u>limited</u>. Individuals must <u>compete</u> for these resources to <u>survive</u> — only some of the individuals will survive.

4) Some genetic <u>variants</u> give rise to <u>characteristics</u> that are <u>better suited</u> to a particular environment (e.g. being able to run away from predators faster). This means that these organisms have an <u>advantageous phenotype</u>. These individuals will have a <u>better chance</u> of survival and so have an increased chance of <u>breeding</u> and passing on their <u>genes</u>.

5) This means that a <u>greater</u> proportion of individuals in the next generation will <u>inherit</u> the <u>advantageous variants</u> and so they'll have the <u>phenotypes</u> that help <u>survival</u>.

6) Over many generations, the characteristic that increases survival becomes more common in the population. The 'best' characteristics are <u>naturally selected</u> and the species becomes more and more <u>adapted</u> to its environment. Here's an example:

> As well as mutations, sexual reproduction also creates genetic variation (see page 51).

> Once upon a time maybe all rabbits had <u>short ears</u> and managed OK. Then one day a <u>mutated gene</u> meant that one rabbit popped out with <u>big ears</u>. This rabbit could hear better and was always the first to dive for cover at the sound of a predator. Pretty soon he's fathered a whole family of rabbits with <u>big ears</u>, all diving for cover before the other rabbits, and before you know it, there are only <u>big-eared</u> rabbits left — because the rest just didn't hear trouble coming quick enough.
>
> FOX!

Evolution is a Change in Inherited Characteristics

1) Natural selection leads to the <u>evolution</u> of species. Here's how evolution is <u>defined</u>:

> Evolution is the change in inherited characteristics of a population over time, through the process of natural selection.

2) The <u>speed</u> at which a species <u>evolves</u> depends partly on how quickly it <u>reproduces</u> — some species reproduce very <u>quickly</u> (e.g. <u>bacteria</u> can be ready to start dividing in just 20 minutes), whereas others reproduce much more <u>slowly</u> (e.g. usually <u>humans</u> only start reproducing after around 20-30 years).

3) Being quick to reproduce means that <u>inherited characteristics</u> are passed on to <u>future generations</u> much more <u>quickly</u>, so the <u>time taken</u> for the population to <u>adapt</u> to its environment is <u>reduced</u>.

4) Evolution can mean that a species' <u>phenotype</u> changes so much that a completely <u>new species</u> is formed (i.e. the old and new version of the species wouldn't be able to breed together to produce fertile offspring).

5) This can happen when a physical barrier <u>separates two populations</u> of a species — conditions on each side of the barrier will be slightly <u>different</u> so the <u>phenotypes</u> that are <u>beneficial</u> will be <u>different</u> for each population. <u>Natural selection</u> acts on each population to increase the <u>proportion</u> of the <u>advantageous phenotype</u> in that population, until they are so <u>different</u> that they can no longer <u>breed together</u>.

'Natural selection' — sounds like vegan chocolates...

It's no good being really great at surviving if for some reason you don't breed and pass on your genes. And you'll only be good at surviving by having great parents or by awesome mutations in your DNA.

Q1   Musk oxen have thick fur, which is an adaptation to the cold climate in which they live. Explain how the musk oxen may have developed this adaptation over many years.   [4 marks]

Topic B5 — Genes, Inheritance and Selection

Evidence for Evolution

If you're sitting there thinking evolution is a load of <u>old codswallop</u>, here's a bit of <u>evidence</u> to help sway you...

There is Good Evidence for Evolution

Scientists believe that all <u>complex organisms</u> on Earth have evolved from <u>simple organisms</u> that existed about <u>3500 million years ago</u>. Of course, they wouldn't think this without good evidence to back it up. <u>Fossil records</u> and <u>antibiotic resistance in bacteria</u> both provide <u>evidence</u> for evolution:

Fossils are the Remains of Plants and Animals

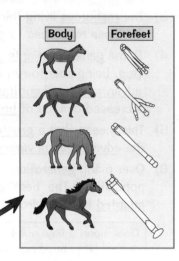

1) A fossil is <u>any trace</u> of an animal or plant that lived <u>long</u> ago. They are most commonly found in <u>rocks</u>.

2) They can tell us a lot about what the organisms <u>looked like</u> and <u>how long ago</u> they existed. Generally, the <u>deeper</u> the rock, the <u>older</u> the fossil.

3) By arranging fossils in <u>chronological</u> (date) order, <u>gradual changes</u> in organisms can be observed. This provides <u>evidence</u> for <u>evolution</u>, because it shows how species have <u>changed</u> and <u>developed</u> over many years. For example, if you look at the <u>fossilised bones</u> of a <u>horse</u>, you can put together a family tree to suggest how the modern horse might have <u>evolved</u>.

Bacteria Can Evolve and Become Antibiotic-Resistant

1) Like all organisms, bacteria sometimes develop <u>random mutations</u> in their DNA, which introduces new <u>variants</u> into the population. These can lead to <u>changes</u> in the bacteria's <u>phenotype</u> — for example, a bacterium could become <u>less affected</u> by a particular <u>antibiotic</u> (a substance designed to kill bacteria or prevent them from reproducing).

2) For the bacterium, this ability to resist antibiotics is a big <u>advantage</u>. The bacterium is better able to <u>survive</u>, even in a host who's being treated with antibiotics, and so it <u>lives for longer</u> and <u>reproduces</u> many more times.

3) This leads to the <u>resistant variant</u> being <u>passed on</u> to offspring and becoming more and more common over time — it's just <u>natural selection</u>.

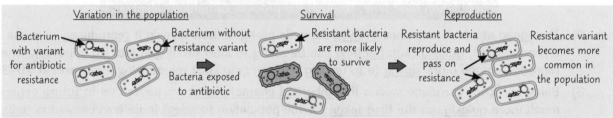

4) The emergence of antibiotic-resistant bacteria provides <u>evidence for evolution</u> (as there is a change in the inherited characteristics of a population over time, through the process of natural selection). What's more, because bacteria <u>reproduce</u> so <u>quickly</u>, scientists are able to <u>monitor</u> the evolution as it's <u>occurring</u>.

The fossil record — it rocks...

Life on Earth is still evolving — the evidence is right under our feet and under our microscopes.

Q1   Which of the following statements best describes how antibiotic resistance provides evidence of evolution?

    A   The proportion of bacteria in a population killed by antibiotics increases over several generations.

    B   Over time, antibiotics are able to kill bacteria with the antibiotic-resistant variant.

    C   In the presence of antibiotics, bacterial cells develop antibiotic-resistant mutations before they die.

    D   Over time, the antibiotic-resistant variant becomes more common in the population.   [1 mark]

Q2   Describe how fossils provide evidence for evolution.   [2 marks]

Revision Questions for Topic B5

Right, that wraps up Topic B5 — time to find out how much of it you've got stored away in your noggin.

- Try these questions and tick off each one when you get it right.
- When you've done all the questions under a heading and are completely happy with it, tick it off.

Genes and Variation (p.49-50) ☑

1) What is an organism's genome?
2) Describe what is meant by the term 'phenotype'.
3) What affects an organism's phenotype apart from its genotype?
4) Give one example of continuous variation.
5) Explain how a mutation leads to the formation of a genetic variant.
6) How likely is it that a variant will have a really big effect on an organism's phenotype?

Reproduction and Sex Determination (p.51-52) ☑

7) What are gametes?
8) What does it mean if a cell is 'haploid'?
9) What are the 23rd pair of chromosomes labelled as in a female?
10) What causes female characteristics in humans?
11) Why does asexual reproduction produce offspring that are genetically identical?

Genetic Diagrams (p.53) ☑

12) In a genetic diagram, is a capital letter used to represent a dominant or recessive allele?
13) What does it mean to be homozygous for a characteristic?
14) Two flowers with the genotypes RR and rr are bred together.
    a) Draw a genetic diagram (e.g. a Punnett square) which shows this cross.
    b) What will the possible genotypes of their offspring be?

Classification (p.54) ☑

15) How are organisms divided into groups in a natural classification system?
16) What is the smallest group that organisms are divided into in the natural classification hierarchy?
17) Describe how the invention of the microscope helped with the classification of organisms.
18) Describe how DNA sequencing is used in classification.

Evolution (p.55-56) ☑

19) How is evolution defined?
20) Why might the speed of evolution vary from species to species?
21) How might evolution lead to the development of new species on Earth?
22) Explain how antibiotic-resistant bacteria provide evidence for evolution.

Investigating Distribution and Abundance

This is where the <u>fun</u> starts. Studying ecology gives you the chance to <u>rummage around</u> in bushes. Hurrah.

Organisms Live in Different Places

1) The <u>abundance</u> of an organism is <u>how many</u> individuals you find in an area (i.e. <u>population size</u>).

2) The <u>distribution</u> of an organism is <u>where</u> an organism is <u>found</u> in a habitat, e.g. in a part of a field.

3) You need to know how to <u>investigate</u> the distribution and abundance of organisms in a <u>habitat</u>.

4) Most of the time it would be <u>too time consuming</u> to measure the <u>number of individuals</u> and <u>distribution</u> of every species in the area you're investigating. So instead you take <u>samples</u>.

5) <u>Abundance</u> can be estimated by <u>counting</u> the number of individuals (or working out <u>percentage cover</u> — see p.61) in samples taken. These results then need <u>scaling up</u> for the total area (see next page).

6) There are a couple of ways to study the <u>distribution</u> of an organism. You can:
   • measure <u>how common</u> an organism is in <u>two sample areas</u> (e.g. using <u>quadrats</u>) and <u>compare</u> them.
   • study how the <u>distribution changes</u> across an area, e.g. by placing quadrats <u>along a transect</u> (p.61).

7) You need to know about the <u>sampling methods</u> coming up below and on the next few pages.

Pooters Are For Collecting Ground Insects*

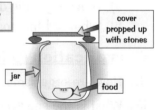

rubber bung

breathe in through flexible tube

long, flexible tube to point at insect

fine mesh stops the insect from being breathed in

1) <u>Pooters</u> are jars that have rubber bungs sealing the top, and <u>two tubes</u> stuck through the bung.

2) If you <u>suck</u> on the shorter tube, and put the end of the longer tube <u>over an insect</u>, it'll be sucked <u>into</u> the jar.

3) In your <u>first sample area</u>, crawl around for a <u>few minutes</u> sucking up as many insects as you can, e.g. from around the <u>base of a tree</u>. Then <u>count</u> the number of insects you've collected.

4) Do this in your <u>second</u> sample area and <u>compare</u> what you find. Spend the <u>same</u> amount of <u>time</u> sampling in each area, and choose sample areas of a <u>similar size</u>.

Pitfall Traps Are Another Way to Investigate Ground Insects

cover propped up with stones

jar

food

A pitfall trap

1) <u>Pitfall traps</u> are <u>steep-sided containers</u> that are sunk in a <u>hole</u> in the ground. The top is <u>partly open</u>.

2) Leave the trap <u>overnight</u> in your first sample area. Insects that come along <u>fall</u> into the container and <u>can't get out</u> again, so you can <u>count</u> them.

3) Then set up a pitfall trap in your second sample area and <u>compare</u> what you find.

Nets Are Used For Collecting Animals From Long Grass and Water

1) A <u>SWEEP NET</u> is a net lined with <u>strong cloth</u> for collecting insects, spiders, etc. from <u>long grass</u>.

2) To use one, <u>stand still</u> in your first sample area and sweep the net <u>once</u> from <u>left to right</u> through the grass. Then <u>quickly</u> sweep the net up and turn the insects out into a <u>container</u> to <u>count</u> them.

3) <u>Repeat</u> the sweep in your second sample area and <u>compare</u> the numbers of organisms you find.

1) A <u>POND NET</u> is a net used for collecting insects, water snails, etc. from <u>ponds</u> and <u>rivers</u>.

2) To use one, stand in your first sample area and sweep the net <u>along the bottom</u> of the pond or river. Turn the net out into a <u>white tray</u> with a bit of water in to <u>count</u> the organisms you've caught.

3) Then sweep your pond net in your second sample area and <u>compare</u> what you find.

Health and safety advises placing tiny cones around pitfall traps...

For these experiments, you should repeat the measurements several times and then take the average result.

Q1　A student wants to find out which ground insects are present in two different areas of a woodland over a 24-hour period. Suggest a method the student could use to sample the areas.　　[3 marks]

　　*That's insects on the ground, not some kind of powdered wasp and ant mixture.

More on Investigating Distribution and Abundance

A bit more on studying the <u>distribution</u> and <u>abundance</u> of organisms. First up, using <u>quadrats</u>...

Use a Quadrat to Study The Distribution of Small Organisms

PRACTICAL

A <u>quadrat</u> is a <u>square</u> frame enclosing a <u>known area</u>, e.g. 1 m². To compare <u>how common</u> an organism is in <u>two sample areas</u>, just follow these simple steps:

1) Place a <u>1 m² quadrat</u> on the ground at a <u>random point</u> within the <u>first</u> sample area. E.g. divide the area into a grid and use a random number generator to pick coordinates. Otherwise, if all your samples are in <u>one spot</u> and everywhere else is <u>different</u>, the results you get won't be <u>valid</u>. For more about <u>random sampling</u> take a look at page 221.

2) <u>Count</u> all the organisms you're interested in <u>within</u> the quadrat.

3) <u>Repeat</u> steps 1 and 2 lots of times. (The <u>larger</u> the <u>sample size</u> the better, see p.4.)

4) <u>Work out</u> the <u>mean</u> number of organisms per quadrat within the first sample area.

5) <u>Repeat</u> steps 1 to 4 in the <u>second</u> sample area.

6) Finally <u>compare</u> the two means. E.g. you might find 2 daisies per m² in the shade, and 22 daisies per m² (lots more) in an open field.

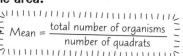
A quadrat

1 m

1 m

$$\text{Mean} = \frac{\text{total number of organisms}}{\text{number of quadrats}}$$

Estimate Population Sizes by Scaling Up from a Small Sample Area

To work out the <u>population size</u> of an organism in one sample area you need to work out the <u>mean number of organisms per m²</u> (if your quadrat has an area of 1 m², this is the same as the mean number of organisms per quadrat, worked out above). Then just <u>multiply the mean</u> by the <u>total area</u> of the habitat.

EXAMPLE: Estimate the population of daisies in a field with an area of 800 m². The mean number of daisies per m² is 22.
Multiply the mean number of daisies per m² by the area.
Population size = 22 × 800 = 17 600 daisies

> If you're given data for the mean number of organisms in a quadrat that's more or less than 1 m² (e.g. per 0.5 m²), you can't just multiply this number by the total area to get your estimate. Calculate organisms per m² first.

You Can Also Estimate Population Sizes Using Capture-Recapture

1) <u>Capture</u> a <u>sample</u> of the population and <u>mark</u> the animals in a <u>harmless</u> way.

2) <u>Release</u> them back into the environment.

3) <u>Recapture</u> another sample of the population. <u>Count</u> how many of this sample are marked.

4) Then <u>estimate</u> population size with this equation:

$$\text{Population Size} = \frac{\text{number in first sample} \times \text{number in second sample}}{\text{number in second sample previously marked}}$$

EXAMPLE: A pitfall trap was set up in an area of woodland. 30 woodlice were caught in an hour and marked on their shell, before being released back into the environment. The next day, 35 woodlice were caught in an hour, only 5 of which were marked. Estimate the population size.

All you need to do is put the numbers into the population size equation (shown above).

Population size = (30 × 35) ÷ 5 = 210 woodlice

number in the first sample   number in the second sample   number in the second sample previously marked

When using the capture-recapture method you have to make a number of <u>assumptions</u>. These include: there has been <u>no change</u> in the <u>population size</u> between the samples (e.g. births and deaths) and the <u>marking</u> hasn't affected individuals' <u>chance of survival</u> (e.g. making them more visible to predators).

Drat, drat and double drat — my favourite use of quadrats...

Choosing which sampling method to use often depends on the type of organism. E.g. quadrats are great for organisms that don't move such as plants, but nets and traps are better for organisms that move around, like insects.

Q1   Capture-recapture was used to estimate the population of crabs on a beach. In the first sample 22 were caught. A second sample had 26 crabs, 4 of which were marked. Estimate the population size. [2 marks]

Using Keys and Factors Affecting Distribution

Yep, there's still some more to learn about this stuff. On this page we cover some practical bits and bobs along with how abiotic and biotic factors affect the distribution of organisms. You're in for a treat, so get excited.

Keys are Used to Identify Creatures

1) A key is a series of questions that you can use to figure out what an unknown organism is.

2) Keys are very useful when you're carrying out sampling as they help you to correctly identify the organisms that you find.

3) To use a key you start at question 1, and the answer to that question (which you know by looking at your mystery organism) is used to narrow down your options of what it could be.

4) Sometimes keys will just have statements, rather than questions, that are followed by a number of options — e.g. 'number of legs' followed by some different options (see below).

5) As you answer more and more questions you narrow down your options further until eventually you're just left with one possible species your organism could be.

Part of a key is shown on the right. It can be used to identify types of organisms that might be found on the ground in a woodland.

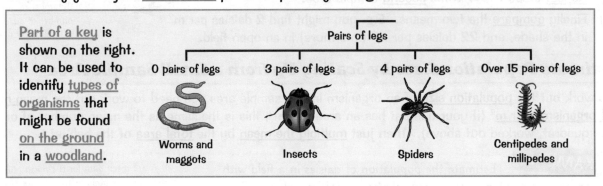

The Distribution of Organisms is Affected by Abiotic and Biotic Factors

1) The distribution of organisms is affected by abiotic factors such as temperature, moisture level, light intensity and soil pH (see page 46). For example, in a playing field, you might find that daisies are more common in the open than under trees, because there's more light available in the open.

2) Biotic factors can also affect the distribution of organisms (see p.46). E.g. competition between species might result in a different distribution of these species than if this competition didn't exist.

You Need to Know How to Measure Abiotic Factors

If you find there's a difference in the distribution of organisms, you can investigate the factors that might be causing it. For example, when looking into the distribution of daisies in the playing field mentioned above, you could measure light intensity both under the trees and in the open — finding a difference in light intensity could provide evidence for the idea that this is affecting the distribution of daisies.

Here's how you can measure the following abiotic factors:

1) Use a thermometer to measure the temperature in different places.

2) Use an electronic device called a light sensor to measure light intensity.

3) Use a soil moisture meter to measure the level of moisture in some soil.

4) Measure soil pH using indicator liquid — water is added to a soil sample and then an indicator liquid (e.g. universal indicator) is added that changes colour depending on the pH. The colour is compared to a chart to find out the pH of the soil. Electronic pH monitors can also be used which produce a pH value for the sample being tested — water is added to the soil sample and an electronic probe is placed into the sample to generate a numerical value for pH.

There's more on measuring temperature and pH on p.219-220.

Identification keys — not much use in the world of home security...

Keys help you identify organisms you've found when sampling. This is pretty important when you want to talk about the different organisms that you've seen — it's not much use saying you found six slimy things in a pond...

Q1   Give two abiotic factors that might be measured on a sandy shore.   [2 marks]

Using Transects

Quadrats back out — transects are another way of investigating the distribution and abundance of organisms...

Transects are Used to Investigate Distribution

PRACTICAL

1) You can investigate how the distribution of an organism gradually changes across an area (e.g. from a hedge towards the middle of a field) using lines called transects.

2) When you sample along the length of a transect using a quadrat (see page 59) this is called a belt transect.

3) To do a belt transect follow the steps below:

> 1) Mark out a line in the area you want to study using a tape measure.
>
> 2) Place a quadrat at the start of the line and count and record the organisms you find in the quadrat.
>
> 3) Then, instead of picking a second sampling site at random (which you'd do if you were sampling a whole area with a quadrat), you take samples by moving your quadrat along the line, e.g. placing the quadrat at intervals of every 2 m.
>
> 4) Alternatively, you could take samples along the entire length of your transect by placing your second quadrat on the transect directly after the first (see diagram above), then the third directly after the second, and so on. This might take ages if you have a long transect though.

4) If it's difficult to count all the individual organisms in the quadrat (e.g. if they're grass) you can calculate the percentage cover. This means estimating the percentage area of the quadrat covered by a particular type of organism, e.g. by counting the number of little squares covered by the organisms.

Measuring % cover

Organism Type A
42 squares = 42%

Organism Type B
47 squares = 47%

You count a square if it's more than half covered.

5) You can plot the results of a transect in a kite diagram (see below). This allows you to map the distribution of organisms in an area.

6) Taking measurements of abiotic factors (see p.46) at points along the transect can show how changes in these affect the distribution and abundance of organisms in the habitat. For example, in a coastal habitat, changes in salinity and soil depth result in zones where different types of plants grow (see below).

Kite Diagrams Show the Abundance and Distribution of Organisms

Kite diagrams can be used to show the data collected in a belt transect — e.g. the kite diagram below shows the distribution and abundance of organisms along a transect in coastal sand dunes:

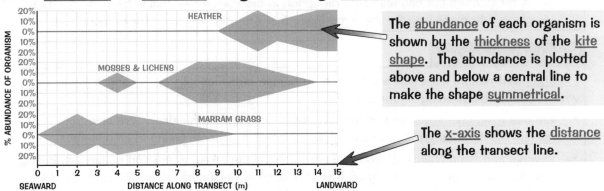

The abundance of each organism is shown by the thickness of the kite shape. The abundance is plotted above and below a central line to make the shape symmetrical.

The x-axis shows the distance along the transect line.

From the kite diagram you can see that marram grass was distributed between 0 and 10 m along the transect. At 2 m along the transect the abundance of marram grass was 20% (i.e. it covered 20% of the quadrat). At 7 m the abundance of marram grass was 10%.

Disclaimer: no kites were harmed in the making of this page...

Transects involve using quadrats in a very organised way. It's exciting, I know, so here's a question to tackle...

Q1 Explain how you would set up a belt transect to record the abundance of species across a field. [5 marks]

Human Impacts on Ecosystems

Time for something less joyous. We humans can have some really damaging negative impacts on ecosystems...

Human Interactions have an Impact on Ecosystems

1) Like all organisms, we humans have an impact on the ecosystems around us.

2) The human population on Earth has grown hugely in the last couple of centuries and is continuing to rise.

3) When the Earth's population was much smaller, the impacts of human activity were usually small and local. Nowadays though, our actions can have a far more widespread effect.

4) Our increasing population puts pressure on the environment, as we take land and resources to survive.

5) But people around the world are also demanding a higher standard of living (and so demand luxuries to make life more comfortable — cars, smartphones, etc.). So we use more raw materials (e.g. oil to make plastics), but we also use more energy for the manufacturing processes. This all means we're taking more and more resources from the environment more and more quickly.

6) Unfortunately, many raw materials are being used up quicker than they're being replaced. So if we carry on like we are, one day we're going to run out.

7) As we produce and consume things we create waste (e.g. waste chemicals), and if we don't handle it properly it can cause harmful pollution like sewage and toxic gases.

8) These human actions are negatively impacting both local biodiversity (the number of species in the local area) and global biodiversity (the number of species on the entire planet) in many ways...

Land Use by Humans is a Negative Interaction with Ecosystems

1) Humans reduce the amount of land and resources available to other animals and plants.

2) The four main human activities that do this are: building, farming, dumping waste and quarrying for metal ores.

3) When land is used by humans, the ecosystem is often changed in a way which has a negative impact on biodiversity. For example:

Habitat destruction

- Woodland clearance — this is often done to increase the area of farmland and can result in a reduction in the number of tree species, so reducing biodiversity. It also destroys the habitats of other organisms — species will die or be forced to migrate elsewhere, further reducing biodiversity.

- Monoculture — this is when areas of land are used to grow a single crop, e.g. in Africa, large areas of land are being used for palm oil plantations. This is an efficient way to grow crops for farmers but can lead to a reduction in biodiversity — this is because habitats are cleared to make way for the large fields that are normally used for monoculture.

Impact of waste on land

Pollution that results from waste produced by human activities kills plants and animals, which reduces biodiversity — for example:

- We use toxic chemicals for farming (e.g. pesticides and herbicides). We also bury nuclear waste underground, and we dump a lot of household waste in landfill sites.

- Sewage and toxic chemicals from industry can pollute lakes, rivers and oceans, affecting the plants and animals that rely on them for survival (including humans). And the chemicals used on land (e.g. fertilisers, pesticides and herbicides) can be washed into water.

- Smoke and gases released into the atmosphere can pollute the air, e.g. sulfur dioxide can cause acid rain.

I'm sorry but I'd prefer it if biodiversity was low inside my house...

I don't know about you but I feel a bit guilty. Our desire for a better standard of living is bad news for the planet.

Q1   Describe how the construction of houses on a meadow could reduce local biodiversity.   [2 marks]

More Human Impacts on Ecosystems

Some more human impacts on ecosystems are on the menu for this page. First up, another negative interaction (crikey), but don't despair, things will start looking up after that...

Hunting is Another Negative Human Interaction with Ecosystems

1) Some animal species are hunted, which (shockingly) reduces their numbers.
   For example:
   > Species of rhino are hunted for their horns and this has contributed to them becoming endangered.

2) If too many individuals are killed, it might result in the extinction of the species.
   For example:
   > Fishing on a big scale can reduce fish stocks to such a low level that it might cause a species to die out completely.

3) The removal of a particular species from an area reduces the biodiversity of that ecosystem. The reduction in number (or complete removal) of a particular species can also have knock-on effects in an ecosystem and negatively impact food chains, which could cause a further decrease in biodiversity.

Conservation of Species is a Positive Interaction with Ecosystems

Conservation schemes can help to protect biodiversity by conserving species or their habitats. Examples of conservation methods include:

Protecting habitats

This includes things such as controlling water levels to conserve wetlands and coppicing (trimming trees) to conserve woodlands. This allows organisms to continue living in their natural habitat.

Controlling or preventing the introduction of harmful species

Some schemes aim to prevent the introduction of harmful species that would threaten local biodiversity — e.g. those that could reduce the numbers of a species by competing with it or eating it. An example of this in the UK is the control of grey squirrels in some areas. Grey squirrels are not native to Britain and they compete with the native red squirrel and have caused their populations to decline.

Creating protected areas for organisms

Protected areas include places like national parks and nature reserves. Both organisms and habitats are protected in these areas by restricting the development of the land — this includes building houses and using the land for farming. Protected areas can also be found in the sea where human activities like fishing are controlled to protect marine ecosystems.

Protecting organisms in safe areas away from their natural habitat

For animals, safe areas include zoos and for plants they include botanical gardens and seed banks. In these areas, organisms can be protected from harmful activities such as hunting and habitat destruction. Safe areas can also be used to increase numbers of particular organisms before they are released into the wild — for animals this is known as captive breeding. This method is useful for reintroducing organisms if they become extinct in the wild.

My room is a protected area from the species Brother Horriblis...

Make sure you get your head around how humans can interact with ecosystems in both positive and negative ways. Negative interactions result in a reduction in the level of biodiversity, whereas positive interactions can maintain or even increase levels of biodiversity. Imagine that, we can have a beneficial effect rather than causing destruction...

Q1 A plant species is nearly extinct in the wild as a result of its habitat being damaged.
    Explain how botanical gardens and habitat protection could be used to increase the
    number of individuals of the plant species growing in the wild.   [2 marks]

Maintaining Biodiversity

Trying to preserve biodiversity can be <u>tricky</u> but there are <u>benefits</u> for doing it, so it's <u>pretty worthwhile</u>...

Maintaining Biodiversity Benefits Wildlife and Humans

Conservation schemes help <u>maintain biodiversity</u> by protecting species (see previous page).
As well as benefitting <u>endangered species</u> they often help <u>humans</u> too:

1) <u>Protecting the human food supply</u> — over-fishing has <u>greatly reduced fish stocks</u> in the world's oceans. Conservation programmes can ensure that future generations will have <u>fish to eat</u>.

2) <u>Ensuring minimal damage to food chains</u> — if <u>one species</u> becomes <u>extinct</u> it will affect all the organisms that feed on and are eaten by that species, so the <u>whole food chain</u> is affected. This means <u>conserving one species</u> may <u>help others</u> to survive.

3) <u>Providing future medicines</u> — many of the medicines we use today come from <u>plants</u>. Undiscovered plant species may contain <u>new medicinal chemicals</u>. If these plants are allowed to become <u>extinct</u>, perhaps through <u>rainforest destruction</u>, we could miss out on valuable medicines.

4) <u>Providing industrial materials and fuels</u> — plant and animal species are involved in the production of <u>industrial materials</u> (e.g. wood, paper, adhesives and oils) and some <u>fuels</u>. If these species become extinct these important resources may become <u>more difficult</u> to produce.

Ecotourism is Another Benefit of Maintaining Biodiversity

1) <u>Ecotourism</u> is tourism that focuses on the <u>appreciation of nature</u> and its <u>conservation</u> whilst having a <u>minimal negative impact</u> on the <u>local ecosystem</u>. Maintaining areas with high biodiversity provides an <u>opportunity</u> for ecotourism to take place in these areas — people are drawn to visit beautiful, unspoilt landscapes.

> The <u>Eden Project</u> in Cornwall is a sort of 'eco theme park', which contains huge plastic domes that represent different ecosystems (e.g. a rainforest) and educates visitors about conservation.

2) Ecotourism helps <u>bring money</u> into areas where conservation work is taking place — e.g. when tourists buy stuff in local shops and cafes it supports the <u>local economy</u>. Tourists spending money at <u>ecotourism attractions</u> (like the Eden project's gift shop) also helps to <u>fund</u> conservation work.

Maintaining Biodiversity can be Challenging

Ways of maintaining biodiversity are <u>great in theory</u> but they can be <u>difficult</u> to do in the real world. Here are a few examples of why:

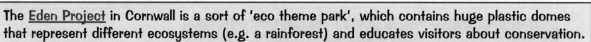

Agreements about conservation schemes can be difficult to arrange

1) Some conservation schemes require several different countries to <u>work together</u>. Sometimes this can be difficult as some countries <u>aren't willing</u> to sign up to an agreement. One example is the efforts of the <u>International Whaling Commission</u> to restrict whaling. Even though lots of countries have signed up to <u>stop whaling</u>, there are still some that haven't — these include Norway, the Faroe Islands and Iceland. Around 2000 whales are killed each year.

2) On a smaller scale, conservation schemes can be <u>objected to</u> by <u>local residents</u>. E.g. people might not be keen if a scheme <u>reduces their income</u> (e.g. a ban on logging or fishing restrictions).

Conservation schemes can be difficult to monitor

E.g. keeping track of <u>fishing quotas</u> (restrictions on the amount of fish that can be caught at sea) can be tricky. This can be a pain if you're trying to work out <u>how successful</u> a scheme is and also if you want to see if people are <u>sticking to it</u>.

It's a shame exams aren't an endangered species...

Hmmm, I guess the maintenance of biodiversity can be a bit tricky but if it keeps food on the table I'm keen...

Q1   Explain why maintaining biodiversity could be important for providing medicines in the future.   [2 marks]

Selective Breeding

'Selective breeding' sounds like it has the potential to be a tricky topic, but it's actually dead simple. You take the best plants or animals and breed them together to get the best possible offspring. That's it.

Selective Breeding is Mating the Best Organisms to Get Good Offspring

Organisms are selectively bred to develop the best features according to what we want from them. This includes things like:

- **Maximum yield** of meat, milk, grain, etc. — this means that food production is as high as possible, which is important for helping make sure there's enough food for people to eat.
- Good health and disease resistance.
- In animals, other qualities like temperament, speed, fertility, good mothering skills, etc.
- In plants, other qualities like attractive flowers, nice smell, etc.

This is the basic process involved in selective breeding:

1) The parent organisms with the best characteristics are selected, e.g. the largest sheep and rams — those with the highest meat yield.

2) They're bred with each other.

3) The best of the offspring are selected and bred.

4) This process is repeated over several generations to develop the desired traits, e.g. to produce sheep with very large meat yields.

Selective breeding is also known as artificial selection.

Selective breeding can also be used to combine two different desirable characteristics:

1) Tall wheat plants have a good grain yield but are easily damaged by wind and rain. Dwarf wheat plants can resist wind and rain but have a lower grain yield.

2) These two types of wheat plant were cross-bred, and the best resulting wheat plants were cross-bred again. This resulted in a new variety of wheat combining the good characteristics — dwarf wheat plants which could resist bad weather and had a high grain yield.

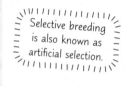

The Main Drawback is a Reduction in the Gene Pool

1) The main problem with selective breeding is that it reduces the gene pool — the number of different alleles (forms of a gene) in a population. This is because the farmer keeps breeding from the "best" animals or plants — which are all closely related. This is known as inbreeding.

2) Inbreeding can cause health problems because there's more chance of the organisms developing harmful genetic disorders when the gene pool is limited.

3) There can also be serious problems if a new disease appears, because there's not much variation in the population. All the stock are closely related to each other, so if one of them is going to be killed by a new disease, the others are also likely to succumb to it.

Oh Eck!

I use the same genes all the time too — they flatter my hips...

Selective breeding's not a new thing. People have been doing it for absolutely yonks. But the basic process has stayed the same — select the best individuals, let them reproduce, repeat over many generations, and voilà...

Q1   A farmer who grows green beans lives in an area that experiences a lot of drought. Explain how he could use selective breeding to improve the chances of his bean plants surviving the droughts.   [3 marks]

Q2   Give two disadvantages of selectively breeding animals.   [2 marks]

Genetic Engineering

Genetic engineering allows humans to change the characteristics of organisms. Here's how it works...

Vectors Can Be Used To Insert DNA Into Other Organisms

The basic idea behind genetic engineering is to move genes for desirable characteristics from one organism to another so that it has those characteristics too. The organism's genome is changed during the process. A vector is something that's used to transfer DNA into a cell. Plasmids (see p.11) are often used as vectors. They are small, circular molecules of DNA that can be transferred between bacteria.

Here's how the process of genetic engineering works:

1) The DNA you want to insert (the gene for the desired characteristic) is cut out with a restriction enzyme. Restriction enzymes recognise specific sequences of DNA and cut the DNA at these points.

2) The plasmid is then cut open using the same restriction enzyme.

3) This creates sticky ends on the DNA — short tails of unpaired bases that are complementary to each other (see p.14).

4) The plasmid and the DNA you're inserting are mixed together with ligase enzymes.

5) The ligases join the sticky ends of the two pieces of DNA together.

6) Plasmid vectors that contain the new DNA are inserted into other cells, e.g. bacteria, known as hosts. The host cells can now use the gene you inserted to produce the desired characteristic.

7) However, not all of the host cells will have been modified successfully, e.g. the vector might not have been transferred properly. So, the last stage is to select (identify) the individuals that have successfully received the desired gene (see below).

Desired gene

Sticky ends

Viruses can also be used as vectors.

Restriction enzymes cut the gene out and cut open the plasmid...

Sticky ends

Plasmid

...ligases join the two pieces of DNA together...

...and the plasmid containing the desired gene is inserted into the host cell.

Genetically engineered organisms can also be called genetically modified or transgenic organisms. Transgenic organisms always contain genes transferred from another species.

Antibiotic Resistance Markers Are Used to Select Cells with the New DNA

To find the host cells that do contain the new DNA, antibiotic resistance markers are used. Here's how they work:

1) A marker gene, which codes for antibiotic resistance, is inserted into the vector at the same time as the gene for the desired characteristic.

2) The host bacteria are grown on a special plate containing antibiotics (see p.72). Only the bacteria that contain the marker gene will be able to survive and reproduce (the antibiotics will kill the rest).

Agrobacterium Tumefaciens is Used to Genetically Modify Plants

Genetic engineering is used in agriculture to produce crops with desirable characteristics that increase yields (see p.65). To genetically modify plants, scientists often use a bacterium called *Agrobacterium tumefaciens*:

1) *Agrobacterium tumefaciens* invades plant cells and inserts its genes into the plant's DNA.

2) Once the *Agrobacterium tumefaciens* bacteria has been genetically modified to include a useful gene (e.g. the gene for herbicide resistance), it's allowed to infect the cells of the 'target' plant. The bacteria will insert their genes (including e.g. the herbicide-resistance gene) into the plant's DNA.

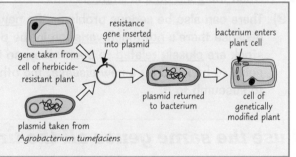

gene taken from cell of herbicide-resistant plant

resistance gene inserted into plasmid

bacterium enters plant cell

plasmid taken from Agrobacterium tumefaciens

plasmid returned to bacterium

cell of genetically modified plant

Using GM bacteria to make GM plants — genius...

Genetically engineer a bacterium, then use that to genetically engineer a plant — cunning.

Q1   What are antibiotic resistance markers used for in genetic engineering?   [1 mark]

More on Genetic Engineering

Genetic engineering sounds great, and there are lots of benefits. But not everyone is happy with it being used.

Genetic Engineering Has Many Benefits...

Many people in the world today don't have enough food to eat. Genetic engineering could help:

Genetic engineering can be used to transfer useful genes into plants and animals so that they have the useful characteristics of the inserted gene. This can help to increase food production in many different ways. E.g:

1) Plants can be genetically modified to make them resistant to insect pests. This prevents the crop being damaged by insects which increases crop yield.

2) There's a bacterium called *Bacillus thuringiensis* (Bt) which produces a toxin (poison) that kills many of the insect larvae that are harmful to crops.

3) The gene for the Bt toxin is inserted into crops, like corn and cotton, which then produce the toxin in their stems and leaves — making them resistant to the insect pests.

4) The toxin is specific to insect pests — it's harmless to humans, animals and other insects.

5) A good thing about Bt crops is that farmers need to apply less pesticide (because the crops already have it built into them). This avoids the negative impacts of pesticide use (see p.62).

6) There's a drawback to Bt crops though. There's a danger that insects might develop resistance to the toxin and no longer be killed by it.

Herbicide and virus resistance can also be engineered into crops.

Genetic engineering can also be used to combat certain deficiency diseases. For example:

In some parts of the world, the population relies heavily on rice for food. In these areas, vitamin A deficiency can be a problem, because rice doesn't contain much of this vitamin, and other sources are scarce. Genetic engineering has allowed scientists to take a gene that controls beta-carotene (which humans can use to make vitamin A) production from carrot plants, and put it into rice plants.

...But It Also Comes With Risks

There are concerns about growing genetically modified crops...

1) Transplanted genes may get out into the environment. E.g. a herbicide resistance gene may be picked up by weeds, creating new 'superweeds'.

2) Another concern is that genetically modified crops could adversely affect food chains — or even human health.

3) Some people are against genetic engineering altogether. They worry that changing an organism's genes might create unforeseen problems — which would then get passed on to future generations. For example, the long-term effects of exposure to Bt crops (see above) aren't yet known.

4) Some people say that growing genetically modified crops will affect the number of weeds and flowers (and therefore wildlife) that usually live in and around the crops — reducing farmland biodiversity (number of species in an ecosystem).

People in developed countries, e.g. those in Europe, tend to be more concerned about the potential risks because food shortages are not as big an issue as in developing countries.

I say it's great.

Genetic Engineering Raises Ethical Issues

You need to be able to discuss the ethical issues surrounding genetic engineering too:

1) Some people think it's wrong to genetically engineer other organisms purely for human benefit. This is a particular problem in the genetic engineering of animals, especially if the animal suffers as a result.

2) People worry that we won't stop at engineering plants and animals. In the future, those who can afford genetic engineering might be able to decide the characteristics they want their children to have — and those who can't afford it may become a 'genetic underclass'.

3) Some people think genetic engineering is irresponsible when there's uncertainty about the consequences.

If only there was a gene to make revision easier...

Genetic engineering is a serious issue — its not just designer food. Make sure you can discuss both pros and cons.

Q1   Give two potential risks of growing genetically engineered crops.   [2 marks]

Health and Disease

If you are feeling <u>bright-eyed</u> and <u>bushy-tailed</u> then you probably won't be for much <u>longer</u> — you're about to find out about lots of lovely <u>diseases</u> and all the <u>nasties</u> that can <u>cause</u> them. Mwah ha ha.

Organisms' Health Can be Affected by Disease

1) A <u>healthy</u> organism is one that is <u>functioning</u> just as it <u>should</u> be — both <u>physically</u> and <u>mentally</u>.

2) A <u>disease</u> is a condition that <u>impairs</u> the <u>normal functioning</u> of an organism.
Both <u>plants</u> and <u>animals</u> can get diseases.

3) Most organisms will experience disease <u>at some point</u>.

4) There are many <u>causes</u> of disease. For example:
   - the organism may become <u>infected</u> by a <u>pathogen</u> (see below),
   - there may be a <u>mutation</u> in the organism's <u>genes</u> (see page 50),
   - the organism may be affected by <u>environmental conditions</u>, e.g. if a plant <u>doesn't get enough light</u> it won't grow properly (see page 49), or a human may be affected by issues such as <u>poor diet</u> or <u>lack of exercise</u>.

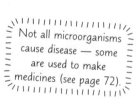

Diseases Can be Communicable or Non-Communicable

1) A <u>pathogen</u> is a type of <u>microorganism</u> (microbe) that causes <u>disease</u>.
Types of pathogen include <u>bacteria</u>, <u>viruses</u>, <u>protists</u> and <u>fungi</u> (see next page).

2) A <u>communicable</u> disease is a disease that can <u>spread</u> between organisms.
They are caused by <u>pathogens</u> infecting the organism, e.g. malaria is caused by a protist, and tobacco mosaic disease in plants is caused by a virus.
Communicable diseases are also known as <u>infectious diseases</u>.

3) <u>Non-communicable</u> diseases <u>cannot</u> be passed from one organism to another, e.g. cardiovascular and respiratory diseases, cancers and diabetes. They generally last for a <u>long time</u> and <u>progress slowly</u>.
They are often linked to <u>unhealthy lifestyles</u> (see page 76-77).

Not all microorganisms cause disease — some are used to make medicines (see page 72).

One Disease Can Lead to Another

Sometimes having <u>one disease</u> can make it <u>more likely</u> that you will suffer from <u>another disease</u>. Here are two <u>examples</u> that you need to know about:

The immune system is the body's way of protecting itself against disease — see page 71.

1) <u>HIV</u> (human immunodeficiency virus) stops the <u>immune system</u> from <u>working properly</u>.

2) The <u>bacteria</u> that cause another communicable disease called <u>tuberculosis</u> are normally <u>destroyed</u> by the immune system <u>before symptoms</u> of the disease can <u>develop</u>.

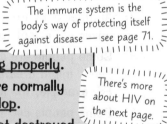
There's more about HIV on the next page.

3) But, if the tuberculosis bacteria infect someone with <u>HIV</u>, the bacteria are <u>not destroyed</u> by the immune system so the disease progresses very <u>rapidly</u> — this means people with HIV are much <u>more likely</u> to show <u>symptoms</u> of tuberculosis. It's also much <u>more difficult</u> for people with HIV to <u>recover</u> from tuberculosis.

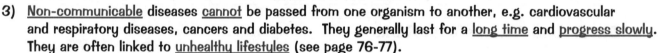

1) <u>HPV</u> (human papillomavirus) is a <u>virus</u> that can infect the <u>reproductive system</u>.
One way that it's transmitted is in <u>body fluids</u> (see next page), usually through sexual activity.

2) An <u>infection</u> by the virus <u>doesn't always</u> cause <u>symptoms</u> and often clears up on its own within a couple of months.

3) However, some <u>HPV infections</u> can cause <u>cell changes</u> resulting in the development of certain types of <u>cancer</u>. It's thought that <u>nearly all</u> cervical cancer cases result from HPV infections.

I have a communicable disease — it's telling me to go to bed...

Communicable diseases can be <u>passed</u> between people because they involve <u>pathogens</u>.

Q1   What is a non-communicable disease?   [3 marks]

How Disease Spreads

Well, here are loads of ways you can catch diseases. As if I wasn't feeling paranoid enough already...

Communicable Diseases are Caused by Pathogens

Pathogens are microbes that cause communicable diseases (see previous page). There are four types:

1) BACTERIA — very small cells (about 1/100th the size of your body cells), which can reproduce rapidly. They make you feel ill by producing toxins (poisons) that damage your cells and tissues.

2) VIRUSES — these are not cells. They're really tiny, about 1/100th the size of a bacterium. They replicate themselves inside the infected organism's cells. These cells then burst, releasing the viruses.

3) PROTISTS — these are eukaryotic (see page 11) usually single-celled and vary in size. Protists that cause disease are often parasites (see page 47).

4) FUNGI — some fungi are single-celled while others have a body, which is made up of thread-like structures called hyphae. These hyphae can grow and penetrate human skin and the surface of plants, causing diseases. They can also produce spores, which can be spread to other plants and animals.

Once inside an organism, pathogens can rapidly multiply, e.g. *E.coli* can divide once every 20 minutes. As this happens, the infected organism will start to show symptoms of the disease.

Communicable Diseases are Transmitted in Different Ways

Pathogens infect both animals and plants and can spread in different ways. For example:

Water	• Some pathogens can be picked up by drinking or bathing in dirty water. E.g. cholera is a bacterial infection that causes diarrhoea and dehydration. It's spread via drinking water containing the diarrhoea of other sufferers.
Air	• Some pathogens are carried in the air. E.g. *Erysiphe graminis* is a fungus that causes barley powdery mildew. It makes white, fluffy patches appear on the leaves of barley plants. This affects the plant's ability to photosynthesise, which can decrease yields. It's spread by spores that are blown between plants by the wind. • Airborne pathogens can be carried in droplets produced when you cough or sneeze — so other people can breathe them in. E.g. the influenza virus that causes flu is spread this way.
Contact	• Some pathogens can be picked up by touching contaminated surfaces. E.g. tobacco mosaic disease affects many species of plants, e.g. tomatoes. It's caused by a virus called tobacco mosaic virus (TMV) that makes the leaves of plants mottled and discoloured. The discolouration means the plant can't photosynthesise as well, so the virus affects growth. It's spread when infected leaves rub against healthy leaves. • Athlete's foot is a fungus which makes skin itch and flake off. It's most commonly spread by touching the same things as an infected person, e.g. shower floors and towels.
Body fluids	• Some pathogens are spread by body fluids such as blood (e.g. by sharing needles to inject drugs), breast milk (through breast feeding) and semen (through sex). HIV is a virus spread by exchanging body fluids. It initially causes flu-like symptoms for a few weeks, but after that, the person doesn't usually experience any symptoms for several years. The virus enters the lymph nodes and attacks the immune cells. If the immune system isn't working properly, it can't cope with other infections (see previous page) or cancers. At this stage, the virus is known as late stage HIV, or AIDS.
Animal vectors	• Animals that spread disease are called vectors. E.g. malaria is caused by a protist. Part of the malarial protist's life cycle takes place inside a mosquito. Mosquitoes act as vectors — they pick up the malarial protist when they feed on an infected animal. Every time the mosquito feeds on another animal, it infects it by inserting the protist into the animal's blood vessels. Malaria causes repeating episodes of fever. It can be fatal.
Soil	• Some pathogens can live in the soil, so plants in the contaminated soil may be infected. E.g. the bacteria, *Agrobacterium tumefaciens*, that cause crown gall disease, are able to live freely in some soils and on the roots of some plants. If the bacteria enter a plant, they can cause growths or tumours called galls on roots, stems and branches. The galls can damage the plant tissue, restricting the flow of water through the plant. This causes the plant to become weaker and it may eventually die.
Food	• Some pathogens are picked up by eating contaminated food. E.g. *Salmonella* bacteria are found in some foods, e.g. raw meat. If these foods are kept too long or not cooked properly the bacteria can cause food poisoning.

You can use sampling techniques to estimate the number of organisms in a population that are infected with a disease. First you'd work out the mean number of infected individuals in some samples, then multiply this mean by the total number of individuals in the population.

Ahh...Ahh... Ahhhhh Choooooooo — urghh, this page is catching...

Pathogens are usually really small — you often need a microscope to see them — but they don't half get about...

Q1   Give three ways in which communicable diseases can be spread.   [3 marks]

Reducing and Preventing the Spread of Disease

Aha, a page about what we can do to <u>avoid</u> catching communicable diseases. Things are definitely <u>looking up</u>.

Communicable Diseases Can Be Affected by Social and Economic Factors

1) The <u>transmission</u> of many communicable diseases <u>increases</u> when lots of people live <u>crowded together</u> in a <u>small space</u> because it's <u>easier</u> for pathogens to <u>pass</u> from one person to another, e.g. if people cough.

2) <u>Poor diet</u> can also <u>increase</u> the risk of infection because the <u>immune system</u> can be <u>weakened</u> by not getting the right nutrients.

3) The risk of infection <u>increases</u> where there is <u>limited access</u> to <u>healthcare</u> and <u>health education</u> too:

   - Having access to <u>healthcare</u> means that people are more likely to be <u>diagnosed</u> and get the <u>treatment</u> they need to get better. This <u>reduces</u> the chance of them <u>passing on</u> the infection.
   - <u>Good education</u> gives people <u>better knowledge</u> of how diseases are <u>transmitted</u> so they can <u>avoid</u> catching the infections in the first place, e.g. through safe-sex practices like using condoms to avoid getting HIV (see previous page).

The Spread of Disease Can Be Reduced or Prevented in Humans...

There are things that we can do to <u>reduce</u>, and even <u>prevent</u>, the spread of disease. For example:

1) <u>Being hygienic</u> — Using simple hygiene measures can prevent the spread of disease. For example, doing things like <u>washing your hands</u> thoroughly before preparing food or after you've sneezed can stop you infecting another person.

2) <u>Destroying vectors</u> — By getting rid of the organisms that spread disease, you can prevent the disease from being passed on. Vectors that are <u>insects</u> can be killed using <u>insecticides</u> or by <u>destroying</u> their <u>habitat</u> so that they can no longer breed.

3) <u>Isolating infected individuals</u> — This <u>prevents</u> people with a communicable disease from <u>passing it on</u>.

4) <u>Vaccination</u> — Vaccinating people and animals against communicable diseases means that they <u>can't</u> develop the infection and then <u>pass it on</u> to someone else.

There's more about how vaccination works on page 72.

The early detection (and treatment) of a disease can be useful for <u>limiting its spread</u>. This can <u>reduce</u> the chance of the disease being passed on to others.

The first step in reducing the spread of disease is identifying the disease — e.g. by detecting antigens, DNA testing or visually identifying the disease.

...And in Plants

Plants are a very important <u>food source</u> throughout the world. Plant <u>diseases</u> can <u>reduce crop yield</u> and the <u>biodiversity</u> of <u>ecosystems</u>, so <u>preventing</u> the spread of disease in plants is <u>really important</u>. Here are some ways that the spread of disease can be <u>controlled</u>:

1) <u>Regulating movement of plant material</u> — this makes sure that <u>infected</u> plants don't come into <u>contact</u> with <u>healthy</u> plants, e.g. plant nurseries are not allowed to sell plants which have crown gall disease.

2) <u>Destroying infected plants</u> — this stops them being <u>sources</u> of infection.

3) <u>Crop rotation</u> — many pathogens are <u>specific</u> to a particular plant. <u>Changing</u> the <u>type of plants</u> that are grown stops the pathogens becoming <u>established</u> in an area.

4) <u>Chemical control</u> — for example, <u>fungicides</u> can be used to kill <u>fungal</u> pathogens or used as a <u>preventative</u> method by <u>coating</u> the bulbs or seeds <u>before</u> they're planted.

5) <u>Biological control</u> — e.g. <u>crown gall disease</u> can be prevented by <u>dipping roots</u> of plants into a suspension of a <u>similar bacterium</u> before they are planted in <u>infected</u> soils. This bacteria doesn't infect the plants — instead, it produces an <u>antibiotic</u> (see p.72) that <u>prevents</u> *Agrobacterium tumefaciens* from <u>reproducing</u>.

The spread of disease — mouldy margarine...

You may be sick of diseases already (geddit?) but don't turn this page until you've got the facts fixed in your brain.

Q1   Malaria is spread by mosquitoes which carry protists. The protists enter the bloodstream of animals when the mosquito feeds on them. Explain one way in which the spread of malaria could be reduced. [2 marks]

The Human Immune System

Right, back to <u>humans</u>. Your body has some pretty neat features when it comes to <u>fighting disease</u>.

Your Body Has a Pretty Sophisticated Defence System

The human body has got features that <u>stop</u> a lot of nasties getting <u>inside</u> in the first place.
These are <u>non-specific</u> defences — they aren't produced in response to a <u>particular</u> pathogen.

1) The <u>skin</u> acts as a <u>barrier</u> to pathogens. It also secretes <u>antimicrobial substances</u> which kill pathogens.

2) The whole <u>respiratory tract</u> (nasal passage, trachea and lungs) is lined with <u>mucus</u> and <u>cilia</u> (hair-like structures) and there are <u>hairs</u> in the nose. The mucus and hairs <u>trap</u> particles that could contain pathogens and the cilia <u>waft the mucus</u> up to the back of the throat where it can be <u>swallowed</u>.

3) <u>Eyes</u> produce (in <u>tears</u>) an enzyme called <u>lysozyme</u> which break down <u>bacteria</u> on the surface of the eye.

4) The <u>stomach</u> produces <u>hydrochloric acid</u>. This <u>kills pathogens</u> that make it that far from the mouth.

5) When you damage a blood vessel, <u>platelets</u> in the blood clump together to 'plug' the damaged area. This is known as <u>blood clotting</u>. Blood clots <u>stop you losing</u> too much <u>blood</u> and prevent <u>microorganisms</u> from entering the wound.

> Platelets are <u>tiny fragments</u> of cells. They contain lots of <u>different substances</u> that are needed to help form the <u>clot</u>. They also have <u>proteins</u> on their surface which help them <u>stick together</u> and to the <u>site of the wound</u>.

Your Immune System Can Attack Pathogens

> You can read more about what's in the blood in Topic B2 — see p.33.

1) If pathogens do make it into your body, your <u>immune system</u> kicks in to destroy them.

2) The most important part of your immune system is the <u>white blood cells</u>. They travel around in your <u>blood</u> and crawl into every part of you, constantly patrolling for <u>pathogens</u>. When they come across an <u>invading</u> pathogen they have <u>three</u> lines of <u>attack</u>:

1. Consuming Them

Some white blood cells (<u>phagocytes</u>) have a <u>flexible membrane</u> and contain lots of <u>enzymes</u>. This enables them to <u>engulf</u> foreign cells and <u>digest</u> them. This is called <u>phagocytosis</u>.

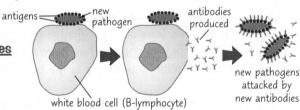

2. Producing Antibodies

1) Every invading pathogen has unique molecules (<u>antigens</u>) on its surface.

2) When your white blood cells come across a <u>foreign antigen</u> (i.e. one they don't recognise), they will start to produce <u>proteins</u> called <u>antibodies</u> to lock onto the invading cells. The antibodies produced are <u>specific</u> to that type of antigen — they won't lock on to any others.

white blood cell (B-lymphocyte)

3) Antibodies are then produced <u>rapidly</u> and carried around the body to <u>lock on</u> to all similar pathogens.

4) The <u>antibodies help</u> the phagocytes <u>find</u> the pathogens, so they can <u>engulf</u> them.

> The white blood cells that produce antibodies are also known as B-lymphocytes.

5) Some white blood cells, called <u>memory cells</u>, <u>stay around</u> in the blood after the pathogen has been fought off. If the person is <u>infected</u> with the <u>same pathogen again</u>, the white blood cells will rapidly produce the antibodies to help destroy it — the person is <u>naturally</u> immune to that pathogen and won't get ill.

3. Producing Antitoxins These counteract toxins produced by the <u>invading bacteria</u>.

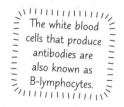

Fight disease — give your nose a blow with boxing gloves...
The <u>body</u> makes antibodies against the antigens on pathogens. There, don't say I never help you. Right, tea...

Q1 Describe the role of platelets in the defence of the body against pathogens. [2 marks]

Vaccines and Medicines

An ounce of <u>prevention</u> is worth a pound of <u>cure</u>. That's what my mum says, anyhow.

Vaccinations Stop You Getting Infections

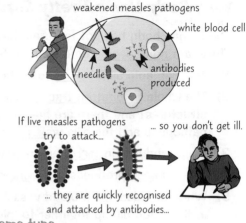

weakened measles pathogens

white blood cell

needle

antibodies produced

1) When you're infected with a <u>new</u> pathogen it can take your white blood cells a while to produce the antibodies to deal with it. In that time you can get <u>very ill</u>, or maybe even die.

2) To avoid this you can be <u>vaccinated</u> (immunised) against some diseases, e.g. polio or measles.

3) Vaccination involves injecting <u>dead, inactive or weakened</u> pathogens into the body. These carry <u>antigens</u>, so even though they're <u>harmless</u> they still trigger an <u>immune response</u> — your white blood cells produce <u>antibodies</u> to attack them.

If live measles pathogens try to attack...

... so you don't get ill.

... they are quickly recognised and attacked by antibodies...

4) Some of these white blood cells will remain in the blood as <u>memory cells</u> (see previous page) so if <u>live</u> pathogens of the <u>same type</u> ever appear, the antibodies to <u>help destroy them</u> will be produced immediately.

5) Big outbreaks of disease — called <u>epidemics</u> — can be prevented if a <u>large percentage</u> of the population is vaccinated. That way, even the people who aren't vaccinated are <u>unlikely</u> to catch the disease because there are <u>fewer</u> people able to <u>pass it on</u>. But if a significant number of people <u>aren't</u> vaccinated, the disease can <u>spread</u> quickly through them and lots of people will be <u>ill</u> at the same time.

Medicines are Used to Treat Disease

1) Drugs are substances which <u>alter the way the body works</u>. Some drugs are <u>medically useful</u>, such as <u>antibiotics</u> (e.g. <u>penicillin</u>). But many drugs are <u>dangerous</u> if misused.

2) This is why you can buy some drugs <u>over the counter</u> at a pharmacy, but others are restricted so you can only get them on <u>prescription</u> — your <u>doctor decides</u> if you should have them.

3) You need to know about <u>antibiotics</u>, <u>antivirals</u> and <u>antiseptics</u>...

Antibiotics

1) <u>Antibiotics</u> are chemicals that kill <u>bacteria</u> without killing your own body cells. Many are produced <u>naturally</u> by <u>fungi</u> and other <u>microbes</u>, e.g. penicillin is made by a type of mould. Pharmaceutical companies can grow them on a <u>large scale</u> in a lab and extract the antibiotics.

2) They're very useful for clearing up bacterial infections that your body is having <u>trouble</u> with, however they <u>don't kill viruses</u>.

Remember, not all microbes are harmful. Many are helpful.

3) Some bacteria are <u>naturally resistant</u> to (not killed by) certain antibiotics (see p.56). <u>Misuse</u> of antibiotics (e.g. doctors <u>overprescribing</u> them or patients <u>not finishing a course</u>) has increased the <u>rate</u> of development of <u>resistant strains</u>. <u>MRSA</u> (the hospital 'superbug') is the best-known example of an antibiotic-resistant strain.

Antivirals

1) <u>Antivirals</u> can be used to treat viral infections. They are <u>difficult</u> to produce because viruses use the <u>host cells</u> to <u>replicate</u> — its hard to target the virus <u>without</u> damaging the cell.

2) Most antivirals don't kill the viruses but <u>stop</u> them from <u>reproducing</u>.

Antiseptics

1) <u>Antiseptics</u> are chemicals that <u>destroy microorganisms</u> or <u>stop them growing</u>.

2) Antiseptics are used <u>outside</u> the body to help to <u>clean wounds</u> and <u>surfaces</u>. They're used to <u>prevent infection</u> rather than treat it.

3) Plenty of <u>household products</u> contain antiseptics, e.g. bathroom cleaners.

4) Antiseptics are used in <u>hospitals</u> and surgeries to try to prevent the spread of infections like MRSA.

GCSEs are like antibiotics — you have to finish the course...

Kapow, down with you nasty pathogens — we will kill you all. Ahem, sorry. You best learn this lot.

Q1　　Explain how vaccines containing dead pathogens can prevent people getting infections.　　[4 marks]

Topic B6 — Global Challenges

Investigating Antimicrobials PRACTICAL

Time to get hands on — you can <u>grow</u> your own <u>microbes</u> to see how <u>effective</u> different <u>antimicrobials</u> are.

You Can do a Practical to Investigate Antimicrobials

You can test the action of <u>antibiotics</u> (or other antimicrobials, e.g. antiseptics) by <u>growing</u> cultures of <u>microorganisms</u>:

1) Pour hot, sterilised <u>agar jelly</u> into a sterile <u>Petri dish</u> (a shallow round plastic dish).

2) When the jelly's cooled and set, <u>inoculating loops</u> (wire loops) can be used to <u>transfer</u> microorganisms to the culture medium. Alternatively, a <u>sterile dropping pipette</u> and <u>spreader</u> can be used to get an <u>even covering</u> of bacteria.

3) Then take three discs of filter paper — soak one disc in an <u>antibiotic</u> (disc A) and another in a <u>different antibiotic</u> (disc B). The third disc (disc C) is a <u>control</u> disc (see below) — it should be soaked in <u>sterile water</u>.

4) Place the discs on the jelly using <u>sterile forceps</u> and tape the <u>lid</u> onto the dish (to prevent contamination by other microbes). The antibiotic will <u>diffuse</u> (soak) into the agar jelly.
Leave some <u>space</u> between the discs and don't forget to <u>label</u> them on the bottom of the dish so you know which one is which.

5) Leave the dish for <u>48 hours</u> at <u>25 °C</u>. The bacteria will <u>multiply</u> and grow into a '<u>lawn</u>' covering the jelly.

6) Anywhere the bacteria can't grow is called a '<u>clear zone</u>'. The <u>more effective</u> the antibiotic is against the bacteria, the <u>larger</u> the <u>clear zone</u> around the paper disc will be — see next page.

7) Using a control disc means that you can be sure that any <u>difference</u> between the <u>growth</u> of the bacteria around the <u>control</u> disc and around the <u>antibiotic</u> discs is due to the <u>effect</u> of the antibiotic <u>alone</u> (and not something weird in the paper, for example).

8) You can carry out the same experiment as above using other <u>antimicrobials</u>.

The jelly is a culture medium — it contains the carbohydrates, minerals, proteins and vitamins that microorganisms need to grow.

Antibiotic A: larger clear zone — more effective
Antibiotic B: smaller clear zone — less effective

No clear zone around an antibiotic disc could mean that the bacteria are resistant to it — see page 56.

You need to control all other variables, such as temperature (e.g. don't leave one side of the dish near a radiator), disc size, etc.

In the <u>lab at school</u>, cultures of microorganisms are kept at about <u>25 °C</u> because <u>harmful pathogens</u> aren't likely to grow at this temperature. In <u>industrial conditions</u>, cultures are incubated at higher <u>temperatures</u> so that they can grow a lot <u>faster</u>. (Not too high though, or the <u>enzymes</u> in the microorganisms could be <u>denatured</u> — see p.16.)

Aseptic Techniques Make Sure the Culture Doesn't Get Contaminated

<u>Contamination</u> by <u>unwanted</u> microorganisms will <u>affect your results</u> and can potentially result in the growth of <u>pathogens</u>. To <u>avoid</u> this:

1) Regularly <u>disinfect</u> work surfaces. (<u>Alcohol</u> works best but can be <u>dangerous</u> because it's <u>flammable</u>.)

2) <u>Sterilise</u> all <u>glassware</u> and other <u>equipment</u>, such as forceps, before and after use, e.g. in an <u>autoclave</u> (a machine which steams equipment at high pressure). The prepared <u>agar jelly</u> should also be put through the autoclave.

3) If an <u>inoculating loop</u> is used to transfer the bacteria to the culture medium, it should be <u>sterilised</u> first by <u>passing it through a hot flame</u>.

4) Work near a <u>Bunsen flame</u>. Hot air rises, so <u>microbes</u> in the <u>air</u> should be <u>drawn away</u> from the <u>culture</u>.

5) Briefly <u>flame</u> the <u>neck</u> of the glass container of bacteria just <u>after</u> it's <u>opened</u> and just <u>before</u> it's <u>closed</u> — this causes air to <u>move out</u> of the container, preventing unwanted <u>microbes</u> from <u>falling in</u>.

inoculating loop

Agar — my favourite jelly flavour after raspberry...

You really don't want to grow microbes that make you ill — that's partly why it's so important to work aseptically.

Q1 Why is it important to work near a Bunsen flame when preparing cultures of microorganisms? [2 marks]

Comparing Antimicrobials

Once you've done all that boring practical stuff, like growing bacterial colonies and using fire, you get to do the really fun stuff — a lovely bit of maths. Woo. Here's how you can compare your clear zones...

Calculate the Sizes of the Clear Zones to Compare Results

You can compare the effectiveness of different antibiotics (or antiseptics) on bacteria by looking at the relative sizes of the clear zones. Remember, the larger the clear zone around a disc, the more effective the antibiotic is against the bacteria.

You can do this by eye if there are large differences in size. But to get more accurate results it's a good idea to calculate the area of the clear zones using their diameter (the distance across).

Don't open the Petri dish to measure the clear zones — they should be visible through the bottom of the dish.

When you calculate the area of the clear zone you should include the area of the disc.

To calculate the area of a clear zone, you need to use this equation:

This is the equation for the area of a circle. You're likely to use the units cm² or mm².

$$\text{Area} = \pi r^2$$

r is the radius of the clear zone — it's equal to half the diameter.

π is just a number. You should have a button for it on your calculator. If not, just use the value 3.14.

EXAMPLE:

The diagram below shows the clear zones produced by antibiotics A and B. Use the areas of the clear zones to compare the effectiveness of the antibiotics.

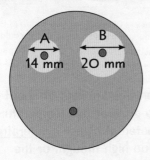

A 14 mm   B 20 mm

1) Divide the diameter of zone A by two to find the radius.

   Radius of A = 14 ÷ 2 = 7 mm

2) Stick the radius value into the equation area = πr^2.

   Area of A = $\pi \times 7^2$ = 154 mm²

3) Repeat steps 1 and 2 for zone B.

   Radius of B = 20 ÷ 2 = 10 mm

4) Compare the sizes of the areas. 314 mm² is just over twice 154 mm²,

   Area of B = $\pi \times 10^2$ = 314 mm²

so you could say that: The clear zone of antibiotic B is roughly twice the size of the clear zone of antibiotic A, so antibiotic B is more effective than antibiotic A.

My brother's football socks create a clear zone...

Bacteria might be the perfect pets. You don't have to walk them, they won't get lonely and they hardly cost anything to feed. But whatever you do, do not feed them after midnight. Oh, and it's probably a good idea if you learn how to calculate the area of a clear zone for your exams. Just a thought.

Q1 A researcher was investigating the effect of three different antiseptics on the growth of bacteria. The diagram on the right shows the results.

a) Which antiseptic was most effective against the bacteria? [1 mark]

b) Calculate the size of the clear zone for Antiseptic C. Give your answer in mm². [2 marks]

c) Describe a control that could have been used for this investigation. [1 mark]

d) Explain why a control should be used. [1 mark]

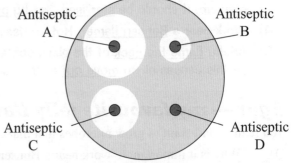

Antiseptic A   Antiseptic B   Antiseptic C   Antiseptic D

Developing New Medicines

You can't just get a random drug and give it to a poor unsuspecting person. That's unethical and thankfully there are laws against it. No, you've got to go through a rigorous testing process that starts with a computer...

New Drugs are Tested First in Pre-Clinical Trials in a Laboratory

New drugs developed to treat any kind of disease need to be thoroughly tested before they can be used to make sure they're safe and that they work. New drugs first go through pre-clinical trials, which usually involve computer simulations, testing on human cells and tissues, and finally testing on animals:

Computer models are often used first of all — these simulate a human's response to a drug, so you don't need to test on live animals at this stage. They can identify promising drugs to be tested in the next stage, but it's not as accurate as actually seeing the effect on a live organism.

The drugs are then developed further by testing on human tissues. However, you can't use human tissue to test drugs that affect whole/multiple body systems, e.g. testing a drug for blood pressure must be done on a whole animal, i.e. one that has an intact circulatory system.

The last step is to develop and test the drug using animals. The law in Britain states that any new drug must be tested on two different live mammals. Some people think it's cruel to test on animals, but others believe this is the safest way to make sure a drug isn't dangerous before it's given to humans.

Drugs are Then Tested on Humans in Clinical Trials

After the drug has been tested on animals, it's tested on humans — this is known as a clinical trial.

1) First, the drug is tested for safety on healthy volunteers. This is to make sure it doesn't have any harmful side effects when the body is working normally. Sick people are likely to be more vulnerable to any damage the drug could do, which is why the drug isn't tested on them yet.

2) If the results of the tests on healthy volunteers are good, the drugs can be tested on people suffering from the illness. These are tests for both safety and effectiveness.

3) Human drug trials usually last a very long time, but it's important that they do. In some cases it takes a while for a drug to have the effect it was designed for, e.g. treating cancer. It's also important to find out if a drug has any side effects which may only appear after a long time.

4) There are usually two groups of patients in clinical trials. One is given the new drug, the other is given a placebo (a substance that looks like the real drug but doesn't do anything). This is done so scientists can see the actual difference the drug makes — it allows for the placebo effect (when the patient expects the treatment to work and so feels better, even though the treatment isn't doing anything).

5) In some trials where patients are seriously ill placebos aren't used because it's unethical not to allow all patients to get the potential benefits of the new drug.

6) Scientists sometimes test new drugs against the best existing treatment rather than a placebo. This tells them how well the new drug compares to what we already have.

Clinical trials are blind — the patient in the study doesn't know whether they're getting the drug or the placebo. In fact, they're often double blind — neither the patient nor the scientist knows until all the results have been gathered. This is so the doctors monitoring the patients and analysing the results aren't subconsciously influenced by their knowledge.

Double Blindman's Buff — now that's got to be fun...

A trial in London in March 2006 left six men seriously ill after a new anti-inflammatory drug caused 'completely unanticipated' effects. But then, if nobody ever took part in trials, there would never be any new drugs.

Q1   a) What is a placebo?   [1 mark]
       b) Explain why placebos are used in clinical trials.   [2 marks]

Non-Communicable Diseases

You may remember non-communicable diseases from page 68. Well, here's a bit more about them...

Lots of Factors Interact to Cause Non-Communicable Diseases

1) All diseases have risk factors — things that increase a person's chance of getting that disease. Risk factors are often aspects of a person's lifestyle (e.g. how much exercise they do). They can also be the presence of certain substances in the environment (e.g. air pollution can contribute to the symptoms of asthma) or a genetic predisposition for a disease (e.g. inheriting particular mutated alleles increases your risk of developing coronary heart disease).

2) Many non-communicable diseases (e.g. many types of cancer, cardiovascular disease (CVD) (diseases of the heart or blood vessels, see p.78), some lung diseases, liver diseases, and some nutrition-related diseases, e.g. type 2 diabetes, see p.43) are caused by several different risk factors interacting with each other rather than one factor alone. For example:

> Normally, when cells have divided enough times to make enough new cells, they stop. But if there's a mutation in a gene that controls cell division, the cells can grow out of control. The cells keep on dividing by mitosis to make more and more cells, which form a tumour. Cancer is a tumour that invades surrounding tissue.

> Sometimes you can inherit faulty genes that make you more susceptible to cancer. The genes alone don't mean you will get cancer but the chance is increased if you have other risk factors too, such as poor diet, high alcohol consumption and smoking (see below and next page).

> Loads of things are known to be risk factors for cancer, e.g. HPV (see p.68), UV exposure, radiation, etc.

3) Risk factors are identified by scientists looking for correlations in data, but correlation doesn't always equal cause (see p.9). Sometimes a risk factor is linked to another factor, and it's this other factor that actually causes the disease. For example, a lack of exercise and a high fat diet are heavily linked to an increased chance of CVD, but they can't cause it directly. It's the resulting high blood pressure and high 'bad' cholesterol levels (see below) that can actually cause it.

4) There are some examples where scientists have found evidence to support a risk factor being a cause of a disease though, e.g. the fact that smoking can cause lung disease and lung cancer (see next page).

Lifestyle Factors Can Increase the Risk of Non-Communicable Diseases

Exercise

1) Exercise increases the amount of energy used by the body and decreases the amount of stored body fat. It also builds muscle, which helps to boost your metabolic rate (see p.39). So people who exercise are less likely to suffer from health problems such as obesity (see below) and CVD.

2) A lack of exercise increases the risk of CVD because it increases blood pressure.

Diet

1) Eating too much can lead to obesity. Obesity is linked to type 2 diabetes, high blood pressure and CVD. It's also a risk factor for some cancers.

> Obesity is defined as being >20% over the maximum recommended body mass.

2) Too much saturated fat in your diet can increase your blood cholesterol level. Cholesterol is an essential lipid that your body produces and needs to function properly. However, too much of a certain type of cholesterol (known as 'bad' or LDL cholesterol) can cause fatty deposits to form inside arteries, which can lead to coronary heart disease (see p.78).

3) Eating too little can cause problems too:
- Some people suffer from lack of food. The effects of malnutrition vary depending on what foods are missing from the diet. But problems commonly include slow growth (in children), fatigue, poor resistance to infection, and irregular periods in women.
- Deficiency diseases are caused by a lack of vitamins or minerals. E.g. a lack of vitamin C can cause scurvy, a deficiency disease that causes problems with the skin, joints and gums.

> People whose diet is badly out of balance are said to be malnourished.

Best put down that cake and go for a run...

You might be asked to interpret data about risk factors. Remember, correlation doesn't necessarily mean cause.

Q1 Explain how exercising can reduce the risk of obesity. [2 marks]

More on Non-Communicable Diseases

Unfortunately, you're not finished with <u>risk factors</u> for <u>non-communicable diseases</u> yet. Here are some more...

Alcohol and Smoking Can Also Lead to Non-Communicable Diseases

Alcohol

1) <u>Alcohol</u> is <u>poisonous</u>. It's <u>broken down</u> by <u>enzymes</u> in the liver and some of the <u>products</u> are <u>toxic</u>. If you drink <u>too much</u> alcohol over a <u>long period</u> of time these toxic products can cause the <u>death</u> of liver cells, forming <u>scar tissue</u> that stops <u>blood</u> reaching the liver — this is called <u>cirrhosis</u>.

2) Drinking too much alcohol <u>increases blood pressure</u> which can lead to <u>CVD</u>.

3) Many <u>cancers</u> including those of the <u>mouth</u>, <u>throat</u>, <u>bowels</u> and <u>liver</u> have all been linked to alcohol consumption because the toxic products <u>damage DNA</u> and cause cells to <u>divide faster</u> than normal.

Smoking

Burning cigarettes produce <u>nicotine</u>, which is what makes smoking <u>addictive</u>. They also produce <u>carbon monoxide</u>, <u>tar</u>, and <u>particulates</u> — which can all cause <u>illness</u> and other <u>problems</u>. E.g:

1) <u>CVD</u> — <u>carbon monoxide</u> reduces the oxygen carrying capacity of the blood. If the <u>cardiac muscle</u> doesn't receive enough oxygen it can lead to a <u>heart attack</u> (see next page). Nicotine increases <u>heart rate</u>. The heart contracts more often increasing <u>blood pressure</u>, which also increases the risk of <u>CVD</u>.

2) <u>Lung</u>, <u>throat</u>, <u>mouth</u> and <u>oesophageal cancer</u> — <u>tar</u> from cigarette smoke is full of toxic chemicals, some of which are <u>carcinogens</u> (cause <u>cancer</u>). Carcinogens make <u>mutations</u> in the DNA <u>more likely</u>, which can lead to <u>uncontrolled cell division</u> (see previous page).

3) Lung diseases, such as <u>chronic bronchitis</u> — cigarette smoke can cause <u>inflammation</u> of the lining of the <u>bronchi</u> and <u>bronchioles</u> (tubes in the lungs), which can result in <u>permanent damage</u>. Symptoms of chronic bronchitis include a <u>persistent cough</u> and <u>breathing problems</u>.

4) <u>Smoking</u> when <u>pregnant</u> can cause <u>lots</u> of <u>health problems</u> for the <u>unborn baby</u>.

Lifestyle Factors Cause Different Trends

Global

Non-communicable diseases are <u>more common</u> in <u>developed countries</u>, where people generally have a <u>higher income</u>, than in <u>developing countries</u>. However, these diseases are now becoming much <u>more common</u> in <u>developing</u> countries too. Different <u>lifestyle factors</u> contribute to these trends, but a lot of it is to do with <u>income</u>. For example:

- <u>Lack of exercise</u> and <u>higher alcohol consumption</u> are associated with <u>higher income</u>.

- <u>Smoking</u> varies massively between countries, but smoking-related deaths are <u>more common</u> in <u>poorer countries</u>.

- In both developed and developing countries, <u>obesity</u> is associated with <u>higher incomes</u> as people are able to afford lots of <u>high-fat food</u>. However, obesity is now associated with <u>lower incomes</u> too, as people are eating <u>cheaper</u>, <u>less healthy</u> foods.

National

Non-communicable diseases are the <u>biggest cause of death</u> in the <u>UK</u>. However, there are <u>differences</u> across the country. For example:

- People from <u>deprived areas</u> are much <u>more likely to smoke</u>, have a <u>poor diet</u>, and <u>not</u> take part in <u>physical activity</u> than those who are better off financially. This means that the incidence of heart disease, obesity, type 2 diabetes, and cancers is higher in those areas. People from deprived areas are also more likely to suffer from <u>alcohol-related disorders</u>.

Local

<u>Individual lifestyle choices</u> affect the incidence of non-communicable diseases at the local level — if you choose to smoke, drink, not take part in exercise or have a poor diet, then the <u>risk increases</u>.

Too many exams are a risk factor for stress...

Trends in non-communicable diseases are often to do with income, because it can have a big effect on lifestyle.

Q1   Give two non-communicable diseases that excessive alcohol consumption is a risk factor for.   [2 marks]

Treating Cardiovascular Disease

Cardiovascular disease is a big, big problem in the UK. The good news is there are lots of ways to treat it.

Cardiovascular Disease Affects The Heart and Blood Vessels

See p.31-32 for more on the heart and blood vessels.

Cardiovascular disease (CVD) are diseases to do with your heart and blood vessels. **E.g.**

1) High blood pressure and lots of LDL cholesterol can lead to the build up of fatty deposits inside arteries, narrowing them. Over time the fatty deposits harden, forming atheromas. **CORONARY HEART DISEASE** is when the coronary arteries have lots of atheromas in them, which restricts blood flow to the heart.

2) Sometimes bits of atheromas can break off or damage the blood vessel, causing a blood clot. Complete blockage of an artery by atheromas or blood clots can lead to a **HEART ATTACK**, where part of the cardiac muscle is deprived of oxygen. If the blockage occurs in the brain, it can cause a **STROKE**.

There are Different Ways of Treating CVD

See pages 76-77 for more about risk factors for CVD.

Healthy Lifestyle

1) Making changes to your lifestyle can reduce the risk of CVD, even if you've already had problems, e.g. a heart attack. People at risk of CVD are encouraged to eat a healthy diet that is low in saturated fat, exercise regularly and stop smoking.

2) Lifestyle changes can also help other forms of treatment (see below) be more effective.

Drugs

Sometimes drugs are needed to help control the effects of CVD. For example:

1) Statins can reduce the amount of cholesterol present in the bloodstream. This slows down the rate of fatty deposits forming, reducing the risk of CVD. However, statins can sometimes cause negative side effects, e.g. aching muscles. Some of these side effects can be serious, e.g. kidney failure, liver damage and memory problems.

2) Anticoagulants are drugs which make blood clots less likely to form. However, this can cause excessive bleeding if the person is hurt in an accident.

3) Antihypertensives reduce blood pressure. This reduces the risk of atheromas and blood clots forming. Their side effects can include headaches or fainting.

> Some antihypertensives reduce blood pressure by widening the blood vessels, some decrease the strength of the heartbeat and some reduce the blood volume.

Surgical Procedures

If the heart or blood vessels are too badly damaged then surgery may be needed.

1) Stents are tubes that are inserted inside arteries. They keep them open, making sure blood can pass through to the cardiac muscle. Stents are a way of lowering the risk of a heart attack in people with coronary heart disease. But over time, the artery can narrow again as stents can irritate the artery and make scar tissue grow. The patient also has to take drugs to stop blood clotting on the stent.

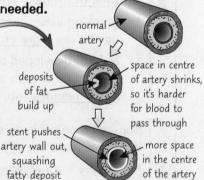

normal artery

space in centre of artery shrinks, so it's harder for blood to pass through

deposits of fat build up

stent pushes artery wall out, squashing fatty deposit

more space in the centre of the artery

2) If part of a blood vessel is blocked, a piece of healthy vessel taken from elsewhere can be used to bypass the blocked section. This is known as coronary bypass surgery.

3) The whole heart can be replaced with a donor heart. However, the new heart does not always start pumping properly. The new heart can also be rejected because the body's immune system recognises it as 'foreign'. Drugs have to be taken to prevent this from happening, and these can have side effects, e.g. making you more vulnerable to infections.

Heart surgery is a major procedure and, as with all surgeries, there is risk of bleeding, clots and infection.

Look after yerselves me hearties...

...and make sure you're aware of the drawbacks as well as the advantages for the above ways of treating CVD.

Q1   Anticoagulants make blood clots less likely. Give a disadvantage of their use in treating CVD.   [1 mark]

Stem Cells in Medicine

Stem cells could be the next big thing in medicine — imagine being able to grow a new body part from your own supply of cells. Maybe I could even grow a new brain to help me with all this revision...

Stem Cells May Be Able to Cure Many Diseases

You may remember from page 25 that stem cells are found in both embryos and adults. They have the potential to be really useful in treating some medical conditions because of their ability to differentiate into different cell types.

1) Medicine already uses adult stem cells to cure some diseases:

> Leukaemia is a cancer of the blood or bone marrow. It's been successfully treated using stem cell technology. Bone marrow transplants can be used to replace the faulty bone marrow in patients suffering from leukaemia. Bone marrow contains stem cells that can become specialised to form any type of blood cell. The stem cells in the transplanted bone marrow produce healthy blood cells.

2) Scientists can also extract stem cells from very early human embryos and grow them.

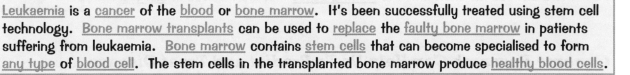

Embryos are created in a laboratory using *in vitro* fertilisation (IVF) — egg cells are fertilised by sperm outside the womb (see p. 51). Once the embryos are approximately 4 to 5 days old, stem cells are removed from them and the rest of the embryo is destroyed.

3) These embryonic stem cells could be used to replace faulty cells in sick people — you could make beating heart muscle cells for people with heart disease, insulin-producing cells for people with diabetes, nerve cells for people paralysed by spinal injuries, and so on.

4) To get cultures of one specific type of cell, researchers try to control the differentiation of the stem cells by changing the environment they're growing in. So far, it's still a bit hit and miss — lots more research is needed.

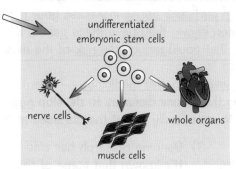

undifferentiated embryonic stem cells

nerve cells

muscle cells

whole organs

5) There are concerns that transplanting tissues and organs grown from embryonic stem cells or from donor stem cells may lead to rejection because the patient's immune system recognises the cells as foreign and attacks them (see page 71). However, if a patient needs a stem cell transplant and their own adult stem cells can be used (from elsewhere in their body) it's thought that there'll be less risk of rejection.

Some People Are Against Stem Cell Research

1) Some people are against stem cell research because they feel that human embryos shouldn't be used for experiments since each one is a potential human life. Others think that curing patients who already exist and who are suffering is more important than the rights of embryos.

2) Sometimes unwanted embryos from fertility clinics are used for research. One fairly convincing argument in favour of stem cell research is that if these embryos weren't used by scientists they would probably just be destroyed. Campaigners for the rights of embryos generally want this banned too.

3) As the use of stem cells is controversial, governments often make laws about how they can be used for research and medicine. Around the world, there are now 'stocks' of stem cells that scientists can use for their research. Some countries (e.g. the USA) won't fund research to make new stem cell stocks, but in the UK it's allowed as long as it follows strict guidelines.

But florists cell stems, and nobody complains about that...

The potential of stem cells is huge — but it's early days yet. There's still lots of work to be done getting stem cells to behave as we want them. And you've got lots of work to be doing too — this page isn't going to learn itself.

Q1   a)   Tissues can be grown from donor stem cells or embryonic stem cells and transplanted into a patient. Explain why these tissues can be rejected by the patient. [1 mark]

        b) How could the risk of rejection be reduced? [1 mark]

Q2   Give one reason why some people are against stem cell research. [1 mark]

Using Genome Research in Medicine

Wow. Science is <u>amazing</u> — this page is all about how scientists might be able to use <u>genes</u> to <u>predict</u> <u>diseases</u> and provide us with <u>new and better drugs</u>. How cool is that. Alright, maybe I should get out more...

The Human Genome Project Identified All Our Genes

1) Human DNA is made up of about <u>25 000 genes</u>.

2) The <u>Human Genome Project</u> (HGP) was a 13 year long project that identified <u>all of the genes</u> found in <u>human DNA</u> (the human genome).

3) <u>Understanding</u> the human genome is an important tool for <u>science</u> and <u>medicine</u> — we can use the information to <u>identify genes</u> that are involved in <u>disease</u>.

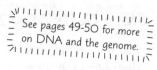
See pages 49-50 for more on DNA and the genome.

Genome Research Can Help Us To Predict and Treat Disease...

1) <u>Predict and prevent diseases</u> — many <u>common diseases</u> like cancers and heart disease are caused by the <u>interaction</u> of <u>different genes</u> as well as <u>lifestyle factors</u> (see pages 76-77). If doctors knew <u>what genes</u> predisposed people to <u>what diseases</u>, we could all get <u>individually tailored</u> advice on the best diet and lifestyle to avoid our likely problems.

> <u>Inheriting particular genes</u> increases your <u>risk</u> of developing certain <u>cancers</u>. If a person <u>knows</u> they have these genes, it might help them to make <u>choices</u> that could <u>reduce the risk</u> of the disease developing (see page 76).

Doctors could also check us regularly to ensure early treatment if we do develop the diseases we're susceptible to.

2) <u>Develop new and better medicines</u> — scientists can use <u>information</u> about the <u>genes</u> that cause diseases to develop <u>new medicines</u>. The new medicines are able to specifically <u>target</u> the diseases at the <u>molecular level</u>.

3) Genome research has also highlighted <u>common genetic variations</u> between people. It's known that <u>some</u> of these <u>variations</u> make <u>some drugs less effective</u>, e.g. some asthma drugs are less effective for people with a particular mutation. Scientists can use this knowledge to <u>design new drugs</u> that are <u>tailored</u> to people with these variations.

... But There are Risks with Using Gene Technology in Medicine

1) <u>Increased stress</u> — if someone knew from an early age that they're susceptible to a nasty brain disease, they could <u>panic</u> every time they get a <u>headache</u> (even if they never get the disease).

2) <u>Gene-ism</u> — people with genetic problems could come under <u>pressure</u> not to have <u>children</u>.

3) <u>Discrimination</u> by employers and insurers — life insurance could become <u>impossible</u> to get (or blummin' expensive at least) if you have any <u>genetic likelihood</u> of serious disease. And <u>employers</u> may discriminate against people who are genetically likely to get a <u>disease</u>.

4) <u>Unfair health system</u> — creating <u>specific</u> drugs for <u>different people</u> will increase costs for companies that develop the drugs. So the <u>new drugs</u> will be more <u>expensive</u>, which could lead to a <u>two-tier health service</u> — only wealthier people could afford these new drugs.

5) <u>Practical risks</u> — some people worry that we may do more <u>harm</u> than <u>good</u> by using gene technology. We <u>don't know</u> what <u>effects</u> there may be in <u>future generations</u>.

New medicines coming soon — in skinny, bootcut, hipster...

These new medicines are only possibilities — some may happen soon, some will take ages, and others might not happen at all. You must know the benefits and the risks. No problem — you were going to learn it all anyway.

Q1   Type 2 diabetes is caused by a combination of genetic and lifestyle factors. Explain how our understanding of the human genome may help doctors prevent more cases of type 2 diabetes.   [2 marks]

Revision Questions for Topic B6

Wow, that was a massive topic. It's time to put yourself to the test and find out <u>how much you really know</u>.

- Try these questions and <u>tick off each one</u> when you <u>get it right</u>.
- When you've done <u>all the questions</u> under a heading and are <u>completely happy</u> with it, tick it off.

Investigating Distribution and Abundance (p.58-61)

1) What would you use a sweep net for?
2) Describe how you would use a quadrat to compare the distribution of dandelions in two areas.
3) Give two abiotic factors that can affect the distribution of organisms.
4) Describe how you can estimate the percentage cover of an organism in a quadrat.

Ecosystems and Maintaining Biodiversity (p.62-64)

5) Give three human activities which reduce the amount of land available to other organisms.
6) Describe how preventing the introduction of harmful species can help protect biodiversity.
7) Explain why maintaining biodiversity by setting up conservation schemes can be challenging.

Selective Breeding and Genetic Engineering (p.65-67)

8) What is selective breeding?
9) In genetic engineering, what is a vector?
10) Give one example of how crops could be genetically modified to increase yields.
11) Describe two ethical issues that genetic engineering raises.

Health and Disease (p.68-71)

12) What is a communicable disease?
13) Explain how the tobacco mosaic virus is transmitted between plants.
14) Give three ways that the spread of disease in plants can be controlled.
15) Explain how the production of antibodies helps the body defend itself against disease.

Treating Disease and the Development of Medicines (p.72-75)

16) What are antiseptics?
17) Describe an experiment you could do to investigate the effectiveness of different antibiotics.
18) Give the formula you need to calculate the area of a clear zone in a bacterial lawn.
19) Give three things that can happen when a drug is at the pre-clinical testing stage of development.

Non-Communicable Diseases and Advances in Medicine (p.76-80)

20) Give three health problems that are linked to eating too much.
21) Describe a global trend in the incidence of non-communicable diseases.
22) Describe the risks of using surgical procedures to treat cardiovascular disease.
23) Why do stem cells have the potential to be useful in the treatment of disease?
24) Give three potential risks of using gene technology in medicine.

States of Matter

All stuff is made of <u>particles</u> (molecules, ions or atoms). The <u>forces</u> between these particles can be weak or strong, depending on whether it's a <u>solid</u>, <u>liquid</u> or a <u>gas</u>. Want to find out more? Then read on...

States of Matter Depend on the Forces Between Particles

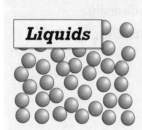

Solids
1) There are <u>strong forces</u> of attraction between particles, which hold them in <u>fixed positions</u> in a very regular <u>lattice arrangement</u>.
2) The particles <u>don't move</u> from their positions, so all solids keep a <u>definite shape</u> and <u>volume</u>, and don't flow like liquids.
3) The particles <u>vibrate</u> about their positions — the <u>hotter</u> the solid becomes, the <u>more</u> they vibrate (causing solids to <u>expand</u> slightly when heated).
4) If you <u>heat</u> the solid (give the particles <u>more energy</u>), eventually the solid will <u>melt</u> and become <u>liquid</u>.

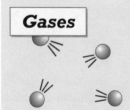

Liquids
1) There is <u>some force</u> of attraction between the particles. They're <u>free</u> to <u>move</u> past each other, but they do tend to <u>stick together</u>.
2) Liquids <u>don't</u> keep a <u>definite shape</u> and will flow to fill the bottom of a container. But they do keep the <u>same volume</u>.
3) The particles are <u>constantly</u> moving with <u>random motion</u>. The <u>hotter</u> the liquid gets, the <u>faster</u> they move. This causes liquids to <u>expand</u> slightly when heated.
4) If you <u>cool</u> a liquid, it will <u>freeze</u> and become <u>solid</u>. If you <u>heat</u> a liquid enough, it evaporates (or <u>boils</u>) and becomes a <u>gas</u>.

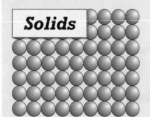

Gases
1) There's next to <u>no force</u> of attraction between the particles — they're <u>free</u> to <u>move</u>. They travel in <u>straight lines</u> and only interact <u>when they collide</u>.
2) Gases <u>don't</u> keep a definite <u>shape</u> or <u>volume</u> and will always <u>fill</u> any container. When particles bounce off the walls of a container, they exert a <u>pressure</u> on the walls.
3) The particles move <u>constantly</u> with <u>random motion</u>. The <u>hotter</u> the gas gets, the <u>faster</u> they move. Gases either <u>expand</u> when heated, or their <u>pressure increases</u>.
4) If you <u>cool</u> a gas, it will <u>condense</u> and become a liquid.

Particle theory is a great <u>model</u> for explaining the three states of matter, but it <u>isn't perfect</u>. In reality, the particles aren't solid and they aren't spheres — they're atoms, ions or molecules. The model doesn't give you any idea of the size of the particles, or the space between them. Also, the model doesn't <u>show</u> any of the <u>forces</u> between the particles, so there's no way of knowing just <u>how strong</u> they are.

Atoms are Rearranged During Chemical Reactions

1) When a substance changes from one state of matter to another (e.g. by melting, boiling, condensing or freezing), it's a <u>physical change</u>. No new substances are made — the original chemicals just <u>change state</u>.
2) Physical changes are pretty easy to undo by <u>heating</u> or <u>cooling</u>. Chemical reactions are a bit different...
3) During a <u>chemical reaction</u>, bonds between atoms break and the atoms <u>change places</u> — the atoms from the substances you <u>start off</u> with (the <u>reactants</u>) rearrange themselves to form <u>different chemicals</u>. These new chemicals are called the <u>products</u>.
4) Compared to physical changes, chemical changes are often <u>hard to reverse</u>.

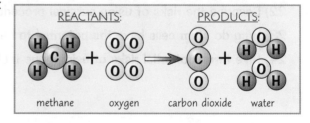

methane   oxygen   carbon dioxide   water

I felt like changing state, so I moved from Texas to Michigan...

After all this stuff about chemical reactions, let's see how you react to a practice question...

Q1   Describe the forces and the arrangement of particles in: a) solids,   b) gases,   c) liquids.   [9 marks]

The History of the Atom

<u>Atoms</u> are pretty tiny. But what exactly are they like? Scientists have been trying to work it out for <u>years</u>...

The Theory of Atomic Structure Has Changed

<u>Atoms</u> are the tiny particles of matter (stuff that has a mass) which make up <u>everything</u> in the universe...

1) At the start of the 19th century, <u>John Dalton</u> described atoms as <u>solid spheres</u> and said that different spheres made up the different <u>elements</u>.

2) In 1897, <u>J J Thomson</u> concluded from his experiments that atoms <u>weren't</u> solid spheres. His measurements of <u>charge</u> and <u>mass</u> showed that an atom must contain even smaller, negatively charged particles — <u>electrons</u>. The 'solid sphere' idea of atomic structure had to be changed. The new theory was known as the '<u>plum pudding model</u>'.

electrons

positively charged 'pudding'

delicious pudding

Rutherford Showed that the Plum Pudding Model Was Wrong

1) In 1909, Ernest <u>Rutherford</u> and his students, Hans <u>Geiger</u> and Ernest <u>Marsden</u>, conducted the famous <u>gold foil experiment</u>. They fired positively charged alpha particles at an extremely thin sheet of gold.

2) From the plum pudding model, they were <u>expecting</u> the particles to <u>pass straight through</u> the sheet or be <u>slightly deflected</u> at most. This was because the positive charge of each atom was thought to be very <u>spread out</u> through the 'pudding' of the atom. But, whilst most of the particles <u>did</u> go <u>straight through</u> the gold sheet, some were deflected <u>more than expected</u>, and a small number were <u>deflected backwards</u>. So the plum pudding model <u>couldn't</u> be right.

3) Rutherford came up with the theory of the <u>nuclear atom</u> to explain this new evidence. In this, there's a tiny, positively charged <u>nucleus</u> at the centre, surrounded by a 'cloud' of negative electrons — most of the atom's <u>empty space</u>.

A few particles are deflected backwards by the nucleus.

Most of the particles pass through empty space.

The Refined Bohr Model Explains a Lot

1) Scientists realised that electrons in a 'cloud' around the nucleus of an atom, as Rutherford described, would be attracted to the nucleus, causing the atom to <u>collapse</u>. Niels Bohr proposed a new model of the atom where all the electrons were contained in <u>shells</u>.

nucleus   shells

electrons

2) Bohr suggested that electrons can only exist in <u>fixed orbits</u>, or <u>shells</u>, and not anywhere in between. Each shell has a <u>fixed energy</u>.

3) Bohr's theory of atomic structure was supported by many <u>experiments</u> and it helped to explain lots of other scientists' <u>observations</u> at the time. It was <u>pretty close</u> to our currently accepted version of the atom (see next page).

Scientific Theories Have to be Backed Up by Evidence

1) So, our current model of the atom is <u>different</u> to what people thought the atom looked like in the past. These different ideas were <u>accepted</u> because they fitted the <u>evidence</u> available at the time.

2) As scientists did more <u>experiments</u>, new evidence was found and our theory of the <u>structure</u> of the atom was <u>modified</u> to fit it. This is nearly always the way <u>scientific knowledge</u> develops — new evidence prompts people to come up with new, <u>improved ideas</u>. These ideas can be used to make <u>predictions</u> which, if proved correct, are a pretty good indication that the ideas are <u>right</u>.

3) Scientists also put their ideas and research up for <u>peer-review</u>. This means everyone gets a chance to see the new ideas, check for errors and then other scientists can use it to help <u>develop</u> their own work.

I love a good model — Kate Moss is my personal favourite...

This is a great example of how science works. Scientists working together to find evidence. Lovely.

Q1 Describe how the gold foil experiment disproved the plum pudding model of the atom.   [3 marks]

Q2 Draw and label a diagram to show the Bohr model of the atom.   [2 marks]

The Atom

There are quite a few <u>different</u> (and equally useful) <u>modern</u> models of the atom — but chemists tend to like this model best. You can use it to explain loads of chemistry... which is nice. Well, here goes...

The Atom is Made Up of Protons, Neutrons and Electrons

The atom is made up of three <u>subatomic particles</u> — protons, neutrons and electrons.

- <u>Protons</u> are <u>heavy</u> and <u>positively charged</u>.
- <u>Neutrons</u> are <u>heavy</u> and <u>neutral</u>.
- <u>Electrons</u> have <u>hardly any mass</u> and are <u>negatively charged</u>.

Particle	Relative Mass	Relative Charge
Proton	1	+1
Neutron	1	0
Electron	0.0005	−1

Relative mass (measured in atomic mass units) measures mass on a scale where the mass of a proton or neutron is 1.

In reality, protons and neutrons are still teeny tiny. They're just heavy compared to electrons.

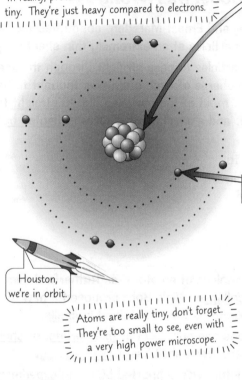

Houston, we're in orbit.

Atoms are really tiny, don't forget. They're too small to see, even with a very high power microscope.

The Nucleus

1) The nucleus is in the <u>middle</u> of the atom.

2) It contains <u>protons</u> and <u>neutrons</u>.

3) It has a <u>positive charge</u> because of the protons.

4) Almost the <u>whole</u> mass of the atom (between about 10^{-23} g and 10^{-21} g) is <u>concentrated</u> in the nucleus.

5) Compared to the overall size of the atom, the nucleus is <u>tiny</u> (the nucleus has a radius of between about 10^{-15} m and 10^{-14} m).

The Electrons

1) Electrons move <u>around</u> the nucleus in electron <u>shells</u> (or orbitals).

2) They're <u>negatively charged</u>.

3) They're <u>tiny</u>, but their orbitals cover <u>a lot of space</u>.

4) The <u>volume</u> of their orbitals determines the size of the atom — atoms have a radius (known as the atomic radius) of about 10^{-10} m.

5) Electrons have virtually <u>no</u> mass — it's often taken as zero.

Molecules Form When Atoms Bond Together

1) <u>Molecules</u> are made up of two or more atoms.

2) Molecules can be made of the <u>same element</u> (e.g. hydrogen), or <u>different elements</u> (e.g. ammonia).

3) Simple molecules (see page 90), like atoms, are pretty tiny. The <u>bonds</u> that form between these molecules are generally a similar length to the atomic radius — <u>about 10^{-10} m</u>.

hydrogen molecule

ammonia molecule

Don't trust atoms — they make up everything...

You need to learn what's in that table with the relative masses and charges of the different parts of the atom. Try remembering **P**rotons are **P**ositive, **N**eutrons are **N**eutral and **E**lectrons are **E**... Never mind.

Q1   What is the charge on: a) a proton,   b) a neutron,   c) an electron?   [1 mark]

Q2   Where is most of the mass of an atom to be found?   [1 mark]

Q3   Put the following things in order of size, starting with the smallest: atomic radius, nuclear radius, simple molecule (e.g. Cl_2).   [1 mark]

Atoms, Ions and Isotopes

As if <u>atoms</u> weren't fiddly enough, time to meet those pesky <u>ions</u>. Oh, and don't get me started on <u>isotopes</u>...

Atomic Number and Mass Number Describe an Atom

These two numbers tell you how many of each kind of particle an atom has.

In some notations and periodic tables (like the one on the data sheet in the exam), these numbers are the other way round. Just remember the bigger one is the mass number.

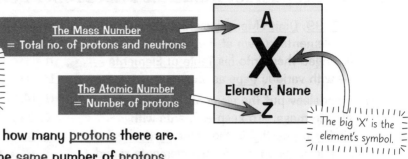

The Mass Number = Total no. of protons and neutrons

The Atomic Number = Number of protons

A
X
Z
Element Name

The big 'X' is the element's symbol.

1) The <u>atomic (proton) number</u> tells you how many <u>protons</u> there are.

2) Atoms of the <u>same</u> element all have the <u>same</u> number of <u>protons</u> — so atoms of <u>different</u> elements will have <u>different</u> numbers of protons.

3) To get the number of <u>neutrons</u>, just subtract the <u>atomic number</u> from the <u>mass number</u>.

4) The <u>mass (nucleon) number</u> is always the <u>biggest</u> number. On a periodic table the mass number is actually the <u>relative atomic mass</u> (see page 100).

5) Neutral atoms have <u>no charge</u> overall (unlike ions, see below). This is because they have the <u>same number</u> of <u>protons</u> as <u>electrons</u>. The charge on the electrons is the same size as the charge on the protons, but opposite — so the charges cancel out. So, the number of electrons in a neutral atom is also <u>equal</u> to the <u>atomic number</u>.

Ions have Different Numbers of Protons and Electrons

1) Ions form when atoms (or groups of atoms) <u>gain</u> or <u>lose electrons</u> (see page 88 for more).

2) <u>Negative ions</u> form when atoms <u>gain electrons</u> — they have more electrons than protons. <u>Positive ions</u> form when atoms <u>lose electrons</u> — they have more protons than electrons.

- F^- — there's a <u>single negative charge</u>, so there must be one more electron than protons. F has an atomic number of 9, so has 9 protons. So F^- must have $9 + 1 = $ <u>10 electrons</u>.

- Fe^{2+} — there's a <u>2+ charge</u>, so there must be two more protons than electrons. Fe has an atomic number of 26, so has 26 protons. So Fe^{2+} must have $26 - 2 = $ <u>24 electrons</u>.

Isotopes are the Same Except for the Number of Neutrons

Isotopes are different forms of the same element, which have the same number of protons but a different number of neutrons.

1) Isotopes have the <u>same atomic number</u> but <u>different mass numbers</u>.

2) If they had <u>different</u> atomic numbers, they'd be <u>different</u> elements altogether.

3) A famous example is the two main isotopes of carbon.

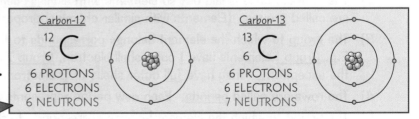

Carbon-12
12
6 C
6 PROTONS
6 ELECTRONS
6 NEUTRONS

Carbon-13
13
6 C
6 PROTONS
6 ELECTRONS
7 NEUTRONS

Na⁺ was positive that he'd misplaced one of his electrons...

There's a smattering of maths here, but it's just some adding and subtracting, so don't worry too much.

Q1 Work out the number of neutrons in the following atoms: a) $^{16}_{8}O$, b) $^{40}_{20}Ca$, c) $^{127}_{53}I$. [3 marks]

Q2 a) Chlorine has an atomic number of 17. It exists naturally with 2 isotopes, chlorine-35 and chlorine-37. Work out how many neutrons, protons and electrons are in each isotope. [2 marks]

b) Chlorine tends to react by forming Cl⁻ ions. How many electrons are in a Cl⁻ ion? [1 mark]

The Periodic Table

We haven't always known as much about chemistry as we do now. No sirree. Take the periodic table. Early chemists looked to try and understand patterns in the elements' properties to get a bit of understanding.

Dmitri Mendeleev Made the First Proper Periodic Table

1) In 1869, Dmitri Mendeleev took the 50 or so elements known at the time and arranged them into his Table of Elements — with various gaps as shown.

Mendeleev's Table of the Elements

```
H
Li  Be                                               B  C  N  O  F
Na  Mg                                               Al Si P  S  Cl
K   Ca  *  Ti V  Cr Mn Fe Co Ni Cu Zn  *  *  As Se Br
Rb  Sr  Y  Zr Nb Mo *  Ru Rh Pd Ag Cd In Sn Sb Te I
Cs  Ba  *  *  Ta W  *  Os Ir Pt Au Hg Tl Pb Bi
```

2) Mendeleev put the elements in order of atomic mass. To keep elements with similar properties in the same vertical groups, he had to swap one or two elements round and leave a few gaps. He was prepared to leave some very big gaps in the first two rows before the transition metals come in on the third row.

3) The gaps were the really clever bit because they predicted the properties of so far undiscovered elements. When they were found and they fitted the pattern, it helped confirm Mendeleev's ideas. For example, Mendeleev made really good predictions about the chemical and physical properties of an element he called ekasilicon, which we know today as germanium.

This is How the Periodic Table Looks Today

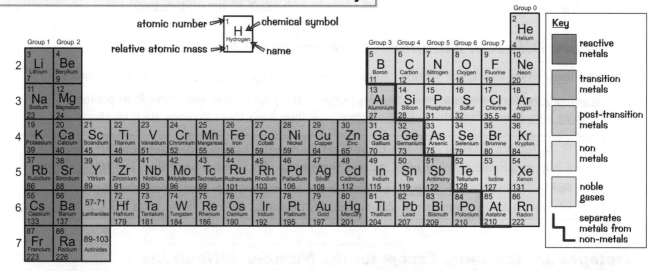

1) Once protons and electrons were discovered, the atomic number (see p.85) of each element could be found, based on the number of protons in its nucleus. The modern periodic table shows the elements in order of ascending atomic number — and they fit the same patterns that Mendeleev worked out.

2) The periodic table is laid out so elements with similar chemical properties form columns — these are called groups. (Elements with similar chemical properties react in similar ways.)

3) The group to which the element belongs corresponds to the number of electrons it has in its outer shell. E.g. Group 1 elements have 1 outer shell electron, Group 7 elements have 7, etc. Group 0 elements are the exception — they have full outer shells of 8 electrons (or 2 in the case of helium).

4) The rows are called periods. Each new period represents another full shell of electrons (see next page).

5) The period to which the element belongs corresponds to the number of shells of electrons it has.

I'm in a chemistry band — I play the symbols...

Because of how the periodic table is organised in groups and periods, you can see the trends in the reactivity (and other properties) of the elements and therefore make predictions on how reactions will occur. How neat is that?

Q1   Using a periodic table, state how many electrons beryllium has in its outer shell.   [1 mark]

Q2   Based on its position in the periodic table, would you expect the chemical properties of potassium to be more similar to those of sodium or calcium? Explain your answer.   [2 marks]

Electron Shells

Like snails, electrons live in shells. Unlike snails, electrons won't nibble on your petunias...

Electron Shell Rules:

1) Electrons occupy shells (sometimes called energy levels).
2) The lowest energy levels are always filled first.
3) Only a certain number of electrons are allowed in each shell:

1st shell	2nd shell	3rd shell
2 electrons	8 electrons	8 electrons

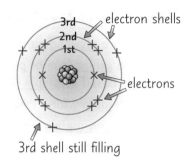

Working Out Electronic Structures

The electronic structures for the first 20 elements are shown in the diagram below.
They're not hard to work out. For a quick example, take nitrogen:

1) The periodic table tells you that nitrogen has seven protons, so it must have seven electrons.
2) Follow the 'Electron Shell Rules' above. The first shell can only take 2 electrons and the second shell can take a maximum of 8 electrons.
3) So the electronic structure for nitrogen must be 2.5 — easy peasy.

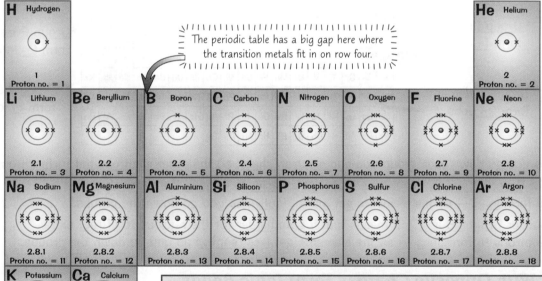

The periodic table has a big gap here where the transition metals fit in on row four.

Example: To calculate the electronic structure of argon, follow the rules. It's got 18 protons, so it must have 18 electrons. The first shell must have 2 electrons, the second shell must have 8, and so the third shell must have 8 as well. It's as easy as 2.8.8.

You can also work out the electronic structure of an element from its period and group.

• The number of shells which contain electrons is the same as the period of the element.
• The group number tells you how many electrons occupy the outer shell of the element.

Example: Sodium is in period 3, so it has 3 shells occupied — so the first two shells must be full (2.8). It's in Group 1, so it has 1 electron in its outer shell. So its electronic structure is 2.8.1.

The electronic structure of the fifth element — it's a bit boron...

Electronic structures may seem a bit complicated at first but once you learn the rules, it's a piece of cake.

Q1 Give the electronic structure of aluminium (atomic number = 13). [1 mark]

Q2 In which group and period of the periodic table would you expect to find the element with electronic structure 2.8.8.2? [2 marks]

Ionic Bonding

Ions crop up all over the place in chemistry — some atoms just can't wait to get rid of electrons, others wish they had just one or two more. It's like... something, I don't know... just make up your own metaphor...

Simple Ions Form When Atoms Lose or Gain Electrons

1) Ions are charged particles — they can be single atoms (e.g. Cl⁻) or groups of atoms (e.g. NO_3^-).

2) When atoms lose or gain electrons to form ions, all they're trying to do is get a full outer shell (also called a "stable electronic structure"). Atoms like full outer shells — it's atom heaven.

3) When metals form ions, they lose electrons to form positive ions.

4) When non-metals form ions, they gain electrons to form negative ions.

5) The number of electrons lost or gained is the same as the charge on the ion.
E.g. If 2 electrons are lost the charge is 2+. If 3 electrons are gained the charge is 3−.

Groups 1 & 2 and 6 & 7 are the Most Likely to Form Ions

1) The elements that most readily form ions are those in Groups 1, 2, 6 and 7.

2) Group 1 and 2 elements are metals. They lose electrons to form positive ions (cations).

3) Group 6 and 7 elements are non-metals. They gain electrons to form negative ions (anions).

4) Elements in the same group all have the same number of outer electrons. So they have to lose or gain the same number to get a full outer shell. And this means that they form ions with the same charges.

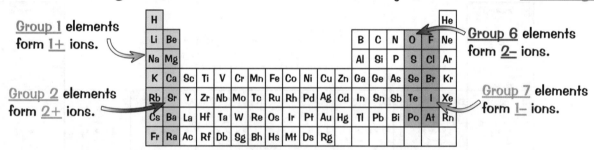

Group 1 elements form 1+ ions.
Group 2 elements form 2+ ions.
Group 6 elements form 2− ions.
Group 7 elements form 1− ions.

5) As you go down each group you add electron shells, so the outer electrons get further from the nucleus.

6) For Groups 1 and 2, this means that it gets easier to remove the outer electrons to form ions — so the elements get more reactive as you go down the groups.

7) But for Groups 6 and 7, it means that it gets harder for the nucleus to attract extra electrons to form ions — so the elements get less reactive as you go down the groups.

Ions With Opposite Charges Form Ionic Bonds

When a metal and a non-metal react together, the metal can lose electrons to form a positively charged ion and the non-metal can gain electrons to form a negatively charged ion. These oppositely charged ions are then strongly attracted to one another by electrostatic forces and form an ionic bond.

To find the formula of an ionic compound, you balance the positive and the negative charges. For example:

Sodium chloride	Magnesium chloride	Potassium oxide
$Na^+ + Cl^- \longrightarrow NaCl$	$Mg^{2+} + 2Cl^- \longrightarrow MgCl_2$	$2K^+ + O^{2-} \longrightarrow K_2O$
The sodium ion has a 1+ charge and the chloride ion has a 1− charge, so they balance.	The magnesium ion has a 2+ charge and the chloride ion has a 1− charge, so you need two Cl⁻ ions to balance the Mg^{2+} ion.	The potassium ion has a 1+ charge and the oxygen ion has a 2− charge, so you need two K⁺ ions to balance the O^{2-} ion.

Any old ion, any old ion — any, any, any old ion...

Make sure you know why ions form, how to work out what ions different elements form, and how ionic bonds form.

Q1   Describe, in terms of electron transfer, how potassium (K) and chlorine (Cl) react to form potassium chloride (KCl).

[3 marks]

Ionic Compounds

Here's a bit more about how ionic compounds form and the properties that make them special...

You Can Show Ionic Bonding Using Dot and Cross Diagrams

Dot and cross diagrams show the arrangement of electrons in an atom or ion. They can also show what happens to the electrons when atoms react with each other. Each electron is represented by a dot or a cross.

Sodium Chloride (NaCl)
The sodium atom gives up its outer electron, becoming an Na^+ ion. The chlorine atom picks up the electron, becoming a Cl^- (chloride) ion.

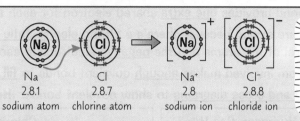

Na
2.8.1
sodium atom

Cl
2.8.7
chlorine atom

Na^+
2.8
sodium ion

Cl^-
2.8.8
chloride ion

Here, the dots represent the Na electrons and the crosses represent the Cl electrons (all electrons are really identical, but this is a good way of following their movement).

Magnesium Chloride (MgCl₂)
The magnesium atom gives up its two outer electrons, becoming an Mg^{2+} ion. The two chlorine atoms pick up one electron each, becoming two Cl^- (chloride) ions.

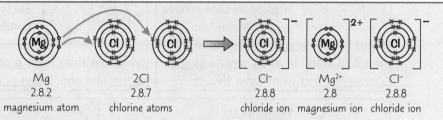

Mg
2.8.2
magnesium atom

2Cl
2.8.7
chlorine atoms

Cl^-
2.8.8
chloride ion

Mg^{2+}
2.8
magnesium ion

Cl^-
2.8.8
chloride ion

Dot and cross diagrams are really useful for showing how ionic compounds are formed, but they don't show the structure of the compound. For that, you'll need a different type of diagram.

Ionic Compounds Have a Regular Lattice Structure

Ionic compounds always have giant ionic lattice structures. The ions form a closely packed regular lattice. There are very strong electrostatic forces of attraction between oppositely charged ions, in all directions.

A single crystal of sodium chloride (salt) is one giant ionic lattice. The Na^+ and Cl^- ions are held together in a regular lattice.

This model shows the scale of the ions, but it only lets you see the outer layer of the compound.

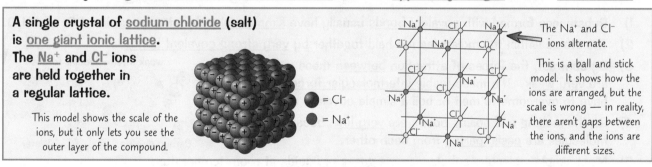

= Cl^-
= Na^+

The Na^+ and Cl^- ions alternate.

This is a ball and stick model. It shows how the ions are arranged, but the scale is wrong — in reality, there aren't gaps between the ions, and the ions are different sizes.

Ionic Compounds All Have Similar Properties

1) Ionic compounds have high melting and boiling points due to the strong attraction between the ions. It takes a large amount of energy to overcome this attraction.

2) Solid ionic compounds don't conduct electricity because the ions are fixed in place and can't move. But when an ionic compound melts, the ions are free to move and will carry an electric current.

3) Many also dissolve easily in water. The ions separate and are all free to move in the solution, so they'll carry an electric current.

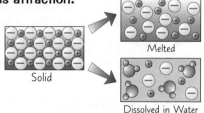

Melted

Solid

Dissolved in Water

Giant ionic lattices — all over your chips...

Make sure you know the advantages and disadvantages of each of the ways of drawing an ionic compound.

Q1   Draw a dot and cross diagram to show how potassium (electronic structure 2.8.8.1) and chlorine (electronic structure 2.8.7) react to form potassium chloride (KCl).   [3 marks]

Q2   Explain why the ionic compound caesium chloride conducts electricity when it is molten.   [1 mark]

Topic C2 — Elements, Compounds and Mixtures

Simple Molecules

Ionic bonding isn't the only way atoms join together. They can also <u>share</u> electrons to form <u>covalent bonds</u>.

Covalent Bonds — Sharing Electrons

1) When <u>non-metal atoms</u> combine together they form <u>covalent bonds</u> by <u>sharing</u> pairs of electrons.

2) This way <u>both atoms</u> feel that they have <u>a full outer shell</u>, and that makes them happy.

3) <u>Each</u> covalent bond provides <u>one extra</u> shared electron for each atom.

4) Covalent bonds are strong because there's a strong <u>electrostatic attraction</u> between the <u>positive</u> nuclei of the atoms and the <u>negative</u> electrons in each shared pair.

5) Usually, each atom involved makes <u>enough</u> covalent bonds to <u>fill up</u> its outer shell.

6) You can use <u>dot and cross diagrams</u> to show covalent bonds. Here are a few examples:

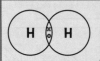
<u>Hydrogen Gas H$_2$</u>
Hydrogen atoms have just one electron.
They need <u>one more</u> to complete the first shell, so they form a <u>single covalent bond</u> to achieve this.

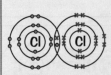
<u>Chlorine Gas Cl$_2$</u>
Each chlorine atom needs <u>one electron</u> to complete its outer shell, so they form <u>a single covalent bond</u> and share <u>one pair</u> of electrons.

As in the dot and cross diagrams for ionic bonds on page 89, the dots and crosses here represent electrons from different atoms — but in reality all the electrons are identical.

<u>Water H$_2$O</u>
Oxygen needs <u>two</u> more electrons to fill its outer shell. In a molecule of water, it <u>shares</u> electrons with two hydrogen atoms, forming two single covalent bonds.

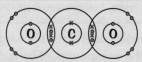
<u>Carbon Dioxide CO$_2$</u>
Carbon needs <u>four</u> more electrons to fill its outer shell, oxygen needs <u>two</u>. So <u>two double covalent bonds</u> are formed. A double covalent bond has <u>two shared pairs</u> of electrons.

Simple Molecular Substances Have Low Melting and Boiling Points

1) Substances formed with <u>covalent bonds</u> usually have <u>simple molecular structures</u>, like CO$_2$ and H$_2$O.

2) The atoms within the molecules are held together by <u>very strong covalent bonds</u>.

3) By contrast, the forces of attraction <u>between</u> these molecules are <u>very weak</u>. It's these <u>feeble intermolecular forces</u> that you have to overcome to melt or boil a simple covalent compound.

4) So the melting and boiling points are <u>very low</u>, because the molecules are <u>easily parted</u> from each other.

5) Most simple molecular substances are <u>gases or liquids</u> at room temperature.

6) Simple molecular substances <u>don't conduct electricity</u>, because they <u>don't</u> have free electrons or ions.

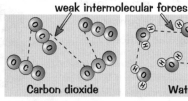
weak intermolecular forces
Carbon dioxide   Water

<u>Ball and stick models</u> show how the atoms in covalent molecules are connected. You can make them with plastic molecular model kits, or as computer models.

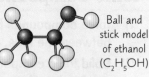
Ball and stick model of ethanol (C$_2$H$_5$OH)

- They're great for helping to <u>visualise</u> the structure of molecules, as they show you the shape of the molecule in <u>3D</u>.

- They're <u>more realistic</u> than 2D drawings, but they're still a bit <u>misleading</u>. They make it look like there are <u>massive gaps</u> between the atoms — in reality this is where the <u>electron clouds</u> interact.

Is it just me, or does ethanol look like a little doggie...

Covalent bonding is all about what's in an atom's outer electron shell. Make sure you're up to speed with electronic structures (see page 87) so you can work out how many covalent bonds an atom can form.

Q1   Given that fluorine atoms have the electronic structure 2.7, draw a dot and cross
diagram to show the covalent bonding in a fluorine molecule, F$_2$.   [1 mark]

Q2   In a methane molecule, CH$_4$, a carbon atom is covalently bonded to four hydrogen atoms.
Draw a dot and cross diagram to show the bonding in a methane molecule.   [1 mark]

Giant Covalent Structures and Fullerenes

Most of the covalent molecules you'll meet at GCSE contain only a few atoms. But not these beauties...

Giant Covalent Structures Contain Many Covalent Bonds

1) Giant covalent structures are similar to giant ionic lattices except that there are no charged ions.
2) The atoms are bonded to each other by strong covalent bonds.
3) This means that they have very high melting and boiling points.
4) They don't conduct electricity — not even when molten (except for graphite, graphene and fullerenes — see below).

> Giant covalent structures are sometimes called 'macromolecules'. 'Macro-' means 'big'. They're called that because they're molecules, and they're big. Big for molecules, anyway.

5) The examples of giant covalent structures you need to know about are made from carbon atoms.
6) Carbon can form loads of different types of molecule (including the examples below), because carbon atoms can form up to four covalent bonds, and bond easily to other carbon atoms to make chains and rings.

Diamond

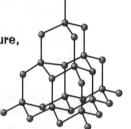

1) Pure diamonds are lustrous (sparkly) and colourless. Ideal for jewellery.
2) Each carbon atom forms four covalent bonds in a very rigid giant covalent structure, which makes diamond really hard. This makes diamonds ideal as cutting tools.
3) All those strong covalent bonds take a lot of energy to break and give diamond a very high melting point, which is another reason diamond is a good cutting tool.
4) It doesn't conduct electricity because it has no free electrons or ions.

Graphite and Graphene

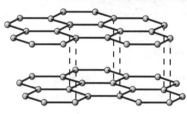

1) Graphite is black and opaque, but still kind of shiny.
2) Each carbon atom only forms three covalent bonds, creating sheets of carbon atoms which are free to slide over each other.
3) The layers are held together weakly so they are slippery and can be rubbed off onto paper to leave a black mark — that's how a pencil works. This also makes graphite ideal as a lubricating material.
4) Graphite's got a high melting point — the covalent bonds need loads of energy to break.
5) Since only three out of each carbon's four outer electrons are used in bonds, there are lots of delocalised (free) electrons that can move. This means graphite conducts electricity.

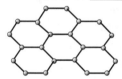

6) A single sheet of graphite is called graphene. Graphene's a bit of a wonder material — its covalent bonds make it extremely strong and a sheet of graphene is so thin that it's transparent and incredibly light. Its delocalised electrons are completely free to move about, which makes it even better at conducting electricity than graphite.

Fullerenes are Large Carbon Molecules

1) Fullerenes are another form of carbon. They aren't giant covalent structures, they're large molecules shaped like hollow balls or tubes. Different fullerenes contain different numbers of carbon atoms.
2) The carbon atoms in fullerenes are arranged in rings, similar to those in graphite. And like graphite, they have delocalised electrons so they can conduct electricity.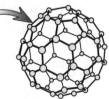
3) Their melting and boiling points aren't anything like as high as those of diamond and graphite, but they're pretty high for molecular substances because they're big molecules (and bigger molecules have more intermolecular forces).

So that pencil I gave her was just the same as a diamond, really...

Make sure you can explain how the structures of each of the substances on this page give rise to their properties.

Q1 Give two similarities and two differences between diamond and graphite, in terms of their structure and properties.

[4 marks]

Polymers and Properties of Materials

Polymers are yet another type of structure that you'll come across. They're a type of covalent molecule — but they behave differently to simple covalent substances because of the long, thin shapes of their molecules.

Plastics are Long-Chain Molecules Called Polymers

1) Polymers are formed when lots of small molecules called monomers join together.
   This reaction is called polymerisation — and it usually needs high pressure and a catalyst.

2) Plastics are polymers. They're usually carbon based and their monomers are often alkenes (a type of hydrocarbon containing a carbon-carbon double bond).

Forces Between Molecules Determine the Properties of Polymers

Strong covalent bonds hold the atoms together in polymer chains.
But it's the forces between the different chains that determine the properties of the plastic.

Squawk! Pretty polymers!

Weak Forces:

If the plastic is made up of chains that are only held together by weak intermolecular forces, then the chains will be free to slide over each other. This means that the plastic can be stretched easily, and will have a low melting point.

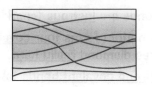

Strong Forces:

Some plastics have stronger bonds between the polymer chains — these might be covalent bonds (sometimes called cross-links). These plastics have higher melting points, are rigid and can't be stretched, as the cross-links hold the chains firmly together.

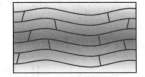

Properties of Materials Depend on Structure and Bonding

1) All the different types of material in this topic have their own special properties. What they've all got in common is the fact that their properties are down to the structures and bonding in the material.

2) The individual atoms in the material don't have these properties themselves — it's the type and strength of the bonds in a material that determines its properties.

> For example, chlorine is pretty good at forming both ionic and covalent bonds.
>
> - It's found in many common ionic compounds like sodium chloride. The ionic bonds in sodium chloride are really strong, because there's strong electrostatic attraction between the ions, which acts in all directions within the lattice structure. The strength of these bonds is what gives sodium chloride its high melting and boiling point.
>
> - Chlorine also forms simple molecular substances such as chloromethane. Although the covalent bonds which hold together the atoms in each molecule of chloromethane are very strong, the intermolecular forces which attract the molecules to each other are weak and easily overcome. So chloromethane has a low melting and boiling point.
>
> - Some polymers, such as polyvinyl chloride (PVC), also contain chlorine. PVC is strong and rigid, because the intermolecular forces between the polymer chains in PVC are relatively strong.
>
> Sodium chloride, chloromethane and PVC have these different properties because of the structure and bonding of each substance, not because they contain chlorine atoms.
> Chlorine just happens to be able to form the bonds you need to make these structures.

My cat Molly loves plastics — in fact, Molly purrs for polymers...

Polymers are really useful. So useful in fact that I think they deserve a question on them. Oh, and here's one...

Q1   Two polymers, A and B, are both composed entirely of carbon and hydrogen. Polymer A has a high melting point and is very rigid. Polymer B has a low melting point and is fairly flexible. Suggest why these polymers have different properties, despite being composed of the same elements.   [3 marks]

Metals

BONG. Here is the news. BONG. Metals have some really useful properties. BONG. These properties come from the bonding in metals. BONG. Okay, I'll stop hitting myself with this metal pan now.

Metals Have a Crystal Structure

1) All metals have the same basic properties, due to the special type of bonding that exists in metals.

2) In metals, the outer electron(s) of each atom can move freely. The atoms become positive ions in a 'sea' of delocalised (free) electrons.

3) Metallic bonding is the electrostatic attraction between these ions and electrons. The ions are surrounded by the electrons, so the attraction acts in all directions.

4) This bonding is what gives rise to many of the properties of metals.

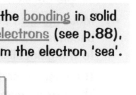
Metal ions   Free electrons

Metals generally hang out on the left-hand side of the periodic table. This explains the bonding in solid metals — elements on the left of the table normally get a full outer shell by losing electrons (see p.88), so metal atoms find it easy to become positive ions. The electrons they give up form the electron 'sea'.

Most Have High Melting and Boiling Points, and High Density

1) Metals are very hard, dense and lustrous (i.e. shiny).

2) There's a strong attraction between the delocalised electrons and the closely packed positive ions — causing very strong metallic bonding.

3) Metals generally have high melting and boiling points because of these strong metallic bonds. You need to use a lot of energy to break them apart.

They're Strong, but Also Bendy and Malleable

1) Metals have a high tensile strength — they're strong and hard to break.

2) But they can also be hammered into different shapes (they're malleable).

They're Good Conductors of Heat and Electricity

1) This is entirely due to the sea of delocalised electrons which move freely through the metal, carrying the electrical current.

2) They can also carry heat energy through the metal.

Don't try this at home. You'll die.

They React with Oxygen to Form Metal Oxides

Most metals can react with oxygen to form metal oxides. Most metal oxides are solid at room temperature and form basic solutions when you dissolve them in water (see page 113 for more on bases).

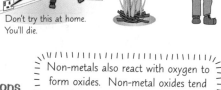
Non-metals also react with oxygen to form oxides. Non-metal oxides tend to form acidic solutions in water.

They Can be Mixed with Other Elements to Make Alloys

1) Pure metals often aren't quite right for certain jobs. You can change their properties by mixing them with other elements (either metals or non-metals) to make alloys.

2) Alloys have different properties from the main metal (or metals) they contain. For example, they may be stronger, more malleable or more corrosion resistant.

Non-metal elements generally have different properties from metals. Non-metals usually have low melting and boiling points. When solid, they tend to be weak and brittle. They have lower densities than metals and don't conduct electricity. (But there are exceptions, e.g. carbon breaks some of these rules — see p.91.)

I saw a metal on the bus once — he was the conductor...

If your knowledge of metals is still feeling a bit delocalised, the question below will help...

Q1   Copper is a metallic element. State what property of copper makes it suitable for using in electrical circuits, and explain why it has this property.

[2 marks]

States, Structure and Bonding

Bridge vs lighthouse... Phone box vs pyramid... It's time to start <u>comparing</u> different types of structure...

Structure and Bonding Affect Melting and Boiling Points

1) The <u>type of bonding</u> in a substance affects its <u>melting point</u> and <u>boiling point</u>. It's all to do with how much <u>energy</u> you need to put in to get the atoms, ions or molecules apart.

2) The <u>stronger</u> the <u>bonds</u> are that keep the particles together in a solid or liquid, the more <u>heat energy</u> you need to put in to overcome those bonds and separate the particles.

3) <u>Simple covalent</u> substances have strong bonds <u>within</u> each molecule, but only <u>weak intermolecular forces</u> between the molecules (see p.90). It doesn't take much energy to overcome these forces, so simple covalent substances melt and boil at fairly low temperatures.

4) Most <u>metals</u> have high melting and boiling points because the metal ions are very strongly attracted to the <u>delocalised electron 'sea'</u> (see p.93).

Structure	Melting / boiling point
simple covalent	low
metallic	high
ionic	high
giant covalent	high

5) The positive and negative ions in <u>ionic lattices</u> are strongly attracted to each other. This strong <u>electrostatic attraction</u> means ionic substances have high melting and boiling points.

6) <u>Giant covalent lattices</u> are held together by <u>strong covalent bonds</u>. These bonds take a lot of energy to break, so giant covalent substances have very high melting and boiling points. (In fact, some giant covalent substances <u>sublime</u> instead — that means they go straight from solid to gas.)

Making Predictions about Substances from their Properties

You might be asked to use data about substances to work out <u>what type</u> of substance they are or <u>how they behave</u> in certain conditions.

EXAMPLE: The table below give information about the properties of four different substances.

Substance	Melting point / °C	Boiling point / °C	Good electrical conductor?
A	−218.4	−183.0	No
B	1535	2750	Yes
C	1410	2355	No
D	801	1413	When molten

How well different types of substance conduct electricity is covered on p.89-91 and p.93.

a) Predict the structure of substance C.

1) C has a <u>high</u> melting and boiling point, so it's <u>unlikely</u> to be a <u>simple molecular</u> substance.

2) It <u>doesn't</u> conduct electricity well, so that means it's <u>unlikely</u> to be a <u>metal</u>. Ionic substances don't conduct electricity when they're solid, but they do when they're liquid, so we can <u>rule out</u> ionic too.

3) <u>Giant covalent</u> structures <u>don't</u> usually conduct electricity, and they have <u>high</u> melting and boiling points, so this is probably the structure of C.

Substance C is likely to have a giant covalent structure.

b) Predict the state of substance D at 1000 °C.

1) The <u>melting point</u> of D is 801 °C and its <u>boiling point</u> is 1413 °C.

2) That means it's a solid <u>below 801 °C</u>, a gas <u>above 1413 °C</u>, and a liquid <u>in between</u>.

3) <u>1000 °C</u> is between 801 °C and 1413 °C, so D is a <u>liquid</u> at this temperature.

Substance D will be a liquid at 1000 °C.

I predict a tall, dark examiner will set you a question on this...

Questions on this sort of stuff may well require you to put all the bits of info from the last few pages together. Remember, you need to know what properties the different types of structure have <u>and</u> why they have them too.

Q1 Using the table in the example above:
a) Predict the states of substances A, B and C at 1500 °C. [3 marks]
b) Predict the structures of substances A, B and D. Explain your answers. [6 marks]

Purity

Purity — one of those special <u>science words</u> that has a special <u>science meaning</u> that doesn't quite match the normal meaning people use in real life... *sigh*...

Pure Substances Contain Only One Thing

1) In <u>everyday life</u>, the word '<u>pure</u>' is often used to mean 'clean' or 'natural'.

2) In <u>chemistry</u>, it's got a more <u>specific</u> meaning — a substance is <u>pure</u> if it's completely made up of a <u>single element or compound</u>.

3) If you've got <u>more than one</u> compound present, or different elements that aren't all part of a single compound, then you've got a <u>mixture</u>, not a pure substance.

4) So, for example, <u>fresh air</u> might be thought of as nice and 'pure', but it's <u>chemically impure</u>, because it's a mixture of nitrogen, oxygen, argon, carbon dioxide, water vapour and various other gases.

5) Lots of <u>mixtures</u> are really <u>useful</u> — <u>alloys</u> (see p.93) are a great example. But sometimes chemists need to obtain a <u>pure sample</u> of a substance.

Having impure thoughts again, Henry?

Test For Purity Using Boiling and Melting Points

1) Every <u>pure</u> substance has a <u>specific melting point</u> and <u>boiling point</u>. For example, pure ice melts at 0 °C, and pure water boils at 100 °C.

2) So you can test the <u>purity</u> of a sample of a substance by comparing the <u>actual</u> melting or boiling point of the sample to the <u>expected value</u>.

3) If a substance is <u>impure</u>, the <u>melting point</u> will be too <u>low</u>. So if some ice melts at –2 °C, it's probably got an impurity in it (e.g. salt).

4) The <u>boiling point</u> of an impure substance will be too <u>high</u>. For example, seawater contains salt (and other impurities). Its boiling point tends to be around 100.6 °C.

You can also sometimes tell if a sample of a solid or liquid is a <u>mixture</u> by <u>heating it up</u>.
In a mixture, the <u>different components</u> will melt or boil at <u>different temperatures</u>, so part of the mixture will melt or boil first, while the rest will stay in its original state for longer. This means mixtures will often melt over a <u>range</u> of temperatures.

> <u>Example:</u> Adil is testing a sample of a compound for <u>purity</u> by determining its <u>melting point</u>. The <u>pure compound</u> has a melting point of <u>55 °C</u>. Adil believes his sample contains a small number of <u>impurities</u>.
>
> If Adil is correct, which of the following results should he expect from his test?
>
> A. The sample melts at a temperature <u>below 55 °C</u>.
> B. The sample melts at <u>exactly 55 °C</u>.
> C. The sample melts at a temperature <u>above 55 °C</u>.
> D. The sample melts gradually over a <u>range of temperatures</u> which includes 55 °C.
>
> Answer: Impurities <u>lower</u> the melting point of a substance, so if his sample is impure, Adil should expect it to melt <u>below</u> the normal value.
>
> A. The sample melts at a temperature below 55 °C.

If in doubt, heat it up until it melts — that's my motto...

There are lots of ways to extract a pure substance out of a mixture. The ones you need to know about are covered over the next few pages. But first, let's check you've got your head around the concept of purity.

Q1 Rachel buys a carton of juice labelled '100% pure orange juice'. Explain why the use of the word 'pure' on this label doesn't match the scientific definition. [2 marks]

Q2 Steel is produced by adding carbon to iron to make it stronger. Would you expect steel to have a higher or lower melting point then pure iron? Explain your answer. [2 marks]

 **PRACTICAL**

Distillation

Distillation is used to separate mixtures that contain <u>liquids</u>.
There are two types that you need to know about — <u>simple</u> and <u>fractional</u>.

Simple Distillation is Used to Separate Out Solutions

<u>Simple distillation</u> is used for separating out a <u>liquid</u> from a <u>solution</u>.
Here's how to use simple distillation to get <u>pure water</u> from <u>seawater</u>:

1) Pour your sample of seawater into the <u>distillation flask</u>.

2) Set up the <u>apparatus</u> as shown in the diagram. Connect the bottom end of the <u>condenser</u> to a cold tap using <u>rubber tubing</u>. Run <u>cold water</u> through the condenser to keep it cool.

3) Gradually heat the distillation flask. The part of the solution that has the lowest boiling point will <u>evaporate</u> — in this case, that's the water.

4) The water <u>vapour</u> passes into the condenser where it <u>cools</u> and <u>condenses</u> (turns back into a liquid). It then flows into the beaker where it is <u>collected</u>.

5) Eventually you'll end up with just the <u>salt</u> left in the flask.

The <u>problem</u> with simple distillation is that you can only use it to separate things with <u>very different</u> boiling points.

If you have a <u>mixture of liquids</u> with <u>similar boiling points</u>, you need another method to separate them out — like fractional distillation...

> If the liquid you're heating is flammable, use an electric heater or a water bath to heat it rather than a Bunsen burner.

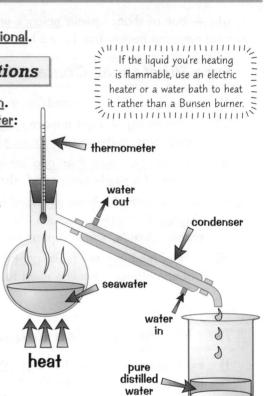

thermometer

water out

condenser

seawater

water in

heat

pure distilled water

Fractional Distillation is Used to Separate a Mixture of Liquids

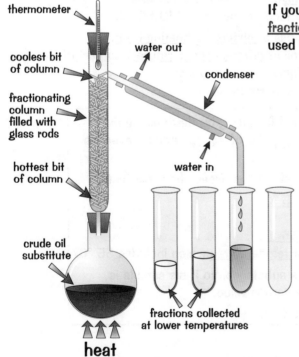

thermometer

coolest bit of column

water out

condenser

fractionating column filled with glass rods

hottest bit of column

water in

crude oil substitute

fractions collected at lower temperatures

heat

If you've got a <u>mixture of liquids</u> you can separate it using <u>fractional distillation</u>. Here's a lab demonstration that can be used to model <u>fractional distillation of crude oil</u> at a <u>refinery</u>:

1) Put your <u>mixture</u> in a flask. Attach a <u>fractionating column</u> and condenser above the flask as shown.

2) Gradually heat the flask. The <u>different liquids</u> will all have <u>different boiling points</u> — so they will evaporate at <u>different temperatures</u>.

3) The liquid with the <u>lowest boiling point</u> evaporates first. When the temperature on the thermometer matches the boiling point of this liquid, it will reach the <u>top</u> of the column.

4) Liquids with <u>higher boiling points</u> might also start to evaporate. But the column is <u>cooler</u> towards the <u>top</u>, so they will only get part of the way up before <u>condensing</u> and running back down towards the flask.

5) When the first liquid has been collected, <u>raise the temperature</u> until the <u>next one</u> reaches the top.

Fractionating — sounds a bit too much like maths to me...

The industrial method for fractional distillation of crude oil isn't quite as... well... crude as the one shown here. If you're desperate to find out what goes on in oil refineries, have a look at page 141.

Q1   Propan-1-ol, methanol and ethanol have boiling points of 97 °C, 65 °C and 78 °C respectively.
      A student uses fractional distillation to separate a mixture of these compounds.
      State which liquid will be collected in the second fraction and explain why.   [2 marks]

Filtration and Crystallisation

If you've mixed a solid with a liquid, it should be pretty easy to separate them out again.
Which method you'll need to use depends on whether or not the solid can dissolve in the liquid.

Filtration is Used to Separate an Insoluble Solid from a Liquid `PRACTICAL`

1) If the product of a reaction is an insoluble solid, you can use
filtration to separate it out from the liquid reaction mixture.

Filter paper folded
into a cone shape.

2) It can be used in purification as well. For example, solid impurities
can be separated out from a reaction mixture using filtration.

The solid is left in
the filter paper.

3) All you do is pop some filter paper into a funnel and pour your mixture into it.
The liquid part of the mixture runs through the paper, leaving behind a solid residue.

Crystallisation Separates a Soluble Solid from a Solution `PRACTICAL`

Here's how you crystallise a product...

1) Pour the solution into an evaporating dish and gently heat the solution. Some of the solvent
(which will usually be water) will evaporate and the solution will get more concentrated.

evaporating
dish

2) Once some of the solvent has evaporated, or when you see crystals
start to form (the point of crystallisation), remove the dish from the
heat and leave the solution to cool.

3) The salt should start to form crystals as it becomes insoluble in the cold, highly concentrated solution.

4) Filter the crystals out of the solution, and leave them in a warm place to dry. You could also use a
drying oven or a desiccator (a desiccator contains chemicals that remove water from the surroundings).

Choose the Right Purification Method

You might have to pick one of the techniques covered in this section
to separate a mixture. The best technique to use will depend on the
properties of the substances in the mixture.

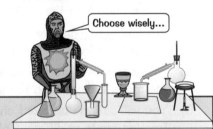

Choose wisely...

Example:
A mixture is composed of two substances, X and Y.
Substance X is a liquid at room temperature, has a melting point of 5 °C and a boiling point of 60 °C.
Substance Y is a solid at room temperature. It has a melting point of 745 °C and a boiling point of
1218 °C. Substance Y dissolves completely in substance X.

Suggest a purification method you could use to obtain:
a) A pure sample of substance X,   b) A pure sample of substance Y.

Answer:
a) To get X on its own, you need to distil it from the solution. You can use simple distillation here
— there's no need for fractional distillation as there's only one liquid in the solution.
You could obtain a pure sample of substance X using simple distillation.

b) To get a soluble solid out of a solution, you should use crystallisation.
In theory, if you distilled the mixture until all of the liquid had evaporated off, you'd end up with just substance Y left in the flask.
But there might be traces of substance X still hanging around too — crystallisation's a better way to be sure of getting a
pure sample of a solid from a solution.
You could obtain a pure sample of substance Y using crystallisation.

Its mum calls it Philliptration...

Some mixtures are made up of several components, so you might need to use a combination of the methods
covered in this section to get all the different components out.

Q1   You are given a solution that has been made by dissolving copper sulfate crystals in water.
Describe a method you could use to extract pure copper sulfate crystals from the solution.   [4 marks]

Chromatography

Chromatography is one analytical method that you need to know inside out and upside down... read on.

Chromatography uses Two Phases

Chromatography is a method used to separate and identify the substances in a mixture.
There are lots of different types of chromatography — but they all have two 'phases':

- A mobile phase — where the molecules can move. This is always a liquid or a gas.
- A stationary phase — where the molecules can't move. This can be a solid or a really thick liquid.

1) The components in the mixture separate out as the mobile phase moves over the stationary phase — they all end up in different places in the stationary phase.

2) This happens because each of the chemicals in a mixture will spend different amounts of time dissolved in the mobile phase and stuck to the stationary phase (see below for more).

3) How fast a chemical moves through the stationary phase depends on how it 'distributes' itself between the two phases.

In Thin-Layer Chromatography the Mobile Phase is a Solvent | PRACTICAL

In thin-layer chromatography (TLC), the stationary phase is a thin layer of a solid (e.g. silica gel or aluminium oxide powder) on a glass or plastic plate. The mobile phase is a solvent (e.g. ethanol).
Here's the method for setting it up:

1) Draw a line near the bottom of the plate. (Use a pencil to do this — pencil marks are insoluble and won't react with the solvent.) Put a spot of the mixture to be separated on the line.

2) Put some of the solvent into a beaker. Dip the bottom of the plate (not the spot) into the solvent.

3) Put a watch glass over the beaker to stop any solvent from evaporating away.

4) The solvent will start to move up the plate. When the chemicals in the mixture dissolve in the solvent, they will move up the plate too.

5) You will see the different chemicals in the sample separate out, forming spots at different places on the plate.

6) Remove the plate from the beaker before the solvent reaches the top. Mark the distance the solvent has moved (the solvent front) in pencil.

watch glass
solvent front
plate
spot of unknown substance
point of origin
solvent

You could use this technique to separate the different components of a dye.

The amount of time the molecules spend in each phase depends on two things:

- How soluble they are in the solvent.
- How attracted they are to the stationary phase.

Molecules with a higher solubility in the solvent (and which are less attracted to the stationary phase) will spend more time in the mobile phase than the stationary phase — so they'll be carried further up the plate.

Paper Chromatography is Similar to TLC

1) Paper chromatography is very similar to TLC, but the stationary phase is a sheet of chromatography paper (often filter paper).

2) The mobile phase is a solvent such as ethanol (just like in TLC).

What's up with Barry?

He's going through a stationery phase.

Give that mixture a bit of TLC, baby...

You might get asked about TLC or paper chromatography in the exams — lucky they're so similar then...

Q1   A mixture of two chemicals, A and B, is separated using thin-layer chromatography.
Chemical A is more soluble in the solvent than B is. Which chemical, A or B,
will end up closer to the solvent front? Explain your answer.

[2 marks]

Interpreting Chromatograms

So, what use is chromatography, apart from making a pretty pattern of spots? Let's find out...

You can Calculate the R_f Value for Each Chemical

1) The result of chromatography analysis is called a chromatogram.

2) Sometimes, the spots on a chromatogram might be colourless. If they are, you'll need to use a locating agent to show where they are (e.g. you might have to spray the chromatogram with a special reagent).

3) You need to know how to work out the R_f values for spots (solutes) on a chromatogram.

4) An R_f value is the ratio between the distance travelled by the dissolved substance (the solute) and the distance travelled by the solvent. You can find R_f values using the formula:

$$R_f = \frac{\text{distance travelled by solute}}{\text{distance travelled by solvent}}$$

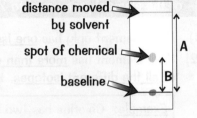

R_f value of this chemical = B ÷ A

5) To find the distance travelled by the solute, measure from the baseline to the centre of the spot.

6) Chromatography is often carried out to see if a certain substance is present in a mixture. You run a pure sample of the substance alongside the unknown mixture. If the R_f values match, the substances may be the same (although it doesn't definitely prove they are the same).

7) Chemists sometimes run samples of pure substances called standard reference materials (SRMs) next to a mixture to check the identities of its components. SRMs have controlled concentrations and purities.

8) You can also use chromatography to do a purity test. A pure substance won't be separated by chromatography — it'll always move as one blob, while a mixture can produce multiple blobs.

Gas Chromatography is a Bit More High-Tech

Gas chromatography (GC) is used to analyse unknown substances too. If they're not already gases, then they have to be vaporised. The mobile phase is an unreactive gas, such as nitrogen and the stationary phase is a viscous (thick) liquid, such as an oil.

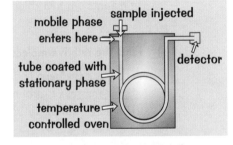

The process is quite different from paper chromatography and TLC:

1) The unknown mixture is injected into a long tube coated on the inside with the stationary phase.

2) The mixture moves along the tube with the mobile phase until it comes out the other end. As in the other chromatography methods, the substances are distributed between the phases (so each substance spends different amounts of time dissolved in the mobile phase and stuck to the stationary phase).

3) The time it takes a chemical to travel through the tube is called the retention time.

4) The retention time is different for each chemical — that's what's used to identify it.

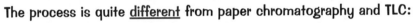

The chromatogram from GC is a graph. Each peak on the graph represents a different chemical.

- The distance along the x-axis is the retention time — which can be looked up to find out what the chemical is.

- The relative areas under the peaks show you the relative amounts of each chemical in the sample.

- There's one peak for each chemical, which means a sample of a pure substance will produce a single peak.

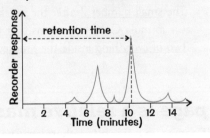

J'aime la chromatographie... hmm, I think I need an interpreter...

GC is used a lot by scientists in real-life chemical analysis. Just don't try it in your oven at home.

Q1   On a paper chromatogram, chemical X travelled 2.1 cm, chemical Y travelled 3.6 cm and the solvent front travelled 6.0 cm. Calculate the R_f value of chemical Y.   [2 marks]

Relative Masses

The <u>mass of an atom</u> is really, really tiny. To make it easier to <u>calculate</u> with and <u>compare</u> the masses of different atoms, you usually use <u>relative masses</u> instead of their actual masses.

Relative Atomic Mass, A_r — Easy Peasy

In the periodic table, the elements all have <u>two</u> numbers next to them. The <u>bigger one</u> is the <u>relative atomic mass</u> (A_r) of the element.

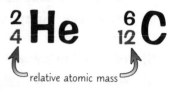

$$^{2}_{4}He \quad ^{6}_{12}C$$

relative atomic mass

> The <u>relative atomic mass</u> of an element is the <u>average mass</u> of <u>one atom</u> of the element, compared to $\frac{1}{12}$ of the <u>mass</u> of <u>one atom</u> of <u>carbon-12.</u>

1) If an element only has <u>one isotope</u> (see p.85), its A_r will be the same as its <u>mass number</u>.

2) If an element has <u>more than one</u> isotope, its A_r will be the <u>average</u> of the <u>mass numbers</u> of <u>all the different isotopes</u>, taking into account <u>how much</u> there is of each one.

> <u>Example:</u> Chlorine has two stable isotopes, <u>chlorine-35</u> and <u>chlorine-37</u>. There's <u>quite a lot</u> of chlorine-35 around and <u>not so much</u> chlorine-37 — so chlorine's A_r works out as <u>35.5</u>.

Relative Formula Mass, M_r — Also Easy Peasy

The <u>relative formula mass</u>, <u>M_r</u>, of a compound is all the relative atomic masses in its formula <u>added together</u>.

For simple covalent compounds, the relative formula mass is usually called the relative molecular mass.

EXAMPLE:

a) Find the relative formula mass of magnesium chloride, $MgCl_2$.

Use the <u>periodic table</u> to find the <u>relative atomic masses</u> of magnesium and chlorine.

$Mg + (2 \times Cl) = 24.3 + (2 \times 35.5)$
$= 24.3 + 71.0 = 95.3$

M_r of $MgCl_2$ = 95.3

b) Find the relative molecular mass of ethanoic acid, CH_3COOH.

Again, use the <u>periodic table</u> to find the <u>relative atomic masses</u> of carbon, hydrogen and oxygen. Then add them all up in the right proportions.

$C + (3 \times H) + C + O + O + H$
$= 12.0 + (3 \times 1.0) + 12.0 + 16.0 + 16.0 + 1.0$
$= 12.0 + 3.0 + 12.0 + 16.0 + 16.0 + 1.0 = 60.0$

M_r of CH_3COOH = 60.0

Compounds with Brackets in...

EXAMPLE:

Calcium hydroxide has the formula $Ca(OH)_2$.
Find the relative formula mass of calcium hydroxide.

The <u>small number 2</u> after the bracket in the formula $Ca(OH)_2$ means that <u>there's two of everything inside the brackets</u>.

$Ca + [(O + H) \times 2] = 40.1 + [(16.0 + 1.0) \times 2]$
$= 40.1 + 34.0 = 74.1$

M_r of $Ca(OH)_2$ = 74.1

This page is a relative masterpiece...

This stuff comes up a fair bit in chemistry, so make sure you've got to grips with it by doing loads of practice questions. Start with these. Use the periodic table on the back cover to find the A_r values you need.

Q1   Find the relative formula mass of sodium chloride, NaCl.   [1 mark]

Q2   Calculate the relative molecular mass of ethanol, C_2H_5OH.   [1 mark]

Q3   Find the relative formula mass of copper nitrate, $Cu(NO_3)_2$.   [2 marks]

Molecular and Empirical Formulas

Three types of <u>formula</u> to cover here. <u>Molecular</u> and <u>displayed</u> are pretty easy (and should already be familiar). <u>Empirical formulas</u> are a bit less fun, because they involve ratios, but I'm sure you'll learn to love them too...

Molecular Formulas and Displayed Formulas Show Numbers of Atoms

You can work out <u>how many atoms</u> of each type there are in a substance when you're given its <u>formula</u>.

This is called a <u>molecular</u> formula. It shows the <u>number</u> and <u>type</u> of <u>atoms</u> in a molecule.

CH_4

Methane contains 1 carbon atom and 4 hydrogen atoms.

$$H-C-H$$ with H above and H below

This is called a <u>displayed</u> formula. It shows the <u>atoms</u> and the <u>covalent bonds</u> in a molecule as a picture.

Don't panic if a molecular formula has <u>brackets</u> in it — they're easy to deal with.

$$CH_3(CH_2)_2CH_3$$

For example, the 2 after the bracket here means that there are 2 lots of CH_2. So altogether there are 4 carbon atoms and 10 hydrogen atoms.

If you have the <u>displayed formula</u> of a molecule, you can use it to write the <u>molecular formula</u> (and vice versa) — each carbon atom in the molecular formula matches up with one carbon in the displayed formula.

$$H-C-C-C-C-H$$ with H H H H above and H H H H below

$$CH_3(CH_2)_2CH_3$$

The Empirical Formula is the Simplest Ratio of Atoms

An <u>empirical formula</u> of a compound tells you the <u>smallest whole number ratio</u> of atoms in the compound.

EXAMPLE: Find the empirical formula of: a) Ethane, C_2H_6 b) Glucose, $C_6H_{12}O_6$

a) The numbers in the <u>molecular formula</u> of <u>ethane</u> are <u>2</u> and <u>6</u>.
To simplify the ratio, divide by the largest number that goes into 2 and 6 <u>exactly</u> — that's <u>2</u>.

C: $2 \div 2 = 1$
H: $6 \div 2 = 3$
The empirical formula of ethane is CH_3.

b) The numbers in the <u>molecular formula</u> of <u>glucose</u> are <u>6</u>, <u>12</u> and <u>6</u>.
To simplify the ratio, divide by the largest number that goes into 6, 12 and 6 <u>exactly</u> — that's <u>6</u>.

C: $6 \div 6 = 1$
H: $12 \div 6 = 2$
O: $6 \div 6 = 1$
The empirical formula of glucose is CH_2O.

You can use the <u>empirical formula</u> of a compound, together with its M_r, to find its molecular formula.

EXAMPLE: Compound X has the empirical formula C_2H_6N. The M_r of compound X is 88. Find the molecular formula of compound X.

1) Start by finding the M_r of the <u>empirical formula</u>. The A_r of carbon is <u>12</u>, the A_r of hydrogen is <u>1</u> and the A_r of nitrogen is <u>14</u>.

M_r of C_2H_6N = $(2 \times C) + (6 \times H) + N$
= $(2 \times 12.0) + (6 \times 1.0) + 14.0$
= $24.0 + 6.0 + 14.0$
= 44.0

2) Divide the M_r of compound X by the M_r of the empirical formula.

$88 \div 44.0 = 2$

3) Now to get the <u>molecular formula</u> of compound X, you just <u>multiply</u> everything in the empirical formula by your answer to step 2) — in this case, that's <u>2</u>

C: $2 \times 2 = 4$
H: $6 \times 2 = 12$
N: $1 \times 2 = 2$
The molecular formula of compound X is $C_4H_{12}N_2$.

I believe in empiricals...

Another page with lots of maths — which means the best way to learn this stuff is by doing some questions. Wait, what's that on the next line? A question on empirical formulas? It's almost like it's your destiny to answer it...

Q1   What is the empirical formula of a compound with the molecular formula $C_4H_8Cl_2$?   [1 mark]

Revision Questions for Topics C1 and C2

That's <u>Topic C1</u> and <u>Topic C2</u> done and dusted. Time to take a look back at the best bits.

- Try these questions and <u>tick off each one</u> when you <u>get it right</u>.
- When you've done <u>all the questions</u> under a heading and are <u>completely happy</u> with it, tick it off.

<u>States of Matter and the Atom (p.82-85)</u> ☐

1) What are the three states of matter? ☑
2) Describe the gold foil experiment carried out by Rutherford, Geiger and Marsden. ☑
3) Draw a diagram of an atom. Label the nucleus and the electrons on your diagram. ☑
4) What are isotopes? ☑

<u>The Periodic Table and Electronic Structures (p.86-87)</u> ☐

5) Outline how Mendeleev arranged the elements in his version of the periodic table. ☑
6) How many electrons would you expect an element in Group 7 to have in its outer shell? ☑
7) What's the maximum number of electrons that each of the first three electron shells will hold? ☑
8) The proton number of aluminium is 13. What is its electronic structure? ☑

<u>Structure, Bonding and Properties of Materials (p.88-94)</u> ☐

9) What is an ion? ☑
10) Why does magnesium form ions with a 2+ charge, while sodium only forms ions with a 1+ charge? ☑
11) Explain why ionic compounds conduct electricity when they're molten, but not when they're solid. ☑
12) Describe how a covalent bond forms. ☑
13) Why do simple molecular substances have low melting and boiling points? ☑
14) List three typical properties of giant covalent structures. ☑
15) Name three substances that have a giant covalent structure. ☑
16) Name the type of molecules that plastics are made from. ☑
17) List three typical properties of metals that are due to their metallic bonding. ☑
18) Out of the four main types of structure (ionic, simple covalent, giant covalent and metallic),
     which one is most likely to have a low melting point? ☑

<u>Purity and Separating Mixtures (p.95-99)</u> ☐

19) In chemistry, what is meant by the term 'a pure substance'? ☑
20) Does adding an impurity to a substance raise or lower its boiling point? ☑
21) List the equipment that you would need to do a fractional distillation in the lab. ☑
22) What purification technique should you use to obtain a pure sample of a soluble solid from a solution? ☑
23) In chromatography, what do the terms 'mobile phase' and 'stationary phase' mean? ☑
24) Describe the method for separating a mixture by thin-layer chromatography. ☑
25) How do you calculate the R_f value of a substance from a chromatogram? ☑

<u>Relative Masses and Formulas (p.100-101)</u> ☐

26) What is the 'relative atomic mass' of an element? ☑
27) How do you work out the relative formula mass of a compound? ☑
28) What is the empirical formula of a compound? ☑

Conservation of Mass

Being a diva, I prefer the conservation of sass. Conservation of mass is more useful in science exams though.

In a Chemical Reaction, Mass is Always Conserved

1) During a chemical reaction no atoms are destroyed and no atoms are created.

2) This means there are the same number and types of atoms on each side of a reaction equation.

3) Because of this no mass is lost or gained — we say that mass is conserved during a reaction.
   Example: $2Li + F_2 \rightarrow 2LiF$. There are 2 lithium atoms and 2 fluorine atoms on each side of the equation.

4) By adding up the relative masses (see page 100) on each side of
   the equation you can see that mass is conserved.

 **EXAMPLE:**

Use relative formula masses to show that
mass is conserved in the following reaction: $2Li + F_2 \rightarrow 2LiF$

1) Work out the total of the relative formula masses of the reactants.
   M_r reactants $= 2 \times M_r(Li) + M_r(F_2)$
   $= (2 \times 6.9) + (2 \times 19.0) = 51.8$

2) Work out the total of the relative formula masses of the products.
   M_r products $= 2 \times M_r(LiF)$
   $= 2 \times (6.9 + 19.0) = 51.8$

3) Compare the total relative formula masses of the reactants and products.
   M_r products $= 51.8$ M_r reactants $= 51.8$
   So M_r reactants $= M_r$ products

There's more about balanced symbol equations on page 105.

I have literally no idea what I'm doing.

If the Mass Seems to Change, There's Usually a Gas Involved

In some experiments, you might observe a change of mass of an unsealed reaction vessel during a reaction. There are two reasons why this happens:

1 If the mass increases, it's probably because at least one of the reactants is a gas that's found in air (e.g. oxygen) and the products are solids, liquids or aqueous.

- Before the reaction, the gas is floating around in the air. It's there, but it's not contained in the reaction vessel, so you can't account for its mass.

- When the gas reacts to form part of the product, it becomes contained inside the reaction vessel.

- So the total mass of the stuff inside the reaction vessel increases.

- For example, when a metal reacts with oxygen in an unsealed container, the mass inside the container increases. The mass of the metal oxide produced equals the total mass of the metal and the oxygen that reacted from the air.
  $metal_{(s)} + oxygen_{(g)} \rightarrow metal\ oxide_{(s)}$

2 If the mass decreases, it's probably because some, or all, of the reactants are solids, liquids or aqueous and at least one of the products is a gas.

- Before the reaction, any solid, liquid or aqueous reactants are contained in the reaction vessel.

- If the vessel isn't enclosed, then the gas can escape from the reaction vessel as it's formed. It's no longer contained in the reaction vessel, so you can't account for its mass.

- So the total mass of the stuff inside the reaction vessel decreases.

- For example, when a metal carbonate thermally decomposes to form a metal oxide and carbon dioxide gas, the mass of the reaction vessel will appear to decrease if it isn't sealed as the carbon dioxide escapes. But in reality, the mass of the metal oxide and the carbon dioxide produced will equal the mass of the metal carbonate that reacted.
  $metal\ carbonate_{(s)} \rightarrow metal\ oxide_{(s)} + carbon\ dioxide_{(g)}$

Remember the particle model on page 82. A gas will expand to fill any container it's in. So if the reaction vessel isn't sealed the gas expands out from the vessel, and escapes into the air around.

Conservation of Mass — protecting mass for future generations...

Never, ever forget that, in a reaction, the total mass of reactants is the same as the total mass of products.

Q1   Using the balanced equation, show that mass is conserved in the following reaction:

$H_2SO_{4(aq)} + 2NaOH_{(aq)} \rightarrow Na_2SO_{4(aq)} + 2H_2O_{(l)}$ [3 marks]

Chemical Formulas

Make sure you've really got your head around the idea of <u>ionic bonding</u> (pages 88-89) before you start this.

You Need to be Familiar with Some Common Ions

1) You met <u>ions</u> back on page 88. They form when atoms, or groups of atoms, lose or gain electrons.

2) Here are some common ions you may meet throughout the course.
Sometimes you can <u>predict</u> the charge from where they are in the periodic table.
Others, e.g. the ions made up of more than one atom, you just have to learn.

Look back at page 88 for how to predict what ion an element will form from its position in the periodic table.

Positive Ions		Negative Ions	
1+ ions	2+ ions	2− ions	1− ions
Lithium, Li^+	Magnesium, Mg^{2+}	Carbonate, CO_3^{2-}	Hydroxide, OH^-
Sodium, Na^+	Calcium, Ca^{2+}	Sulfate, SO_4^{2-}	Nitrate, NO_3^-
Potassium, K^+		Oxide, O^{2-}	Fluoride, F^-
		Sulfide, S^{2-}	Chloride, Cl^-
			Bromide, Br^-
			Iodide, I^-

3) Any of the positive ions above can <u>combine</u> with any of the negative ions to form an <u>ionic compound</u> (see pages 88-89). For example, Na and Cl form NaCl, where sodium becomes a <u>positive ion</u> and chlorine becomes a <u>negative ion</u>.

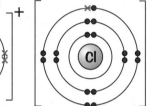

You Can Work Out the Formula of an Ionic Compound

1) Ionic compounds are made up of a <u>positively charged</u> part and a <u>negatively charged</u> part.

2) The <u>overall charge</u> of <u>any compound</u> is <u>zero</u>. So all the <u>negative charges</u> in the compound must <u>balance</u> all the <u>positive charges</u>.

3) You can use the charges on the <u>individual ions</u> present to work out the formula for the ionic compound.

4) You need to be able to write formulas using <u>chemical symbols</u>.

EXAMPLE: What is the chemical formula of calcium nitrate?

1) Write out the <u>formulas</u> for the calcium and nitrate ions. Ca^{2+}, NO_3^-

The brackets show you need two of the whole nitrate ion.

2) The <u>overall charge</u> on the formula must be <u>zero</u>, so work out the ratio of Ca : NO_3 that gives an overall neutral charge. To balance the 2+ charge on Ca^{2+}, you need two NO_3^- ions. So formula = $Ca(NO_3)_2$

$(+2) + (2 \times -1) = 0$

You Need to Learn the Formulas of Some Molecules

1) <u>Prefixes</u> can tell you how many of a certain atom are in a molecule. The main ones you'll need to know are <u>mono-</u> = one, <u>di-</u> = two and <u>tri-</u> = three. E.g. each molecule of carbon <u>mono</u>xide contains <u>one</u> oxygen atom and each molecule of carbon <u>di</u>oxide contains <u>two</u> oxygen atoms.

2) It's a good idea to <u>learn</u> the chemical formulas of these common molecules. They crop up all the time.

- Water — H_2O
- Ammonia — NH_3
- Carbon dioxide — CO_2
- Hydrogen — H_2
- Chlorine — Cl_2
- Oxygen — O_2

These three molecules are all called <u>diatomic</u> molecules, as they contain <u>two</u> atoms.

 tricycle dicycle monocycle

Group 1 ions — positively wonderful, but for a small charge...

Chemical formulas pop up everywhere. Make sure you can write 'em or you'll be stumped in the exam.

Q1   Write the formula, with the charge, of the following ions:
     a) bromide ion,   b) carbonate ion,   c) lithium ion,   d) nitrate ion.   [4 marks]

Q2   What is the chemical formula of magnesium hydroxide?   [1 mark]

Topic C3 — Chemical Reactions

Chemical Equations

If you're going to get anywhere in chemistry you need to know about <u>chemical equations</u>...

Chemical Changes are Shown Using Chemical Equations

One way to show a chemical reaction is to write a <u>word equation</u>. It's not as <u>useful</u> as using chemical symbols because you can't tell straight away <u>what's happened</u> to each of the <u>atoms</u>, but it's <u>dead easy</u>.

Here's an example — <u>methane</u> burns in <u>oxygen</u> giving <u>carbon dioxide</u> and <u>water</u>:

The molecules on the <u>left-hand side</u> of the equation are called the <u>reactants</u> (because they react with each other).

methane + oxygen → carbon dioxide + water

The molecules on the <u>right-hand side</u> are called the <u>products</u> (because they've been produced from the reactants).

Symbol Equations Show the Atoms on Both Sides

Chemical <u>changes</u> can be shown in a kind of <u>shorthand</u> using symbol equations. Symbol equations just show the <u>symbols or formulas</u> of the <u>reactants</u> and <u>products</u>...

$$magnesium + oxygen \rightarrow magnesium\ oxide$$
$$2Mg + O_2 \rightarrow 2MgO$$

The numbers in front of the formulas show the ratios between the number of moles of each substance (see pages 107-109 for more on moles and equations).

Symbol Equations Need to be Balanced

1) There must always be the <u>same</u> number of atoms on <u>both sides</u> of the equation — they can't just <u>disappear</u>.

2) You <u>balance</u> the equation by putting numbers <u>in front</u> of the formulas where needed. Take this equation for reacting sulfuric acid with sodium hydroxide:

$$H_2SO_4 + NaOH \rightarrow Na_2SO_4 + H_2O$$

3) The <u>formulas</u> are all correct but the numbers of some atoms <u>don't match up</u> on both sides.

4) You <u>can't change formulas</u> like H_2SO_4 to H_2SO_5. You can only put numbers <u>in front of them</u>.

The more you <u>practise</u>, the <u>quicker</u> you get, but all you do is this:

$E=mc^2$

- Find an element that <u>doesn't balance</u> and <u>pencil in a number</u> to try and sort it out.
- <u>See where it gets you.</u> It may create <u>another imbalance</u>, but if so, pencil in <u>another number</u> and see where that gets you.
- Carry on chasing <u>unbalanced</u> elements and the equation will <u>sort itself out</u> pretty quickly.

EXAMPLE: In the equation above you'll notice we're short of <u>H atoms</u> on the RHS (Right-Hand Side).

1) The only thing you can do about that is make it <u>2H₂O</u> instead of just H_2O:

$$H_2SO_4 + NaOH \rightarrow Na_2SO_4 + 2H_2O$$

2) But that now gives <u>too many</u> H atoms and O atoms on the RHS, so to balance that up you could try putting <u>2NaOH</u> on the LHS (Left-Hand Side):

$$H_2SO_4 + 2NaOH \rightarrow Na_2SO_4 + 2H_2O$$

3) And suddenly there it is! <u>Everything balances</u>. And you'll notice the Na just sorted itself out.

Revision is all about getting the balance right...

Balancing equations is all about practice. Once you have a few goes you'll see it's much less scary than it seemed before you took on, challenged and defeated this page. Go grab some chemistry glory.

Q1   Balance the equation: $Fe + Cl_2 \rightarrow FeCl_3$ [1 mark]

Q2   Hydrogen and oxygen molecules are formed in a reaction where water splits apart.
        For this reaction: a) State the word equation.   b) Give a balanced symbol equation.   [3 marks]

More on Chemical Equations

If you thought that was all there was to know about <u>chemical equations</u>, prepare to be sorely disappointed...

State Symbols Tell You the State of a Substance in an Equation

You saw on the last page how a chemical reaction can be shown using a <u>word equation</u> or a <u>symbol equation</u>. Symbol equations can also include <u>state symbols</u> next to each substance — they tell you what <u>physical state</u> (see page 82) the reactants and products are in:

(s) — solid   (l) — liquid   (g) — gas   (aq) — aqueous

'Aqueous' means 'dissolved in water'.

<u>Example</u>: Aqueous hydrochloric acid reacts with solid calcium carbonate to form aqueous calcium chloride, liquid water and carbon dioxide gas: $2HCl_{(aq)} + CaCO_{3(s)} \rightarrow CaCl_{2(aq)} + H_2O_{(l)} + CO_{2(g)}$

Ionic Equations Show Just the Useful Bits of Reactions

1) You can also write an <u>ionic equation</u> for any reaction involving ions that happens in solution.

2) In an ionic equation, only the <u>reacting particles</u> (and the products they form) are included.

3) To write an ionic equation, you've just got to look at the reactants and products. Anything that's <u>exactly the same</u> on <u>both sides</u> of the equation can be left out.

> You should make sure your symbol equation is balanced before you start trying to write the ionic equation (see the last page for more on how to balance symbol equations).

EXAMPLE: Write the ionic equation for the following reaction:
$$CaCl_{2\,(aq)} + 2NaOH_{(aq)} \rightarrow Ca(OH)_{2\,(s)} + 2NaCl_{(aq)}$$

1) Anything that's <u>ionic</u> (i.e. made of ions — see page 88) and aqueous will break up into its ions in solution. So, write out the equation showing all the <u>ions separately</u>.

$$Ca^{2+}_{(aq)} + 2Cl^-_{(aq)} + 2Na^+_{(aq)} + 2OH^-_{(aq)} \rightarrow Ca(OH)_{2\,(s)} + 2Na^+_{(aq)} + 2Cl^-_{(aq)}$$

2) To get to the ionic equation, <u>cross out</u> anything that's the <u>same on both sides</u> of the equation — here, those are the Na^+ and Cl^- ions.

$$Ca^{2+}_{(aq)} + \cancel{2Cl^-}_{(aq)} + \cancel{2Na^+}_{(aq)} + 2OH^-_{(aq)} \rightarrow Ca(OH)_{2\,(s)} + \cancel{2Na^+}_{(aq)} + \cancel{2Cl^-}_{(aq)}$$

$$Ca^{2+}_{(aq)} + 2OH^-_{(aq)} \rightarrow Ca(OH)_{2\,(s)}$$

The overall charge should be the same on both sides of the reaction.

Half Equations Show the Movement of Electrons

<u>Half equations</u> show how electrons are transferred during reactions. In half equations, e^- stands for <u>one electron</u>.

You can't write half equations for all chemical reactions — only the ones where <u>oxidation</u> or <u>reduction</u> happen (see page 117).

> Half equations are really useful for showing what happens at each electrode during electrolysis (see page 117-119).

<u>Examples</u>: In this half equation, sodium is losing one electron to become a sodium ion.

In this equation, two hydrogen ions are each gaining one electron to form a hydrogen molecule.

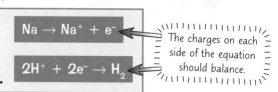

$$Na \rightarrow Na^+ + e^-$$
$$2H^+ + 2e^- \rightarrow H_2$$

The charges on each side of the equation should balance.

You can <u>combine half equations</u> to create <u>full ionic equations</u>.
Full equations <u>never</u> contain electrons — the electrons in the reactants and products should <u>cancel out</u>.
So, in the sodium/hydrogen example above, the <u>full ionic equation</u> would be: $2Na + 2H^+ \rightarrow 2Na^+ + H_2$.
(You need to multiply the sodium half equation by 2 so the electrons on each side balance.)

Half equations — equa, equa, equa, equa, equa, equa...

They may be half equations, but they're double the trouble if you ask me. Better get some practice in...

Q1   Write the ionic equation for the following reaction: $HNO_{3\,(aq)} + NaOH_{(aq)} \rightarrow NaNO_{3\,(aq)} + H_2O_{(l)}$ [1 mark]

Q2   Write a half equation to show a chlorine molecule gaining electrons to become chloride ions.   [2 marks]

Moles

The mole might seem a bit confusing. I think it's the word that puts people off. But it's not that hard really...

"The Mole" is Simply the Name Given to a Certain Number

1) Just like a million is this many: 1 000 000, or a billion is this many: 1 000 000 000, a mole is given by Avogadro's constant, and it's this many: 602 200 000 000 000 000 000 000 or 6.022×10^{23}.

2) But what does Avogadro's constant show? The answer is that when you get that number of atoms or molecules, of any element or compound, then, conveniently, they weigh exactly the same number of grams as the relative atomic mass, A_r, (or relative formula mass, M_r) of the element or compound.

> One mole of atoms or molecules of any substance will have a mass in grams equal to the relative formula mass (A_r or M_r) for that substance.

Look back at page 100 if you've forgotten how to work out A_r and M_r.

Examples:

Carbon has an A_r of 12.   So one mole of carbon weighs exactly 12 g.

Nitrogen gas, N_2, has an M_r of 28 (2×14).   So one mole of nitrogen gas weighs exactly 28 g.

Hexane, C_6H_{14}, has an M_r of 86 ((6×12) + (14×1)).   So one mole of hexane weighs exactly 86 g.

So 12 g of carbon, 28 g of nitrogen gas and 86 g of hexane all contain the same number of particles, namely one mole or 6.022×10^{23} particles.

EXAMPLE: How many atoms are there in 5 moles of oxygen gas?

1) Multiply Avogadro's constant by the number of moles you have to find the number of particles.

$$6.022 \times 10^{23} \times 5 = 3.011 \times 10^{24}$$

2) There are two atoms in each molecule of oxygen gas, so multiply your answer by 2.

$$3.011 \times 10^{24} \times 2 = 6.022 \times 10^{24}$$

Give your answer in standard form (in terms of $\times 10^x$) to save you having to write out lots of O's.

3) To find the mass of an atom of a certain element, just divide its relative atomic mass by Avogadro's constant.

EXAMPLE: What is the mean mass of one atom of iron?

Mass of one atom = $A_r \div$ Avogadro's constant
$$= 55.8 \div (6.022 \times 10^{23}) = 9.27 \times 10^{-23} \text{ g}$$

You Can Find the Number of Moles in a Given Mass

There's a nifty formula you can use to find the number of moles in a certain mass of something. You need to know how to use it, and be able to rearrange it to find mass or M_r.

You can rearrange an equation using a formula triangle. Just cover the thing you want to find, and you're left the expression you need to calculate it.

$$\text{Number of Moles} = \frac{\text{Mass in g (of element or compound)}}{M_r \text{ (of element or compound)}}$$

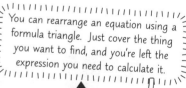

To find the number of moles of atoms in a certain mass of an element, just replace M_r in the formula with A_r.

EXAMPLE:

How many moles are there in 66 g of carbon dioxide?

M_r of carbon dioxide (CO_2) = 12.0 + (2×16.0) = 44.0

moles = mass $\div M_r$ = 66 $\div$ 44.0 = 1.5 moles

EXAMPLE: What mass of carbon is there in 4.0 moles of carbon dioxide?

mass = moles $\times A_r$
$$= 4.0 \times 12.0 = 44 \text{ g}$$

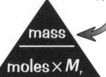

What do moles do for fun? Moller skate...

Moles can give you a bit of a headache — so spend a bit of time getting your head round all this if you need to.

Q1   Calculate the number of moles in 90 g of water. M_r of water = 18.0.   [1 mark]

Q2   Calculate the mass of 0.200 moles of potassium bromide. M_r of KBr = 119.0.   [1 mark]

Q3   0.500 moles of substance X has a mass of 87.0 g. What is the relative formula mass of X?   [1 mark]

Calculating Masses

Unlimited. Together we're unlimited. Unless you're a _limiting reactant_, in which case you're a big ol' limiter.

Reactions Stop When One Reactant is Used Up

1) A reaction stops when all of one of the reactants is _used up_. Any other reactants are said to be in _excess_.

2) The reactant that's _used up_ in a reaction is called the _limiting reactant_ (because it limits the amount of product that's formed).

3) The amount of product formed is _directly proportional_ to the amount of _limiting reactant_. This is because if you add _more of the limiting reactant_ there will be _more reactant particles_ to take part in the reaction, which means _more product particles_ are made (as long as the other reactants are in excess).

The Amount of Product Depends on the Limiting Reactant

You can use a _balanced chemical equation_ to work out the _mass of product formed_ from a given _mass of a limiting reactant_. Here's how...

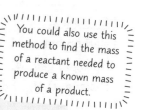

You could also use this method to find the mass of a reactant needed to produce a known mass of a product.

1) Write out the _balanced equation_.

2) _Work out relative formula masses_ (M_r) of the reactant and product you want.

3) Find out _how many moles_ there are of the substance you _know_ the mass of.

4) Use the balanced equation to work out _how many moles_ there'll be of the _other_ substance (i.e. how many moles of product will be made by this many moles of reactant).

5) Use the number of moles to calculate the _mass_.

EXAMPLE: Calculate the mass of aluminium oxide formed when 135 g of aluminium is burned in air.

1) Write out the _balanced equation_:	$4Al + 3O_2 \rightarrow 2Al_2O_3$
2) Calculate the relative atomic or formula masses of the reactants and products you're interested in.	Al: 27.0 Al_2O_3: $(2 \times 27.0) + (3 \times 16.0) = 102.0$
3) _Calculate the number of moles_ of aluminium in 135 g:	moles = mass ÷ M_r = 135 ÷ 27.0 = 5
4) Look at the _ratio_ of moles in the equation:	4 moles of Al react to produce 2 moles of Al_2O_3 — half the number of moles are produced. So 5 moles of Al will react to produce 2.5 moles of Al_2O_3.
5) _Calculate the mass_ of 2.5 moles of aluminium oxide:	mass = moles × M_r = 2.5 × 102.0 = **255 g**

EXAMPLE: Magnesium oxide can be made by burning magnesium in air. What mass of magnesium is needed to make 100 g of magnesium oxide?

1) Write out the balanced equation.	$2Mg + O_2 \rightarrow 2MgO$
2) Work out the relative atomic or formula masses of the reactants and products you're interested in.	Mg: 24.3 MgO: 24.3 + 16.0 = 40.3
3) _Calculate the number of moles_ of magnesium oxide in 100 g:	moles = mass ÷ M_r = 100 ÷ 40.3 = 2.48...
4) Look at the _ratio_ of moles in the equation to work out the no. moles of reactant used, compared to the no. moles of product made.	2 moles of MgO are made from 2 moles of Mg. So 2.48... moles of MgO will be formed from 2.48... moles of Mg.
5) _Calculate the mass_ of 2.5 moles of Mg.	mass = moles × M_r = 2.48... × 24.3 = **60.3 g**

Relative mass — when you go to church with your parents...

A specially organically grown, hand-picked question for you my dear. Don't say I don't spoil you.

Q1 Chlorine and potassium bromide react according to this equation: $Cl_2 + 2KBr \rightarrow Br_2 + 2KCl$
Calculate the mass of bromine produced when 23.8 g of
potassium bromide reacts in an excess of chlorine.

[4 marks]

Topic C3 — Chemical Reactions

More Mole Calculations

You've already seen how to balance equations back on page 105. But, sometimes, you may have to balance equations given the masses of the reactants and products. Your good old friend the mole will come in handy...

You Can Balance Equations Using Reacting Masses

If you know the masses of the reactants and products that took part in a reaction, you can work out the balanced symbol equation for the reaction. Here are the steps you should take:

1) Divide the mass of each substance by its relative formula mass to find the number of moles.

You may need to work out some unknown masses first (see below).

2) Divide the number of moles of each substance by the smallest number of moles in the reaction.

3) If needed, multiply all the numbers by the same amount to make them all whole numbers.

4) Write the balanced symbol equation for the reaction by putting these numbers in front of the formulas.

EXAMPLE: Paula burns a metal, X, in oxygen. There is a single product, an oxide of the metal. Given that 25.4 g of X burns in 3.2 g of oxygen, write a balanced equation for this reaction. A_r of X = 63.5 and M_r of X oxide = 143.0.

1) Work out the mass of metal oxide produced. Because it's the only product, the mass of metal oxide produced must equal the total mass of reactants. 25.4 + 3.2 = 28.6 g of X oxide

2) Divide the mass of each substance by its M_r or A_r to calculate how many moles of each substance reacted or were produced:

X: $\frac{25.4}{63.5}$ = 0.40 mol O_2: $\frac{3.2}{32.0}$ = 0.10 mol   X oxide: $\frac{28.6}{143.0}$ = 0.20 mol

3) Divide by the smallest number of moles, which is 0.10:   X: $\frac{0.40}{0.10}$ = 4.0 O_2: $\frac{0.10}{0.10}$ = 1.0   X oxide: $\frac{0.20}{0.10}$ = 2.0

4) The numbers are all whole numbers, so you can write out the balanced symbol equation straight away. $4X + O_2 \rightarrow 2(X\ oxide)$

5) The oxide of X must have a chemical formula containing X and O atoms. In order for the equation to balance, each molecule of X oxide must contain one O atom and 2 X atoms. $4X + O_2 \rightarrow 2X_2O$

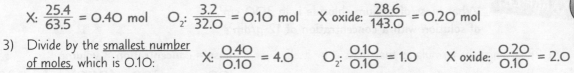

You Can Work Out Limiting Reactants

EXAMPLE: 8.14 g of zinc oxide (ZnO) were put in a crucible with 0.30 g of carbon and heated until they reacted. Given that the balanced chemical equation for this reaction is: $2ZnO + C \rightarrow CO_2 + 2Zn$, work out the limiting reactant in this reaction.

1) Divide the mass of each substance by its M_r or A_r to find how many moles of each substance were reacted: ZnO: $\frac{8.14}{81.4}$ = 0.10 mol C: $\frac{0.30}{12.0}$ = 0.025 mol

2) Divide by the smallest number of moles, which is 0.025:   ZnO: $\frac{0.10}{0.025}$ = 4.0 C: $\frac{0.025}{0.025}$ = 1.0

3) Compare the ratios between the moles of products with the balanced chemical equation.   In the balanced equation, ZnO and C react in a ratio of 2 : 1. Using the masses, there is a 4 : 1 ratio of ZnO to C. So, ZnO is in excess, and C must be the limiting reactant.

What do moles have for pudding? Jam moly-poly...

The best way to get to grips with the maths on this page is by practising. Luckily for you, there is a fine looking question below to get you started. Don't say I don't spoil you. Better get cracking...

Q1   84 g of nitrogen gas are sealed in a vessel with 12 g of hydrogen gas and heated. They react to produce ammonia. The equation for the reaction is: $N_2 + 3H_2 \rightarrow 2NH_3$. What is the limiting reactant?   [3 marks]

Concentration

Concentration is just <u>how much stuff</u> you have in a solution. Brace yourself — it involves some <u>calculations</u>, so don't put your calculator away just yet. There's some more number-crunching to come...

Concentration is a Measure of How Crowded Things Are

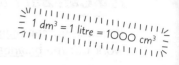

1) The <u>more solute</u> (the solid you're dissolving) you dissolve in a given volume, the <u>more crowded</u> the molecules are and the <u>more concentrated</u> the solution.

2) Concentration can be measured in <u>grams per dm³</u> — so 1 gram of stuff dissolved in 1 dm³ of solution has a concentration of <u>1 gram per dm³</u>.

3) Here's the formula for finding <u>concentration</u> from the <u>mass of solute</u>:

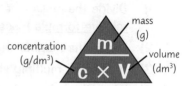

$$\text{concentration} = \text{mass of solute} \div \text{volume of solution}$$

> **EXAMPLE:** 25 g of copper sulfate is dissolved in 500 cm³ of water. What's the concentration in g/dm³?
>
> 1) Make sure the values are in the <u>right units</u>. The mass is already in g, but you need to convert the volume to dm³.
>
> 1000 cm³ = 1 dm³, so
> 500 cm³ = (500 ÷ 1000) dm³ = 0.5 dm³
>
> 2) Now just substitute the values into the formula:
>
> concentration = 25 ÷ 0.5 = **50 g/dm³**

> **EXAMPLE:** What mass of sodium chloride is in 300 cm³ of solution with a concentration of 12 g/dm³?
>
> 1) Rearrange the formula so that mass is by itself.
> 2) Put the volume into the <u>right units</u>.
> 3) Substitute the values into the rearranged formula.
>
> mass = concentration × volume
> 300 cm³ = (300 ÷ 1000) dm³ = 0.30 dm³
> mass = 12 × 0.30 = **3.6 g**

Concentration can also be Measured in mol/dm³

1) As well as measuring concentration in g/dm³, the <u>concentration</u> of a solution can also be measured in <u>moles per dm³</u> — so 1 mole of a substance dissolved in 1 dm³ of solution has a concentration of <u>1 mole per dm³</u> (or 1 mol/dm³).

2) The formula for finding <u>concentrations</u> in <u>mol/dm³</u> is similar to the one for g/dm³:

$$\text{concentration} = \text{number of moles} \div \text{volume of solution}$$

> **EXAMPLE:** 30.0 g of sodium hydroxide was dissolved in 250 cm³ of water. What is the concentration of the resultant solution in mol/dm³?
>
> 1) First, find out <u>how many moles</u> of NaOH are in 30.0 g. You'll need to calculate the M_r of NaOH first (see page 100 for how to do this).
>
> M_r(NaOH) = 23.0 + 16.0 + 1.0 = 40.0
> moles = mass ÷ M_r ◀ This is just the equation from page 107.
> = 30.0 ÷ 40.0 = 0.750 mol
>
> 2) Then, <u>substitute</u> your values for moles and volume into the equation for concentration.
>
> concentration = moles ÷ volume
> = 0.750 ÷ (250 ÷ 1000)
> = **3.0 mol/dm³**

A troop of soldiers standing to attention — it's a mass of salutes...

I know this is chemistry, but unfortunately you have to be able to do a bit of maths too... Best get practising.

Q1   What mass of sodium hydroxide would you need to make up 200 cm³ of a 55 g/dm³ solution?   [2 marks]

Endothermic and Exothermic Reactions

Whenever chemical reactions occur, there are changes in <u>energy</u>. This is kind of interesting if you think of the number of chemical reactions that are involved in everyday life.

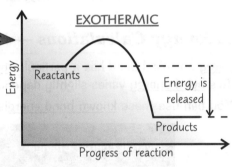

Combustion reactions (where something burns in oxygen) are always exothermic.

Reactions are Exothermic or Endothermic

An <u>EXOTHERMIC reaction</u> is one which <u>gives out energy</u> to the surroundings, usually in the form of <u>heat</u> and usually shown by a <u>rise in temperature</u> of the surroundings.

An <u>ENDOTHERMIC reaction</u> is one which <u>takes in energy</u> from the surroundings, usually in the form of <u>heat</u> and usually shown by a <u>fall in temperature</u> of the surroundings.

Reaction Profiles Show if a Reaction's Exo- or Endothermic

<u>Reaction profiles</u> show the energy levels of the <u>reactants</u> and the <u>products</u> in a reaction. You can use them to work out if energy is <u>released</u> (exothermic) or <u>taken in</u> (endothermic).

1) This shows an <u>exothermic reaction</u> — the products are at a <u>lower energy</u> than the reactants.

2) The <u>difference in height</u> represents the <u>energy given out</u> in the reaction.

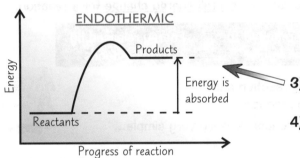

3) This shows an <u>endothermic reaction</u> because the products are at a <u>higher energy</u> than the reactants.

4) The <u>difference in height</u> represents the <u>energy taken in</u> during the reaction.

Activation Energy is the Energy Needed to Start a Reaction

1) The <u>activation energy</u> is the <u>minimum</u> amount of energy needed for <u>bonds to break</u> (see next page) and a reaction to start.

2) On a reaction profile, it's the energy difference between the reactants and the highest point on the curve.

3) It's a bit like having to <u>climb up</u> one side of a hill before you can ski/snowboard/sledge/fall down the <u>other side</u>.

4) If the <u>energy</u> input is <u>less than</u> the activation energy there <u>won't</u> be enough energy to <u>start</u> the reaction — so nothing will happen.

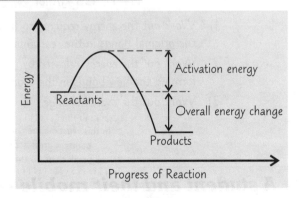

Exothermic reactions are a hot topic right now...

Remember, "exo-" = exit, "-thermic" = heat, so an exothermic reaction is one that gives out heat — and endothermic means just the opposite. To make sure you really understand these terms, try this question.

Q1 The temperature of a reaction mixture increases from 21 °C to 28.5 °C over the course of the reaction.
a) Is the reaction exothermic or endothermic? [1 mark]
b) Sketch a reaction profile to show the reaction. Label the energy of the reactants, the energy of the products and the activation energy. [3 marks]

Topic C3 — Chemical Reactions

Bond Energies

Energy transfer in chemical reactions is all to do with <u>making and breaking bonds</u>.

Energy Must Always be Supplied to Break Bonds

There's more on energy transfer on the previous page.

1) During a chemical reaction, <u>old bonds are broken</u> and <u>new bonds are formed</u>.

2) Energy must be <u>supplied</u> to break <u>existing bonds</u> — so bond breaking is an <u>endothermic</u> process.

3) Energy is <u>released</u> when new bonds are <u>formed</u> — so bond formation is an <u>exothermic</u> process.

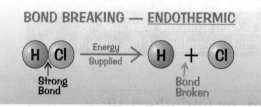

BOND BREAKING — ENDOTHERMIC

H Cl → Energy Supplied → H + Cl

Strong Bond   Bond Broken

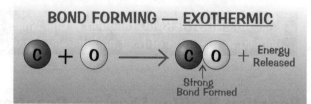

BOND FORMING — EXOTHERMIC

C + O → C O + Energy Released

Strong Bond Formed

4) In <u>endothermic</u> reactions, the energy <u>used</u> to break bonds is <u>greater</u> than the energy <u>released</u> by forming them.

5) In <u>exothermic</u> reactions, the energy <u>released</u> by forming bonds is <u>greater</u> than the energy used to <u>break</u> 'em.

Bond Energy Calculations — Need to be Practised

1) <u>Every</u> chemical bond has a particular <u>bond energy</u> associated with it. This <u>bond energy</u> varies slightly depending on the <u>compound</u> the bond occurs in.

2) You can use these <u>known bond energies</u> to calculate the <u>overall energy change</u> for a reaction.

> Overall Energy Change = Energy required to break bonds − Energy released by forming bonds

3) A <u>positive</u> energy change means an <u>endothermic</u> reaction and a <u>negative</u> energy change means an <u>exothermic</u> reaction.

4) You need to <u>practise</u> a few of these, but the basic idea is really very simple...

EXAMPLE: Using the bond energy values below, calculate the energy change for the following reaction, where hydrogen and chlorine react to produce hydrogen chloride:

$$H—H + Cl—Cl \rightarrow 2H—Cl$$

H—H: 436 kJ/mol   Cl—Cl: 242 kJ/mol   H—Cl: 431 kJ/mol

1) Work out the energy required to break the <u>original bonds</u> in the reactants.

    $(1 \times H—H) + (1 \times Cl—Cl) = 436 + 242$
    $= 678$ kJ/mol

2) Work out the energy released by forming the <u>new bonds</u> in the products.

    $(2 \times H—Cl) = 2 \times 431$
    $= 862$ kJ/mol

3) Work out the overall change.

    overall energy change = energy required to break bonds − energy released by forming bonds
    $= 678 − 862 = −184$ kJ/mol

In this reaction, the energy released by forming bonds is greater than the energy used to break them so the reaction is exothermic.

A student and their mobile — a bond that can never be broken...

This stuff might look hard at the moment, but with a bit of practice it's dead easy and it'll win you easy marks if you understand all the theory behind it. See how you get on with this question:

Q1   During the Haber Process, N_2 reacts with H_2 in the following reaction: $N_2 + 3H_2 \rightleftharpoons 2NH_3$
The bond energies for these molecules are:
N≡N: 941 kJ/mol, H–H: 436 kJ/mol,
N–H: 391 kJ/mol.
Calculate the overall energy change
for the forward reaction, shown on the right.

N≡N + H—H H—H H—H → N (H H H) + N (H H H)

[3 marks]

Acids and Bases

Testing the pH of a solution means using an <u>indicator</u> — and that means pretty <u>colours</u>...

The pH Scale Goes From 0 to 14

1) The pH scale is a measure of <u>how acidic or alkaline</u> a solution is. A <u>neutral</u> substance has <u>pH 7</u>.

2) An <u>acid</u> is a substance with a <u>pH less than 7</u>. Acids form <u>H^+ ions</u> in water.

3) A <u>base</u> is a substance with a <u>pH greater than 7</u>.
An <u>alkali</u> is a base that <u>dissolves in water</u>. Alkalis form <u>OH^- ions</u> in water.

OH⁻ ions are called hydroxide ions.

4) The value of the pH is <u>inversely proportional</u> to the <u>concentration of hydrogen ions</u> in a solution.
So, as the concentration of hydrogen ions <u>increases</u>, the <u>pH decreases</u>. This makes sense, because the higher the hydrogen ion concentration, the <u>more acidic</u> something is, so the lower the pH.

You Can Measure the pH of a Solution

PRACTICAL

An <u>indicator</u> is a <u>dye</u> that <u>changes colour</u> depending on whether it's <u>above or below</u> <u>a certain pH</u>. <u>Universal indicator</u> is a <u>combination of dyes</u>. It's very useful for <u>estimating</u> the pH of a solution. Indicators are simple to use — <u>add a few drops</u> to the solution you're testing, then compare the colour the solution goes to a <u>pH chart</u> for that indicator. Here's a pH chart for Universal indicator:

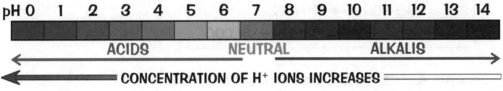

pH 0 1 2 3 4 5 6 7 8 9 10 11 12 13 14

ACIDS   NEUTRAL   ALKALIS

◄──── CONCENTRATION OF H^+ IONS INCREASES ════

A <u>pH probe</u> attached to a <u>pH meter</u> can be used to measure pH <u>electronically</u>. The probe is placed in the solution you are measuring and the pH is given on a digital display as a <u>numerical value</u>. This gives a <u>higher level</u> of accuracy than an indicator. When using a pH probe, it's important you <u>calibrate it correctly</u> (by setting it to read pH 7 in a sample of pure water), and rinse the probe with deionised water in between readings.

Acids and Bases Neutralise Each Other

The reaction between acids and bases is called <u>neutralisation</u>. It produces a <u>salt</u> and <u>water</u> (see page 115 for more on this).

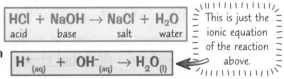

$HCl + NaOH \rightarrow NaCl + H_2O$
acid   base   salt   water

This is just the ionic equation of the reaction above.

Neutralisation reactions in <u>aqueous solution</u> can also be shown as an ionic equation (see p.106) in terms of <u>H^+</u> and <u>OH^- ions</u>:

$H^+_{(aq)} + OH^-_{(aq)} \rightarrow H_2O_{(l)}$

When an acid neutralises a base (or vice versa), the <u>products</u> are <u>neutral</u>, i.e. they have a <u>pH of 7</u>. At pH 7, the concentration of hydrogen ions equals the concentration of hydroxide ions. An indicator can be used to show that a neutralisation reaction is over (Universal indicator will go green).

If you add acid to a base, the pH will decrease. If you add a base to an acid, then the pH will increase.

Titration Curves Show pH Changes with Volume

1) Experiments called <u>titrations</u> are used to work out how much of an acid is used to <u>neutralise</u> a base of unknown concentration (or vice versa).

2) <u>Titration curves</u> are used to show where <u>neutralisation</u> happens during a titration. There's a <u>vertical point</u> in the curve which is where the solution is <u>neutral</u> (at pH 7). This is called the <u>end point</u> of the titration.

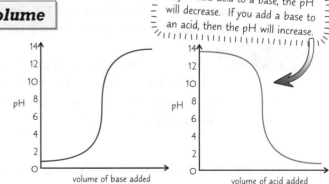

This page should have all bases covered...

pHew, you got to the end of the page, so here's an interesting(ish) fact — your skin is slightly acidic (pH 5.5).

Q1   a) The pH of an unknown solution is found to be 6. Is the solution acidic or alkaline?   [1 mark]
     b) What colour would the solution go if a few drops of Universal indicator were added to it?   [1 mark]

Strong and Weak Acids

Right then. More on acids. Brace yourself.

Acids Produce Protons in Water

An H⁺ ion is just a proton.

The thing about acids is that they ionise — they produce hydrogen ions, H^+.
For example,

$$HCl \rightarrow H^+ + Cl^-$$
$$HNO_3 \rightarrow H^+ + NO_3^-$$

HCl and HNO_3 don't produce hydrogen ions until they meet water.

Acids Can be Strong or Weak

1) <u>Strong acids</u> (e.g. sulfuric, hydrochloric and nitric acids) <u>ionise almost completely</u> in water. A <u>large</u> proportion of acid molecules dissociate to release H^+ ions. They tend to have low pHs (pH 0-2).

2) <u>Weak acids</u> (e.g. ethanoic, citric and carbonic acids) <u>do not fully ionise</u> in solution. Only a <u>small</u> proportion of acid molecules dissociate to release H^+ ions. Their pHs tend to be around 2-6.

3) The ionisation of a <u>weak</u> acid is a <u>reversible reaction</u>, which sets up an <u>equilibrium mixture</u>. Since only a few of the acid molecules release H^+ ions, the <u>equilibrium</u> lies well to the <u>left</u>.

<u>Strong acid</u>: $HCl \longrightarrow H^+ + Cl^-$

<u>Weak acid</u>: $CH_3COOH \rightleftharpoons H^+ + CH_3COO^-$

For more on equilibria turn to page 134.

Don't Confuse Strong Acids with Concentrated Acids

1) Acid <u>strength</u> (i.e. strong or weak) tells you <u>what proportion</u> of the acid molecules <u>ionise</u> in water.

2) The <u>concentration</u> of an acid is different. Concentration measures <u>how much acid</u> there is in a litre (1 dm³) of water. Concentration is basically how <u>watered down</u> your acid is.

3) An acid with a <u>high</u> proportion of <u>acid molecules</u> compared to the volume of water is said to be <u>concentrated</u>. An acid with a <u>low</u> proportion of acid molecules compared to the volume of water is said to be <u>dilute</u>.

Concentration is measured in g/dm³ or mol/dm³.

4) Note that concentration describes the <u>total number</u> of dissolved acid molecules — <u>not</u> the number of molecules that produce hydrogen ions.

5) The more grams (or moles) of acid per dm³, the <u>more concentrated</u> the acid is.

6) So you can have a <u>dilute but strong</u> acid, or a <u>concentrated but weak</u> acid.

Changing the Concentration of an Acid Affects its pH

If the concentration of H^+ ions <u>increases</u> by a factor of <u>10</u>, the pH <u>decreases</u> by <u>1</u>. So if the H^+ ion concentration <u>increases</u> by a factor of <u>100</u> (= 10 × 10), the pH <u>decreases</u> by <u>2</u> (= 1 + 1), and so on. Decreasing the H^+ ion concentration has the opposite effect — a <u>decrease</u> by a factor of <u>10</u> in the H^+ concentration means an <u>increase</u> of <u>1</u> on the pH scale.

A solution with a hydrogen ion concentration of 0.001 mol/dm³ has a pH of 4. What would happen to the pH if you increased the hydrogen ion concentration to 0.01 mol/dm³?

The H^+ concentration has increased by a factor of 10, so the pH would decrease by 1. So the new pH would be 4 − 1 = 3.

Weak acid or strong acid? I know which goes better with chips...

Acids are acidic because of H^+ ions. And strong acids are strong because they let go of all their H^+ ions at the drop of a hat... Well, at the drop of a drop of water.

Q1   Explain the difference between a strong acid and a weak acid.   [2 marks]

Q2   A student added strong acid to a weakly acidic solution of pH 6. The pH of the new solution was found to be pH 3. By how many times did the concentration of H^+ increase or decrease?   [2 marks]

Reactions of Acids

MORE? You want MORE? Well, I'm much kinder than a Dickensian orphanage master, so <u>more acids</u> for you.

Many Metals React With Acids to Give Salts

$$Acid + Metal \rightarrow Salt + Hydrogen$$

A salt is an ionic compound, formed as part of a neutralisation reaction.

Hydrochloric Acid Produces Chloride Salts:
$$2HCl + Mg \rightarrow MgCl_2 + H_2 \quad \text{(Magnesium chloride)}$$
$$6HCl + 2Al \rightarrow 2AlCl_3 + 3H_2 \quad \text{(Aluminium chloride)}$$

Sulfuric Acid Produces Sulfate Salts:
$$H_2SO_4 + Mg \rightarrow MgSO_4 + H_2 \quad \text{(Magnesium sulfate)}$$
$$3H_2SO_4 + 2Al \rightarrow Al_2(SO_4)_3 + 3H_2 \quad \text{(Aluminium sulfate)}$$

Nitric Acid Produces Nitrate Salts When NEUTRALISED, But...

The reaction of nitric acid with metals is more complicated — you get a nitrate salt, but instead of hydrogen gas, the other products are usually a mixture of water, NO and NO_2.

You can't really predict the balanced equation for the reaction of nitric acid with metals.

Metal Carbonates Give Salt + Water + Carbon Dioxide

$$Acid + Metal \; Carbonate \rightarrow Salt + Water + Carbon \; Dioxide$$

<u>Examples:</u>
$$2HCl + Na_2CO_3 \rightarrow 2NaCl + H_2O + CO_2 \quad \text{(Sodium chloride)}$$
$$H_2SO_4 + K_2CO_3 \rightarrow K_2SO_4 + H_2O + CO_2 \quad \text{(Potassium sulfate)}$$
$$2HNO_3 + ZnCO_3 \rightarrow Zn(NO_3)_2 + H_2O + CO_2 \quad \text{(Zinc nitrate)}$$

Again, as above, hydrochloric acid produces chloride salts, sulfuric acid produces sulfate salts, and nitric acid produces nitrate salts.

Acids and Alkalis React to Give a Salt and Water

$$Acid + Alkali \rightarrow Salt + Water$$

<u>Examples:</u>
$$HCl + NaOH \rightarrow NaCl + H_2O \quad \text{(Sodium chloride)}$$
$$H_2SO_4 + Zn(OH)_2 \rightarrow ZnSO_4 + 2H_2O \quad \text{(Zinc sulfate)}$$
$$HNO_3 + KOH \rightarrow KNO_3 + H_2O \quad \text{(Potassium nitrate)}$$

You met neutralisation reactions back on page 113.

You can Make Soluble Salts Using Acid/Alkali Reactions

PRACTICAL

1) Soluble salts (salts that dissolve in water) can be made by reacting an acid with an <u>alkali</u>.

2) But you can't tell whether the reaction has <u>finished</u> — there's no signal that all the acid has been neutralised. You also can't just add an <u>excess</u> of alkali to the acid and filter out what's left because the salt is <u>soluble</u> and would be contaminated with the excess alkali.

3) Instead, you have to add <u>exactly</u> the right amount of alkali to <u>neutralise</u> the acid. You can carry out a <u>titration</u> to work out the <u>exact amount</u> of alkali needed. This involves using a <u>burette</u> (see page 218) to add a volume of alkali to a known volume of acid until the acid's completely neutralised. You should use an <u>indicator</u> (see page 113) that gives a sudden colour change to show when the acid's just been neutralised.

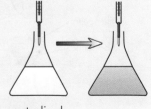

4) Then, carry out the reaction using exactly the right proportions of alkali and acid but with no <u>indicator</u> (because you now know the volumes needed), so the salt <u>won't be contaminated</u> with indicator.

5) The <u>solution</u> that remains when the reaction is complete contains only the <u>salt</u> and <u>water</u>. Slowly <u>evaporate</u> off some of the water and then leave the solution to crystallise. Filter off the solid and dry it — you'll be left with a <u>pure</u>, <u>dry</u> salt (see page 97 for more on crystallisation).

Nitrates — much cheaper than day-rates...

What a lot of reactions. Better take a peek back at page 105 for help with writing and balancing chemical equations.

Q1   Write a balanced chemical equation for the reaction of hydrochloric acid with calcium carbonate.   [2 marks]

PRACTICAL

Making Salts

Making salts can be tricky. You need a different method depending on whether the salt's insoluble or soluble.
You met one technique for making soluble salts on the last page. Time for some more...

Making Soluble Salts Using an Acid and an Insoluble Reactant

1) You can make soluble salts by reacting an acid with an insoluble base.

2) You need to pick the right acid, plus a metal or an insoluble base (a metal oxide or metal hydroxide).

3) Add the base to the acid — the base and acid will react to produce
a soluble salt (and water). You will know when all the acid has been
neutralised because the excess solid will just sink to the bottom of the flask.
You sometimes need to heat the reaction mixture during this step to get the acid and base to react.

filter paper

filter funnel

excess solid

salt and water

4) Then filter off the excess solid to get a solution containing only salt and water.

5) Heat the solution gently to slowly evaporate off some of the water,
then leave the more concentrated solution to cool and allow the salt
to crystallise (see page 97). Filter off the solid and leave it to dry.

> Example: You can add copper oxide to hydrochloric acid to make copper chloride:
> $$CuO_{(s)} + 2HCl_{(aq)} \rightarrow CuCl_{2(aq)} + H_2O_{(l)}$$

Making Insoluble Salts — Precipitation Reactions

1) To make a pure, dry sample of an insoluble salt, you can use a precipitation reaction.
You just need to pick the right two soluble salts, they react and you get your insoluble salt.

2) E.g. to make lead chloride (insoluble), mix lead nitrate and sodium chloride (both soluble).

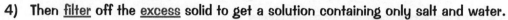
lead nitrate + sodium chloride → lead chloride + sodium nitrate
$$Pb(NO_3)_{2\,(aq)} + 2NaCl_{(aq)} \rightarrow PbCl_{2\,(s)} + 2NaNO_{3\,(aq)}$$

Soluble things dissolve in water. Insoluble things don't.

Method

1) Add 1 spatula of lead nitrate to a test tube. Add deionised water to dissolve
the lead nitrate. Use deionised water to make sure there are no other ions about.
Shake it thoroughly to ensure that all the lead nitrate has dissolved.
Then, in a separate test tube, do the same with 1 spatula of sodium chloride.

precipitate

2) Tip the two solutions into a small beaker, and give it a good stir to make
sure it's all mixed together. The lead chloride should precipitate out.

3) Put a folded piece of filter paper into a filter funnel,
and stick the funnel into a conical flask.

filter paper

filter funnel

4) Pour the contents of the beaker into the middle of the filter paper.
Make sure that the solution doesn't go above the filter paper
— otherwise some of the solid could dribble down the side.

5) Swill out the beaker with more deionised water, and tip this into the filter
paper — to make sure you get all the wanted product from the beaker.

lead chloride

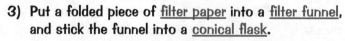

6) Rinse the contents of the filter paper with deionised water to make
sure that all the soluble sodium nitrate has been washed away.

7) Then just scrape the lead chloride onto fresh filter paper and leave to dry.

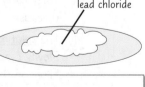

I was attacked by a nasty lead chloride — it was a-salt...

The theory may seem dull, but you'll probably get to make some nice salts in your class, and that's pretty cool.

Q1   Iron nitrate is a soluble salt that can be made from iron oxide (an insoluble base) and nitric acid.
Suggest a method you could use to make a pure sample of iron nitrate from these reactants.   [3 marks]

Oxidation and Reduction

Oxidation can be to do with something gaining oxygen (makes sense), but it can also be to do with electrons...

If Electrons are Transferred, It's a Redox Reaction

1) Oxidation can mean the reaction with, or addition of oxygen, and reduction can be the removal of oxygen.

$$Fe_2O_3 + 3CO \rightarrow 2Fe + 3CO_2$$

- Iron oxide is reduced to iron (as oxygen is removed).
- Carbon monoxide is oxidised to carbon dioxide (as oxygen is added).

Combustion reactions involve oxidation. They're always exothermic (see p.111). E.g. $CH_4 + 2O_2 \rightarrow CO_2 + 2H_2O$

2) But on this page, we're looking at oxidation and reduction in terms of electrons. A loss of electrons is called oxidation. A gain of electrons is called reduction.

3) REDuction and OXidation happen at the same time — so this type of reaction is called a redox reaction.

4) An oxidising agent accepts electrons and gets reduced (it gains electrons or loses oxygen).

5) A reducing agent donates electrons and gets oxidised (it loses electrons or gains oxygen).

When dealing with electrons:
Oxidation Is Loss,
Reduction Is Gain.

Remember it as OIL RIG.

Half Equations Show if Things Have Been Oxidised or Reduced

1) Half equations (see page 106) show how electrons move during a reaction.

2) You could be asked to identify whether something's been oxidised or reduced during a chemical reaction. If you are, looking at half equations is a great way of doing this.

3) Remember, if something loses electrons, then it's been oxidised (and it's a reducing agent). If something gains electrons, then it's been reduced (and it's an oxidising agent).

- Iron atoms are oxidised to Fe^{2+} ions when they react with dilute acid: $Fe + 2H^+ \rightarrow Fe^{2+} + H_2$
- The iron atoms lose electrons. They're oxidised by the hydrogen ions: $Fe \rightarrow Fe^{2+} + 2e^-$
- The hydrogen ions gain electrons. They're reduced by the iron atoms: $2H^+ + 2e^- \rightarrow H_2$

EXAMPLE: Work out which element has been reduced in the following equation: $Cu^{2+} + Mg \rightarrow Cu + Mg^{2+}$

1) Work out whether each element has lost or gained electrons by writing out the half equations.

$Cu^{2+} + 2e^- \rightarrow Cu$
$Mg \rightarrow Mg^{2+} + 2e^-$

Add electrons so the charges on each side of the equation balance.

2) Reduction involves the gain of electrons, so find the element that's gained electrons.

Copper ions have gained two electrons to become copper atoms, so **copper** is reduced.

Electrolysis Involves Oxidation and Reduction

There's more on electrolysis on the next page.

1) Electrolysis is the breaking down of a substance using electricity.

2) An electric current is passed through an electrolyte (a molten or dissolved ionic compound), causing it to decompose.

This creates a flow of charge through the electrolyte.

3) The positive ions (cations) in the electrolyte will move towards the cathode (negative electrode) and are reduced (gain electrons). The negative ions (anions) in the electrolyte will move towards the anode (positive electrode) and are oxidised (lose electrons).

4) As ions gain or lose electrons they form the uncharged substances and are discharged from the solution.

5) An electrochemical cell is a circuit, made up of the anode, cathode, electrolyte, a power source and the wires that connect the two electrodes.

Put your feet up... inhale... exhale... and redox...

It might seem pretty useless now, but if electrolysis comes up in the exam, you'll want to know it...

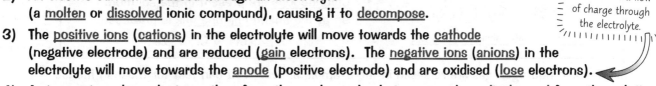

Q1   Identify the oxidising agent in this reaction: $Zn + 2H^+ \rightarrow Zn^{2+} + H_2$ [1 mark]

Q2   In electrolysis, which ions are attracted towards the cathode? [1 mark]

Electrolysis

This stuff is electrifying. You'll be on the edge of your seat with all this fun, fun, fun electrolysis.

In Molten Ionic Solids, There's Only One Source of Ions

1) An ionic solid can't be electrolysed because the ions are in fixed positions and can't move.

2) Molten ionic compounds can be electrolysed because the ions can move freely and conduct electricity.

3) Positive metal ions are reduced (i.e. they gain electrons) to atoms at the cathode.

4) Negative ions are oxidised (i.e. they lose electrons) to atoms at the anode.

5) In the example of $PbBr_2$, you'd see a brown vapour of bromine gas at the anode. Beads of molten lead would form at the cathode.

$$Pb^{2+} + 2e^- \rightarrow Pb \qquad 2Br^- \rightarrow Br_2 + 2e^-$$

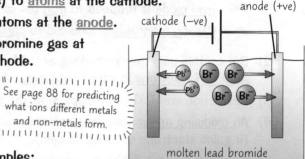

See page 88 for predicting what ions different metals and non-metals form.

molten lead bromide

cathode (−ve) anode (+ve)

6) It's easy to predict what products you get when you electrolyse molten substances — it's getting the half equations right that's tougher. Here are some examples:

Molten Electrolyte	Product at Cathode	Half equation at Cathode	Product at Anode	Half equation at Anode
lead iodide, PbI_2	lead	$Pb^{2+} + 2e^- \rightarrow Pb$	iodine	$2I^- \rightarrow I_2 + 2e^-$
potassium chloride, KCl	potassium	$K^+ + e^- \rightarrow K$	chlorine	$2Cl^- \rightarrow Cl_2 + 2e^-$
aluminium oxide, Al_2O_3	aluminium	$Al^{3+} + 3e^- \rightarrow Al$	oxygen	$2O^{2-} \rightarrow O_2 + 4e^-$

Electrolysis of Aqueous Solutions is a Bit More Complicated

1) In aqueous solutions, as well as the ions from the ionic compound, there will be hydrogen ions (H^+) and hydroxide ions (OH^-) from the water: $H_2O_{(l)} \rightleftharpoons H^+_{(aq)} + OH^-_{(aq)}$

2) At the cathode, if H^+ ions and metal ions are present, hydrogen gas will be produced if the metal is more reactive than hydrogen (e.g. sodium). If the metal is less reactive than hydrogen (e.g. copper or silver), then a solid layer of the pure metal will be produced instead.

Some reactivity series (see page 127) include hydrogen in the list. You can use these to find out which metals are more or less reactive than hydrogen.

3) At the anode, if halide ions (Cl^-, Br^-, I^-) are present, molecules of chlorine, bromine or iodine will be formed. If no halide ions are present, then oxygen will be formed from the hydroxide ions.

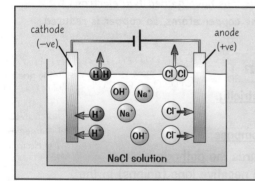

cathode (−ve) anode (+ve)

NaCl solution

A solution of sodium chloride (NaCl) contains four different ions: Na^+, Cl^-, OH^- and H^+.

- Sodium metal is more reactive than hydrogen. So at the cathode, hydrogen gas is produced.

$$2H^+ + 2e^- \rightarrow H_2$$

- Chloride ions are present in the solution. So at the anode chlorine gas is produced.

$$2Cl^- \rightarrow Cl_2 + 2e^-$$

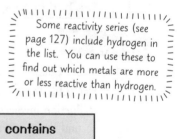

For more on tests for gases, turn to page 120.

Chlorine and hydrogen gas are released in the example above. You can test for these in the lab:

- Chlorine bleaches damp litmus paper, turning it white. (It may turn red for a moment first though — that's because a solution of chlorine is acidic.)

- Hydrogen makes a "squeaky pop" when burnt with a lighted splint.

Faster shopping at the supermarket — use Electrolleys...

So it's kinda confusing this electrolysis malarkey — you need to take it slow and make sure you get it.

Q1   An aqueous solution of copper bromide, $CuBr_2$, is electrolysed using inert electrodes.
Give the half equation to show the reaction occurring at the anode.

[1 mark]

Topic C3 — Chemical Reactions

Electrolysis of Copper Sulfate

You may be yawning now, but electrolysis is a really important step in purifying copper.

Here's How to Set Up an Electrochemical Cell

You'll probably have to do an experiment using electrolysis in the lab, so you need to know how to set up an electrochemical cell. Here's how you'd set up a copper sulfate cell:

1) Get two electrodes (you should use inert electrodes, e.g. platinum or carbon). Clean the surfaces of the electrodes using a piece of emery paper (or sandpaper).

2) From this point on, be careful not to touch the surfaces of the metals with your hands — you could transfer grease back onto the strips.

3) Place both electrodes into a beaker filled with your electrolyte.

4) Connect the electrodes to a power supply using crocodile clips and wires.

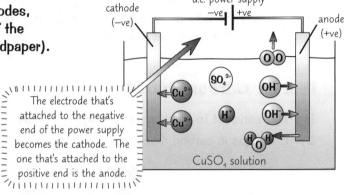

The electrode that's attached to the negative end of the power supply becomes the cathode. The one that's attached to the positive end is the anode.

A solution of copper sulfate ($CuSO_4$) contains four different ions: Cu^{2+}, SO_4^{2-}, H^+ and OH^-.

- Copper metal is less reactive than hydrogen. So at the cathode, copper metal is produced. You'd see a coating of copper forming on the cathode.

$$Cu^{2+} + 2e^- \rightarrow Cu$$

- There aren't any halide ions present. So at the anode, oxygen and water are produced. You'd see bubbles of oxygen gas forming.

$$4OH^- \rightarrow O_2 + 2H_2O + 4e^-$$

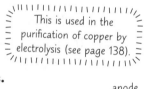

Oxygen relights a glowing splint.

Non-Inert Electrodes Take Part in Electrolysis Reactions

1) Non-inert electrodes can decompose into the electrolyte.

2) For example, you could use copper electrodes in a solution of copper sulfate.

3) To set up this electrochemical cell, you should use the same method as the one above, but use copper electrodes, rather than inert carbon or platinum electrodes.

4) As the reaction continues, the mass of the anode will decrease and the mass of the cathode will increase. This is because copper is transferred from the anode to the cathode.

5) The reaction takes a bit of time to happen, you'll need to leave the cell running for 30 minutes or so to get a decent change in mass.

6) If you want to measure how the mass of your electrodes has changed during an experiment like this one, you should dry the electrodes before weighing them — any copper sulfate solution on the electrodes may mean they appear to have a higher mass than they really do...

This is used in the purification of copper by electrolysis (see page 138).

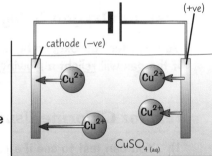

The electrical supply acts by:

- Pulling electrons off copper atoms at the anode, causing them to go into solution as Cu^{2+} ions.

$$\text{Anode: } Cu_{(s)} \rightarrow Cu^{2+}_{(aq)} + 2e^-$$

- Then offering electrons at the cathode to nearby Cu^{2+} ions to turn them back into copper atoms.

$$\text{Cathode: } Cu^{2+}_{(aq)} + 2e^- \rightarrow Cu_{(s)}$$

Electro-lite — low-fat and packed full of important ions...

Well, after all that stuff about electrolysis, it seems only fair you were rewarded with a fun ol' pratical. Hozzah.

Q1 June connects an electrochemical cell, consisting of two copper electrodes and a copper sulfate solution electrolyte, to a power supply and leaves it for 30 minutes. How would you expect the mass of the anode to change during the experiment? Explain your answer. [2 marks]

Tests for Gases

There are lots of ways of <u>testing</u> for different <u>gases</u> — some of them involve bubbling the gas through a liquid, some involve testing it with litmus paper, and some involve trying to set fire to it. Doesn't sound dangerous at all...

Testing for Gases Can be Dangerous

1) When you're testing for a mystery gas, you need to be <u>careful</u>. Some gases are pretty <u>nasty</u>, so you don't want to just go spewing them out into your classroom.

2) So, you should carry out all of the following tests in a <u>fume cupboard</u>, that way there's not as much of a risk that you, or your classmates, will go inhaling a <u>toxic gas</u>.

Test for Carbon Dioxide Using Limewater

1) You can test to see if a gas is <u>carbon dioxide</u> by bubbling it through <u>limewater</u>.

2) If the gas is carbon dioxide, the limewater will <u>turn cloudy</u>.

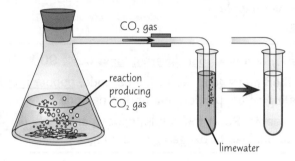

reaction producing CO_2 gas

CO_2 gas

limewater

Test for Hydrogen Using a Lighted Splint

1) Hydrogen makes a '<u>squeaky pop</u>' with a <u>lighted splint</u>.

2) The noise comes from the hydrogen burning with the oxygen in the air to form water.

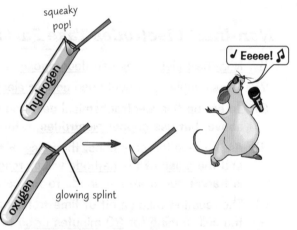

squeaky pop!

✓ Eeeee! ♫

hydrogen

Test for Oxygen Using a Glowing Splint

You can <u>test</u> for oxygen by checking if the gas will <u>relight</u> a <u>glowing splint</u>.

oxygen

glowing splint

Test for Chlorine Using Damp Blue Litmus Paper

1) You can test to see if a gas is <u>chlorine</u> by holding a piece of <u>damp blue litmus paper</u> over it.

2) If the gas is chlorine, it will <u>bleach</u> the litmus paper, turning it <u>white</u>.

3) It may also turn <u>red</u> for a moment first — that's because a solution of chlorine is <u>acidic</u> (see page 113 for more on acids).

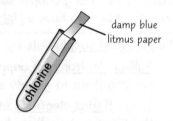

damp blue litmus paper

chlorine

Bleach, cloudy and squeaky pop — the world's worst cereal mascots.

I'm afraid this is just one of those pages where the only thing to do is sit down and learn all four of these gas tests, including what a positive result would be, until they're properly lodged in your memory. Then try the questions...

Q1 Describe how you could test a gas to see if it was oxygen. State what a positive result would be. [2 marks]

Q2 A student performs tests on two gases, gas A and gas B. Gas A bleaches damp blue litmus paper. Gas B ignites with a squeaky pop when tested with a lighted splint. Identify the two gases. [2 marks]

Revision Questions for Topic C3

Well, wasn't that enjoyable? <u>Topic C3</u> has been my favourite topic so far I think.

*   Try these questions and <u>tick off each one</u> when you <u>get it right</u>.
*   When you've done <u>all the questions</u> under a heading and are <u>completely happy</u> with it, tick it off.

<u>Conservation of Mass (p.103)</u>

1) In a reaction, how does the mass of products compare with the mass of reactants?
2) Why might the mass of a reaction that occurs in an open vessel appear to decrease?

<u>Formulas and Calculations (p.104-110)</u>

3) What is the charge on a sulfide ion?
4) What is the overall charge on an ionic compound?
5) What is shown by an ionic equation?
6) What type of chemical equation would you use to show how electrons are transferred in a reaction?
7) What does Avogadro's constant represent?
8) What is meant by a limiting reactant?
9) How can you find the limiting reactant from a balanced equation and the masses of reactants present?
10) Give the formula that links concentration, volume of solution and mass of solute.

<u>Energy Changes and Reactions (p.111-112)</u>

11) What is the difference between an endothermic and an exothermic reaction?
12) Sketch a reaction profile for an exothermic reaction.
13) What is meant by the term 'activation energy'?
14) Is energy released when bonds are broken or when they are made?
15) How would you calculate the overall energy change in a reaction from the bond energies?

<u>Acids and Bases (p.113-116)</u>

16) What is: a) an acid?   b) a base?   c) an alkali?
17) Name two ways that you could measure the pH of a solution.
18) What are the reactants and products of a neutralisation reaction?
19) Sketch a titration curve to show how the pH of a solution of acid changes as a base is added.
20) Write an equation to show the ionisation of ethanoic acid (CH_3COOH), a weak acid, in solution.
21) Write a balanced equation for the reaction of hydrochloric acid with aluminium.
22) Write a balanced equation to show how copper chloride ($CuCl_2$)
    is made from copper oxide (CuO) and hydrochloric acid.
23) Outline how you could make lead chloride ($PbCl_2$) using a precipitation reaction.

<u>Redox, Electrolysis and Tests for Gases (p.117-120)</u>

24) Give the two definitions of: a) oxidation,   b) reduction.
25) What is electrolysis?
26) When a molten ionic compound decomposes during electrolysis, at which electrode does the metal form?
27) Outline how you would set up an electrochemical cell using copper sulfate solution and inert electrodes.
28) Why do the masses of non-inert electrodes change during electrolysis?
29) What is the test for carbon dioxide gas?
30) If you were testing a gas to see if it was chlorine, describe what a positive result would look like.

Group 1 — Alkali Metals

You can predict how different elements will <u>react</u> by looking at where they are in the <u>periodic table</u> — elements in the <u>same group</u> will react in <u>similar ways</u>. Time to take a look at some of the groups, starting with <u>Group 1</u>...

Group 1 Metals are Known as the 'Alkali Metals'

Group 1	Group 2	
3 Li Lithium 7	Be	
11 Na Sodium 23	Mg	
19 K Potassium 39	Ca	Sc
37 Rb Rubidium 86	Sr	Y
55 Cs Caesium 133	Ba	
87 Fr Francium 223	Ra	

The Group 1 metals are lithium, sodium, potassium, rubidium, caesium and francium.

1) The alkali metals all have <u>one outer electron</u>
    — so they have <u>similar chemical properties</u>.

2) They all have the following <u>physical properties</u>:
    * <u>Low melting points</u> and <u>boiling points</u> (compared with other metals).
    * <u>Low density</u> — lithium, sodium and potassium float on water.
    * <u>Very soft</u> — they can be cut with a knife.

3) The alkali metals form <u>ionic</u> compounds. They lose their one outer electron <u>so easily</u> that sharing it would be out of the question, so they <u>don't</u> form covalent bonds.

Group 1 Metals are Very Reactive

1) The Group 1 metals readily <u>lose</u> their single <u>outer electron</u> to form a <u>1+ ion</u> with a <u>stable electronic structure</u>.

2) The <u>more readily</u> a metal loses its outer electrons, the <u>more reactive</u> it is — so the Group 1 metals are very reactive.

3) As you go <u>down</u> Group 1, the alkali metals get <u>more reactive</u>. The <u>outer electron</u> is more easily <u>lost</u> because it's further from the nucleus (the <u>atomic radius</u> is <u>larger</u>) — so it's less strongly attracted to the nucleus and <u>less energy</u> is needed to remove it.

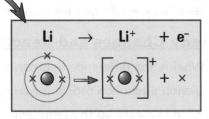

Reaction with Cold Water Produces a Hydroxide and Hydrogen Gas

1) When the <u>alkali metals</u> are put in <u>water</u>, they react <u>vigorously</u>.

2) The reaction produces <u>hydrogen gas</u> and a <u>hydroxide</u> of the metal (an <u>alkali</u> see page 113). For example, here's the overall equation for the reaction of <u>sodium</u> with <u>water</u>:

Squeaky pop!

A squeaky pop shows H_2 gas is present — see p.120 for more.

$2Na$	+	$2H_2O$	$\rightarrow$	$2NaOH$	+	H_2
sodium	+	water	$\rightarrow$	sodium hydroxide	+	hydrogen

The same reaction happens with all of the alkali metals — make sure you can write balanced equations for them all.

3) The reactivity of Group 1 metals with water (and dilute acid — see below) increases down the group.
    * <u>Lithium</u> will <u>move</u> around the surface, <u>fizzing</u> furiously.
    * <u>Sodium</u> and <u>potassium</u> do the same, but they also <u>melt</u> in the heat of the reaction. The potassium even gets hot enough to <u>ignite</u> the hydrogen gas being produced.
    * <u>Rubidium</u> and <u>caesium</u> react <u>violently</u> with water, and tend to <u>explode</u> when they get wet...

The alkali metals also react with <u>dilute acids</u>, but with an <u>acid</u> the products are a <u>salt</u> and hydrogen gas.

For example:
$2Na$	+	$2HCl$	$\rightarrow$	$2NaCl$	+	H_2
sodium	+	hydrochloric acid	$\rightarrow$	sodium chloride	+	hydrogen

These reactions are <u>more violent</u> than the ones with water — they can be <u>dangerous</u> to do in a school lab.

And that's why you don't get caesium teaspoons... *Amongst other reasons...*

Alkali metals are super reactive. In fact they have to be stored in oil — otherwise they just react with the air.

Q1 Explain why the alkali metals become more reactive as you move down Group 1. [3 marks]

Q2 Write a balanced symbol equation for the reaction between lithium (Li) and water. [2 marks]

Group 7 — Halogens

Here's a page on another periodic table group that you need to be familiar with — <u>the halogens</u>.

Group 7 Elements are Known as the Halogens

Group 7 is made up of the elements fluorine, chlorine, bromine, iodine and astatine.

1) All Group 7 elements have <u>7 electrons in their outer shell</u>
— so they all have <u>similar chemical properties</u>.

2) The halogens exist as <u>diatomic molecules</u> (e.g. Cl_2, Br_2, I_2).
Sharing one pair of electrons in a <u>covalent bond</u>
(see page 90) gives both atoms a <u>full outer shell</u>.

3) As you go <u>down Group 7</u>, the <u>melting points</u>
and <u>boiling points</u> of the halogens <u>increase</u>.

4) This means that at <u>room temperature</u>:

- <u>Chlorine</u> (Cl_2) is a fairly reactive, poisonous, <u>green gas</u>
(it has a low boiling point).

- <u>Bromine</u> (Br_2) is a poisonous, <u>red-brown liquid</u>,
which gives off an <u>orange vapour</u> at room temperature.

- <u>Iodine</u> (I_2) is a <u>dark grey crystalline solid</u>
which gives off a <u>purple vapour</u> when heated.

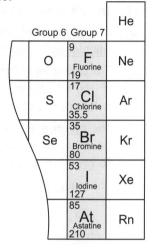

	Group 6	Group 7	Group 0
			9 F Fluorine 19
	O	17 Cl Chlorine 35.5	Ne
	S	35 Br Bromine 80	Ar
	Se	53 I Iodine 127	Kr
		85 At Astatine 210	Xe

Reactivity Decreases Going Down Group 7

1) A halogen atom only needs to <u>gain one electron</u>
to form a <u>1– ion</u> with a <u>stable electronic structure</u>.

2) The <u>easier</u> it is for a halogen atom to <u>attract</u> an
electron, the <u>more reactive</u> the halogen will be.

3) As you go <u>DOWN</u> Group 7, the halogens become <u>less reactive</u> — it gets <u>harder</u> to attract the <u>extra electron</u> to fill the outer shell when it's <u>further away</u> from the nucleus (the <u>atomic radius</u> is <u>larger</u>).

$$Cl + e^- \rightarrow Cl^-$$

The Halogens React With Alkali Metals to Form Salts

The halogens will react vigorously with alkali metals (Group 1 elements, see page 122)
to form <u>salts</u> called '<u>metal halides</u>'. For example:

2Na	+	Cl_2	→	2NaCl
Sodium	+	Chlorine	→	Sodium chloride
2K	+	Br_2	→	2KBr
Potassium	+	Bromine	→	Potassium bromide

All the reactions between Group 1 and Group 7 elements follow this pattern — make sure you can write equations for any of them.

The Halogens Undergo Displacement Reactions

1) A <u>more reactive</u> halogen can <u>displace</u> a <u>less reactive</u> one from a salt solution.

2) There's loads more about these reactions coming up on the next page...

Halogens — one electron short of a full shell...

Another page, another periodic table group to learn the properties and the trends of. When you're pretty confident that you've got all the stuff from this page in your head, have a go at the questions below, just to check.

Q1 The melting point of chlorine (Cl_2) is –101.5 °C. Predict whether bromine (Br_2)
would be a solid, a liquid or a gas at –101.5 °C. Explain your answer. [2 marks]

Q2 Write a balanced symbol equation for the reaction between sodium metal (Na) and iodine (I_2). [2 marks]

Halogen Displacement Reactions

The halogens are a pretty competitive lot really. In fact the more reactive ones will push the less reactive ones out of a compound. How uncivilized — has nobody ever taught them that it's bad manners to push?

A More Reactive Halogen Will Displace a Less Reactive One

1) The elements in Group 7 take part in displacement reactions.

2) A displacement reaction is where a more reactive element 'pushes out' (displaces) a less reactive element from a compound.

3) For example, chlorine is more reactive than bromine (it's higher up Group 7). If you add chlorine water (an aqueous solution of Cl_2) to potassium bromide solution, the chlorine will displace the bromine from the salt solution.

4) The chlorine is reduced to chloride ions, so the salt solution becomes potassium chloride. The bromide ions are oxidised to bromine, which turns the solution orange.

5) The equation for this reaction is shown below:

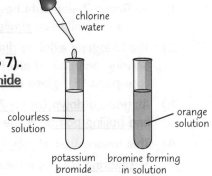

chlorine water

colourless solution

orange solution

potassium bromide

bromine forming in solution

Cl_2	+	2KBr	$\rightarrow$	Br_2	+	2KCl
chlorine	+	potassium bromide	$\rightarrow$	bromine	+	potassium chloride

If you ever need to write an equation for a different halogen displacement reaction, they all follow this pattern.

Displacement Reactions Show Reactivity Trends

You can use displacement reactions to show the reactivity trend of the halogens.

1) Start by measuring out a small amount of a halide salt solution in a test tube.

2) Add a few drops of a halogen solution to it and shake the tube gently.

3) If you see a colour change, then a reaction has happened — the halogen has displaced the halide ions from the salt. If no reaction happens, there won't be a colour change.

You should wear a lab coat and goggles if you do this experiment — some of the chemicals are harmful.

4) Repeat the process using different combinations of halide salt and halogen.

5) The table below shows what should happen when you mix different combinations of chlorine, bromine and iodine water with solutions of the salts potassium chloride, potassium bromide and potassium iodide.

Start with:	Potassium chloride solution $KCl_{(aq)}$ — colourless	Potassium bromide solution $KBr_{(aq)}$ — colourless	Potassium iodide solution $KI_{(aq)}$ — colourless
Add chlorine water $Cl_{2\,(aq)}$ — colourless	no reaction	orange solution (Br_2) formed	brown solution (I_2) formed
Add bromine water $Br_{2\,(aq)}$ — orange	no reaction	no reaction	brown solution (I_2) formed
Add iodine water $I_{2\,(aq)}$ — brown	no reaction	no reaction	no reaction

6) Chlorine displaces both bromine and iodine from salt solutions. Bromine can't displace chlorine, but it does displace iodine. Iodine can't displace chlorine or bromine.

7) This shows the reactivity trend — the halogens get less reactive as you go down the group.

This is to do with how easily they gain electrons — see p.123 for more.

New information displaces old information from my brain...

If you remember that the halogens get less reactive as you go down the group, you can work out what will happen when you mix any halogen with any halide salt. You need to know the colour changes that go with the reactions too.

Q1 A student added a few drops of a halogen solution to some potassium iodide solution. The solution turned brown. She added a few drops of the same halogen solution to some potassium bromide solution. No reaction occurred. Name the halogen solution that the student used.

[1 mark]

Group 0 — Noble Gases

The elements in Group 0 of the periodic table are known as the <u>noble gases</u>. 'Noble' here is just being used in the old chemistry sense of being <u>unreactive</u> — nothing to do with them being particularly honourable or good.

Group 0 Elements are All Inert, Colourless Gases

Group 0 elements are called the <u>noble gases</u>. Group 0 is made up of the elements helium, neon, argon, krypton, xenon and radon.

1) All of the elements in Group 0 are <u>colourless gases</u> at room temperature.

2) The noble gases are all <u>monatomic</u> — that just means that their gases are made up of <u>single atoms</u> (not molecules).

3) They're also more or less <u>inert</u> — this means they <u>don't react</u> with much at all. The reason for this is that they have a <u>full outer shell</u> of electrons. This means they <u>don't</u> easily either <u>give up</u> or <u>gain</u> electrons.

4) As the noble gases are inert, they're <u>non-flammable</u> — they won't set on fire.

5) These properties make the gases pretty <u>hard to observe</u> — it took a long time for them to be discovered.

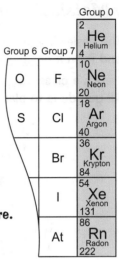

	Group 0
	2 He Helium 4
Group 6 Group 7	10 Ne Neon 20
O F	18 Ar Argon 40
S Cl	36 Kr Krypton 84
Br	54 Xe Xenon 131
I	86 Rn Radon 222
At	

There are Patterns in the Properties of the Noble Gases

1) As with the other groups in the periodic table, there are <u>trends</u> in the <u>properties</u> of the noble gases.

2) For example, <u>boiling point</u>, <u>melting point</u> and <u>density</u> all <u>increase</u> as you go <u>down</u> Group 0.

3) You could be given information about a particular <u>property</u> of the noble gases (or Group 1 and Group 7 elements) and asked to use it to <u>estimate the value</u> of this property for a certain element. For example:

EXAMPLE: Use the densities of helium (0.2 kg/m^3) and argon (1.8 kg/m^3) to predict the density of neon.

Neon comes between helium and argon in the group, so you can predict that its density will be roughly halfway between their densities: $(0.2 + 1.8) \div 2 = 2.0 \div 2 = 1.0$

Neon should have a density of about 1.0 kg/m^3.

There are other methods you could use for these questions, but don't worry — you'd get marks for any sensible answer.

EXAMPLE: The table on the right shows the melting points of the first five noble gases. Predict the melting point of radon.

Melting points increase as you go down the group, so radon's melting point must be higher than xenon's. To predict how much higher, look at the gaps between the melting points of the other elements:

He to Ne: $(-249) - (-272) = 23$ Ne to Ar $(-189) - (-249) = 60$
Ar to Kr: $(-157) - (-189) = 32$ Kr to Xe: $(-112) - (-157) = 45$

Element	Melting point (°C)
He	−272
Ne	−249
Ar	−189
Kr	−157
Xe	−112

The gaps aren't exactly the same, so find the average gap: $(23 + 60 + 32 + 45) \div 4 = 160 \div 4 = 40$ °C
Now you can just add this average gap to the melting point of xenon.

Radon should have a melting point of about $(-112) + 40 = -72$ °C.

4) You could be asked about how an element <u>reacts</u> too, so remember — elements in the <u>same group</u> react in <u>similar ways</u> as they all have the same number of <u>electrons</u> in their <u>outer shells</u>. And, all you need to do to find which group an element is in is look at the <u>periodic table</u>. Simple.

What's a pirate's favourite element? Arrrrgon...

The noble gases might seem a bit dull, given how unreactive they are, but they're not so bad. They'd be pretty good at hide and seek for a start. And what would helium balloon sellers be without them? Deflated — that's what.

Q1   The boiling points of the first four noble gases are: helium = −269 °C, neon = −246 °C, argon = −186 °C and krypton = −153 °C. Predict the boiling point of xenon.   [1 mark]

Topic C4 — Predicting and Identifying Reactions and Products

Reactivity of Metals

<u>Reactive metals</u> tend to do exciting, fizzy things when you drop them into acid or water. If you do the same with an <u>unreactive metal</u>, it'll just sit there. How boring. Here's a bit more detail on <u>reactivity experiments</u>...

How Metals React With Acids Tells You About Their Reactivity

1) The easier it is for a metal atom to lose its outer electrons and form a <u>positive ion</u>, the <u>more reactive</u> it will be.

2) Here's a classic experiment that you can do to show that some metals are <u>more reactive</u> than others. All you do is to place little pieces of various <u>metals</u> into <u>dilute hydrochloric acid</u>:

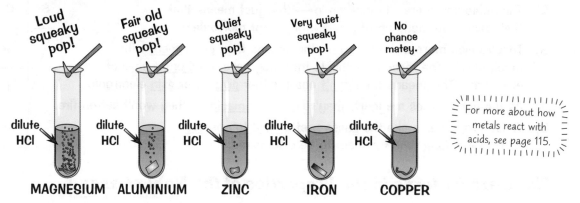

For more about how metals react with acids, see page 115.

MAGNESIUM · ALUMINIUM · ZINC · IRON · COPPER

3) The more <u>reactive</u> the metal is, the <u>faster</u> the reaction will go.

4) Very reactive metals (e.g. <u>magnesium</u>) will <u>fizz vigorously</u>, less reactive metals (e.g. <u>zinc</u>) will <u>bubble a bit</u>, and unreactive metals (e.g. <u>copper</u>) will <u>not</u> react with dilute acids <u>at all</u>.

5) You can show that <u>hydrogen</u> is forming using the <u>burning splint test</u> (see page 120). The <u>louder</u> the squeaky pop, the more hydrogen has been made in the time period and the <u>more reactive</u> the metal is.

6) The <u>speed</u> of reaction is also indicated by the <u>rate</u> at which the <u>bubbles</u> of hydrogen are given off — the faster the bubbles form, the faster the reaction and the more reactive the metal.

You could also follow the rate of the reaction by using a gas syringe to measure the volume of gas given off at regular time intervals.

Metals Also React With Water

The <u>reactions</u> of metals with <u>water</u> also show the reactivity of metals. This is the basic reaction:

> metal + water → metal hydroxide + hydrogen
> (Or: less reactive metal + steam → metal oxide + hydrogen)

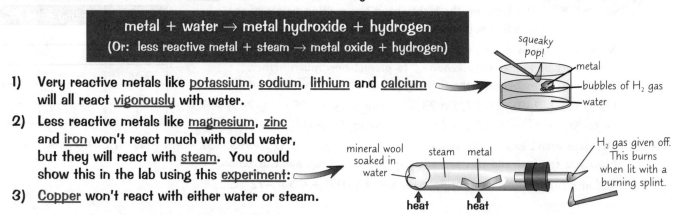

squeaky pop!
metal
bubbles of H_2 gas
water

1) Very reactive metals like <u>potassium</u>, <u>sodium</u>, <u>lithium</u> and <u>calcium</u> will all react <u>vigorously</u> with water.

2) Less reactive metals like <u>magnesium</u>, <u>zinc</u> and <u>iron</u> won't react much with cold water, but they will react with <u>steam</u>. You could show this in the lab using this <u>experiment</u>:

mineral wool soaked in water · steam · metal

H_2 gas given off. This burns when lit with a burning splint.

3) <u>Copper</u> won't react with either water or steam.

heat · heat

I AM NOT HIGHLY REACTIVE — OK...

This stuff isn't too bad — who knows, you might even get to have a go at these experiments in class...

Q1 A student is given small samples of three metals, A, B and C. He places them in dilute hydrochloric acid. Nothing happens to Metal A. Metal B fizzes vigorously. The gas given off gives a loud squeaky pop when lit with a burning splint. Metal C fizzes a bit and the gas given off gives a quiet squeaky pop when lit.

   a) Put the three metals in order, from most reactive to least reactive. [1 mark]

   b) One of the metals was zinc, one was magnesium, and one was copper. Use this information to identify metals A, B and C. [1 mark]

The Reactivity Series and Displacement

On the previous page, you covered some reactions that help you work out how <u>reactive</u> a <u>metal</u> is. You can use information like this to put the metals in order of their <u>reactivity</u>. Which is more useful than it sounds, promise.

The Reactivity Series Shows How Reactive Metals Are

A <u>reactivity series</u> is just a table that lists <u>metals</u> in order of their <u>reactivity</u>. Here's an example:

The Reactivity Series	
Potassium	K
Sodium	Na
Calcium	Ca
Magnesium	Mg
Aluminium	Al
Zinc	Zn
Iron	Fe
Copper	Cu
Silver	Ag

most reactive

least reactive

The reactivity series can help you to work out the best method of extracting a metal from its ore — see page 137 for more.

I shall not react.

More Reactive Metals Displace Less Reactive Ones

1) If you put a <u>more reactive metal</u> into a solution of a <u>less reactive metal salt</u>, the reactive metal will <u>replace</u> the <u>less reactive metal</u> in the salt.

<u>Example</u>: if you put an <u>iron nail</u> in a solution of <u>copper sulfate</u>, the more reactive iron will "<u>kick out</u>" the less reactive copper from the salt. You end up with <u>iron sulfate solution</u> and <u>copper metal</u>.

copper sulfate + iron → iron sulfate + copper
$$CuSO_4 + Fe \rightarrow FeSO_4 + Cu$$

2) If you put a <u>less reactive metal</u> into a solution of a <u>more reactive metal salt</u>, <u>nothing</u> will happen.

<u>Example</u>: if you put a small piece of silver metal into a solution of <u>copper sulfate</u>, nothing will happen. The more reactive metal (copper) is already in the salt.

3) You can use displacement reactions to <u>work out</u> where in the reactivity series a metal should go.

<u>Example</u>: A student adds some <u>metals</u> to <u>metal salt solutions</u> and records whether any <u>reactions</u> happen. Use her table of results, below, to work out an <u>order of reactivity</u> for the metals.

	copper nitrate	magnesium chloride	zinc sulfate
copper	no reaction	no reaction	no reaction
magnesium	magnesium nitrate and copper formed	no reaction	magnesium sulfate and zinc formed
zinc	zinc nitrate and copper formed	no reaction	no reaction

- Magnesium <u>displaces</u> both <u>copper</u> and <u>zinc</u>, so it must be <u>more reactive</u> than both.
- Copper <u>is displaced by</u> both <u>magnesium</u> and <u>zinc</u>, so it must be <u>less reactive</u> than both.
- Zinc <u>can displace copper</u>, but <u>not magnesium</u>, so it must go between them.

The <u>order of reactivity</u>, <u>from most to least</u>, is: <u>magnesium</u>, <u>zinc</u>, <u>copper</u>

And that's why Iron Man never goes swimming in copper sulfate...

You could be given the results of an experiment and have to use them to put the metals into an order of reactivity, or you could be told their reactivities and then asked to predict how they'll react — make sure you can do both.

Q1 State whether magnesium would displace iron from iron sulfate solution. Explain your answer. [1 mark]

Q2 Tin sits between iron and copper in the reactivity series.
State whether tin would displace zinc from zinc sulfate solution and explain your answer. [1 mark]

Revision Questions for Topic C4

Hooray, that's the end of Topic C4 — now have a go at these questions to make sure you've really got it.

- Try these questions and tick off each one when you get it right.
- When you've done all the questions under a heading and are completely happy with it, tick it off.

Group 1 — Alkali Metals (p.122) ☑

1) How many electrons does an alkali metal atom have in its outer shell? ☑
2) List three typical properties of the alkali metals. ☑
3) Explain why Group 1 metals are so reactive. ☑
4) Put these alkali metals in order of reactivity, starting with the least reactive:
   potassium, caesium, lithium, sodium. ☑
5) Write a balanced symbol equation to show the reaction between sodium and water. ☑

Group 7 — Halogens (p.123-124) ☑

6) How many electrons do halogens have in their outer shells? ☑
7) Describe the appearances and physical states of the
   following halogens at room temperature and pressure:
   a) chlorine,
   b) bromine,
   c) iodine. ☑
8) Describe how the reactivity of the elements changes as you go down Group 7. ☑
9) Give the name of the salt formed when potassium reacts with bromine. ☑
10) Chlorine (Cl_2) can displace bromine from potassium bromide (KBr).
    a) Write an equation for this reaction.
    b) Describe the colour change that you would see when this reaction happened. ☑
11) Can iodine displace bromine from potassium bromide solution? ☑

Group 0 — Noble Gases (p.125) ☑

12) True or false? The noble gases generally exist as diatomic molecules. ☑
13) Why are the elements in Group 0 inert? ☑

Metals and Reactivity (p.126-127) ☑

14) True or false? The easier it is for a metal atom to form a positive ion, the more reactive it will be. ☑
15) You are given samples of four mystery metals and some dilute hydrochloric acid.
    Briefly describe how you could use these things to work out a reactivity series for the four metals. ☑
16) In a reactivity series, where do you find the least reactive elements? ☑
17) Magnesium is above zinc in the reactivity series.
    Would any reaction happen if a piece of magnesium metal was put in zinc sulfate solution? ☑

Reaction Rates

Reactions can be <u>fast</u> or <u>slow</u> — you've probably already realised that. It's exciting stuff. Honest.

The Rate of Reaction is a Measure of How Fast the Reaction Happens

The <u>rate of a reaction</u> is how quickly a reaction happens. It can be observed <u>either</u> by measuring how quickly the reactants are used up or how quickly the products are formed. The <u>rate of a reaction</u> can be calculated using the following formula:

$$\text{Rate of Reaction} = \frac{\text{amount of reactant used or amount of product formed}}{\text{time}}$$

It's usually a lot easier to measure products forming.

You Can Do Experiments to Follow Reaction Rates

There are different ways that the rate of a reaction can be <u>measured</u>. Here are three examples:

Precipitation

1) This method works for any reaction where mixing <u>two see-through solutions</u> produces a <u>precipitate</u>, which <u>clouds</u> the solution.

2) You <u>mix</u> the two reactant solutions and put the flask on a piece of paper that has a <u>mark</u> on it.

3) <u>Observe</u> the mark through the mixture and measure how long it takes for the mark to be <u>obscured</u>. The <u>faster</u> it disappears, the <u>faster</u> the reaction.

4) The result is <u>subjective</u> — <u>different people</u> might not agree on <u>exactly</u> when the mark 'disappears'.

You can use this method to investigate how temperature affects the rate of the reaction between sodium thiosulfate and hydrochloric acid (which produces a yellow precipitate of sulfur). You repeat the reaction using solutions at different temperatures — use a water bath to heat both solutions to the right temperature before you mix them.

Change in Mass (Usually Gas Given Off)

1) You can measure the rate of a reaction that <u>produces a gas</u> using a <u>mass balance</u>.

2) As the gas is released, the <u>lost mass</u> is easily measured on the balance. The <u>quicker</u> the reading on the balance <u>drops</u>, the <u>faster</u> the reaction.

3) You can use your results to plot a <u>graph</u> of <u>change in mass</u> against <u>time</u>.

4) This method does release the gas produced straight into the room — so if the gas is <u>harmful</u>, you must take <u>safety precautions</u>, e.g. do the experiment in a <u>fume cupboard</u>.

The cotton wool lets gases through but stops any solid, liquid or aqueous reactants flying out during the reaction.

The Volume of Gas Given Off

1) This involves the use of a <u>gas syringe</u> to measure the <u>volume</u> of gas given off.

2) The <u>more</u> gas given off during a set <u>time interval</u>, the <u>faster</u> the reaction.

3) You can use your results to plot a graph of <u>gas volume</u> against <u>time elapsed</u>.

4) You need to be careful that you're using the <u>right size</u> gas syringe for your experiment though — if the reaction is too <u>vigorous</u>, you can blow the plunger out of the end of the syringe.

Retraction rate — how fast my mates disappear when I tell a joke...

Lots of different ways to follow reaction rates here — well... three. Precipitation, mass loss and gas formation.

Q1   Outline how you could follow the rate of a reaction where mixing two solutions forms a precipitate. [2 marks]

Q2   Give one possible problem with using the change in mass method to follow the rate of a reaction. [1 mark]

Rate Experiments

You'll probably have to <u>measure</u> the <u>rate of a reaction</u> in class at some point. Time to learn how to do it...

Reaction of Hydrochloric Acid and Marble Chips

You can use this experiment to show how <u>surface area</u> affects reaction <u>rate</u>.

1) Set the apparatus up as shown in the diagram on the right.

2) Measure the <u>volume</u> of gas produced using a <u>gas syringe</u>. Take readings at <u>regular time intervals</u> and record your results in a table.

3) You can plot a <u>graph</u> of your results — <u>time</u> goes on the <u>x-axis</u> and <u>volume</u> goes on the <u>y-axis</u>.

4) <u>Repeat</u> the experiment with <u>exactly the same volume</u> and <u>concentration</u> of acid, and <u>exactly the same mass</u> of marble chips, but with the marble <u>more crunched up</u>.

5) Then <u>repeat</u> with the same mass of <u>powdered chalk</u>.

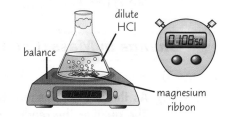

It's important your system is air tight so no gas escapes.

CO_2 gas

dilute HCl

marble chips ($CaCO_3$)

Marble and chalk are both made of calcium carbonate ($CaCO_3$).

Finer Particles of Solid Mean a Higher Rate

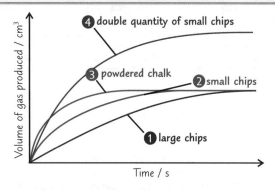

④ double quantity of small chips
③ powdered chalk
② small chips
① large chips

Volume of gas produced / cm^3

Time / s

1) Using <u>finer particles</u> means that the marble has a <u>larger surface area</u>.

2) <u>Lines 1 to 3</u> on the graph on the left show that the <u>finer</u> the particles are (and the <u>greater</u> the surface area of the solid reactants), the <u>faster</u> the reaction goes.

3) <u>Line 4</u> shows the reaction if a <u>greater mass</u> of small marble chips is added. The <u>extra surface area</u> gives a <u>faster reaction</u> and there is also <u>more gas evolved</u> overall.

Reaction of Magnesium Metal with Dilute HCl

1) <u>This reaction</u> is good for measuring the effects of <u>changing the concentration</u> on reaction rate.

2) The reaction gives off <u>hydrogen gas</u>, so you can measure the loss of mass as the gas is formed using a <u>mass balance</u>.

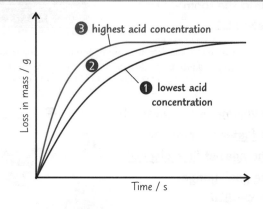

dilute HCl

balance

magnesium ribbon

More Concentrated Solutions Mean a Higher Rate

③ highest acid concentration
②
① lowest acid concentration

Loss in mass / g

Time / s

1) During the experiment, take <u>readings</u> of the mass of the flask and its contents at <u>regular</u> time intervals. Put the results in a <u>table</u> and work out the <u>loss in mass</u> for each reading.

2) You can plot a <u>graph</u> of your results with <u>time</u> on the <u>x-axis</u> and <u>loss in mass</u> on the <u>y-axis</u>.

3) <u>Repeat</u> the experiment with <u>exactly the same mass</u> and <u>surface area</u> of magnesium and <u>exactly the same volume</u> of acid, but using different <u>concentrations</u> of acid.

4) <u>Lines 1 to 3</u> on the graph show that a <u>higher</u> concentration gives a <u>faster reaction</u>, with the reaction <u>finishing</u> sooner.

I prefer chalk to marble chips — I like the finer things in life...

Doing rate experiments lets you collect data. Collecting data lets you plot graphs, and you can use graphs to find reaction rates. But more about that on the next page. I bet you're just itching to read on...

Q1 Describe how you could investigate how the rate of reaction between magnesium and hydrochloric acid varies with the surface area of the sample of magnesium. [3 marks]

Calculating Rates

You can work out rates of reaction using <u>graphs</u> or <u>tables</u>. The choice is yours (well, it's the examiner's really).

Faster Rates of Reaction are Shown by Steeper Gradients

If you have a graph of <u>amount of product formed</u> (or <u>reactant used up</u>) against <u>time</u>, then the <u>gradient</u> (slope) of the graph will be equal to the rate of the reaction — the <u>steeper</u> the slope, the <u>faster</u> the rate.

The gradient of a <u>straight line</u> is given by the equation:

gradient = change in y ÷ change in x

EXAMPLE: Calculate the rate of the reaction shown on the graph on the right.

1) Find two <u>points on the line</u> that are <u>easy to read</u> the x and y values of (ones that pass through grid lines).

2) Draw a line straight <u>down</u> from the higher point and straight <u>across</u> from the lower one to make a <u>triangle</u>.

3) The <u>height</u> of your triangle = <u>change in y</u>
The <u>base</u> of your triangle = <u>change in x</u>
Change in y = 16 − 5 = 11
Change in x = 65 − 20 = 45

4) Use the formula to work out the <u>gradient</u>, and therefore the rate.
Gradient = change in y ÷ change in x = 11 ÷ 45 = 0.24 cm³/s ——— The units of the rate are just 'units of y-axis ÷ units of x-axis'.

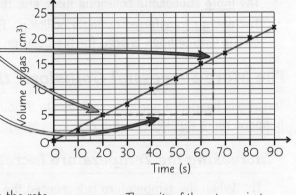

Draw a Tangent to Find the Gradient of a Curve

1) If your graph (or part of it) is a <u>curve</u>, then the gradient, and therefore the <u>rate</u>, is different at different points along the curve.

2) To find the <u>gradient</u> of the graph at a certain point, you'll have to draw a <u>tangent</u> at that point.

3) A tangent is just a line that <u>touches the curve</u> and has the <u>same gradient</u> as the curve at that point.

4) To draw a tangent, place a <u>ruler</u> on the line of best fit at the point you're interested in, so you can see the <u>whole curve</u>. Adjust the ruler so the space between the ruler and the curve is the same on both sides of the point. Draw a line <u>along the ruler</u> to make the <u>tangent</u>.

5) The rate at that point is then just the <u>gradient</u> of the <u>tangent</u>.

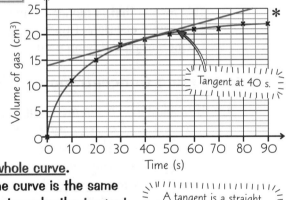

Tangent at 40 s.

A tangent is a straight line, so you can find its gradient using the straight line method shown above.

1 ÷ Time is Proportional to Rate

1) The <u>longer</u> something takes, the <u>slower</u> the <u>rate</u>. Therefore, rate is <u>inversely proportional</u> to time.

2) You can use <u>1/time</u> (or 1 ÷ time) as a measure of the rate of a reaction (1/time is proportional to rate).

EXAMPLE:
Use the table on the right to calculate the relative rate of reaction at each temperature.

Temperature (°C)	20	25	30	35	40
Time taken for mark to disappear (s)	193	151	112	87	52

At 20 °C, 1 ÷ 193 = 0.0052 s⁻¹   At 30 °C, 1 ÷ 112 = 0.0089 s⁻¹   At 40 °C, 1 ÷ 52 = 0.019 s⁻¹
At 25 °C, 1 ÷ 151 = 0.0066 s⁻¹   At 35 °C, 1 ÷ 87 = 0.011 s⁻¹

My interest in gradients is inversely proportional to time...

Lots of nifty graph skills here. Gradients aren't too hard, but make sure those tangents don't trip you up.

Q1   Work out the rate of reaction at 20 seconds using the graph (marked *) shown above.   [2 marks]

Collision Theory

The rate of a reaction depends on these things — <u>temperature</u>, <u>concentration</u> (or <u>pressure</u> for gases) and the <u>size of the particles</u> (for solids). This page explains why these things affect the reaction rate. Let's get cracking.

Particles Must Collide with Enough Energy in Order to React

<u>Reaction rates</u> are explained by <u>collision theory</u>. It's simple really.

<u>The rate of a chemical reaction</u> depends on:

- The <u>collision frequency</u> of reacting particles (<u>how often they collide</u>). The <u>more</u> successful collisions there are, the <u>faster</u> the reaction is.
- The <u>energy transferred</u> during a collision. Particles have to collide with <u>enough energy</u> for the collision to be <u>successful</u>.

A successful collision is a collision that ends in the particles reacting to form products.

The More Successful Collisions, the Higher the Rate of Reaction

Reactions happen if <u>particles collide</u>. So if you <u>increase</u> the <u>number</u> of collisions, the reaction happens <u>more quickly</u> (i.e. the rate increases). The three factors below all lead to more collisions...

Increasing the Temperature Increases Rate

1) When the <u>temperature is increased</u> the particles <u>move faster</u>. If they move faster, they're going to have <u>more collisions</u>.

2) Higher temperatures also increase the <u>energy</u> of the collisions, since the particles are moving <u>faster</u>. Reactions <u>only happen</u> if the particles collide with <u>enough energy</u>.

3) This means that at <u>higher</u> temperatures there will be more <u>successful collisions</u> (<u>more particles</u> will <u>collide</u> with <u>enough energy</u> to react). So <u>increasing</u> the temperature <u>increases</u> the rate of reaction.

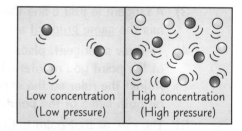

Cold   Hot

Increasing Concentration (or Pressure) Increases Rate

1) If a <u>solution</u> is made more <u>concentrated</u>, it means there are more particles of <u>reactant</u> in the same volume. This makes collisions <u>more likely</u>, so the reaction rate <u>increases</u>.

2) In a <u>gas</u>, increasing the <u>pressure</u> means that the particles are <u>more crowded</u>. This means that the frequency of <u>collisions</u> between particles will <u>increase</u> — so the rate of reaction will also <u>increase</u>.

Low concentration (Low pressure)   High concentration (High pressure)

Smaller Solid Particles (or More Surface Area) Means a Higher Rate

1) If one reactant is a <u>solid</u>, breaking it into <u>smaller</u> pieces will <u>increase its surface area to volume ratio</u> (i.e. more of the solid will be exposed, compared to its overall volume).

2) The particles around it will have <u>more area to work on</u>, so the frequency of collisions will <u>increase</u>.

3) This means that the rate of reaction is faster for solids with a larger <u>surface area to volume</u> ratio.

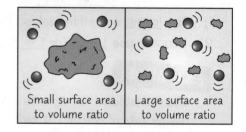

Small surface area to volume ratio   Large surface area to volume ratio

---

Collision theory — it's always the other driver...

Remember — more collisions mean a faster reaction. But don't be fooled, not every collision results in a reaction. The particles have to collide with enough energy to react (otherwise known as the 'activation energy').

Q1   Would you expect the rate of reaction between hydrochloric acid and calcium carbonate to be faster with calcium carbonate in the form of powder or chips? Explain your answer.   [3 marks]

Q2   Why does raising the temperature increase the rate of a reaction?   [3 marks]

Catalysts

Catalysts are very important for commercial reasons — they increase reaction rate and reduce energy costs in industrial reactions. If that's not reason enough to learn this page, I don't know what is. (Oh, apart from "exams"...)

A Catalyst Increases the Rate of a Reaction

1) A catalyst is a substance which increases the rate of a reaction, without being chemically changed or used up in the reaction.

2) Because it isn't used up, you only need a tiny bit to catalyse large amounts of reactants.

3) Catalysts tend to be very fussy about which reactions they catalyse though — you can't just stick any old catalyst in a reaction and expect it to work.

4) Catalysts work by decreasing the activation energy (see page 111) needed for a reaction to occur.

5) They do this by providing an alternative reaction pathway that has a lower activation energy.

6) You can see this if you look at a reaction profile.

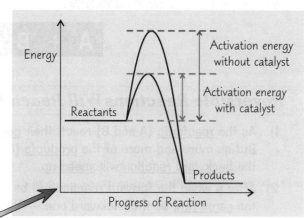

You can Identify Catalysts in Chemical Reactions

1) To find out if a substance is a catalyst for a reaction, you can do an experiment.

2) For example, if you have a solid that you think might be a catalyst for a reaction between two solutions, you could measure the reaction rate without the solid present, and then again with a known mass of the solid added.

3) If the rate increases, but the solid appears to be unchanged, it could be a catalyst.

4) To make it a fair test, you need to keep everything else the same, so that nothing else can affect the rate of reaction — that means volumes and concentrations of solutions, and the temperature.

5) You can check that none of the solid has been used up by filtering it out at the end of the experiment, drying it and measuring the mass to check it's all still there.

> Example: Hydrogen peroxide (H_2O_2) decomposes into water and oxygen: $2H_2O_2 \longrightarrow 2H_2O + O_2$.
> This reaction normally happens very slowly (so slowly that it's hard to record a rate at all). But it's catalysed by manganese(IV) oxide (MnO_2) — if you add MnO_2 powder to hydrogen peroxide solution, the reaction speeds up. Oxygen gas is given off, so you can measure the rate of reaction using the gas syringe method (see page 129). When the reaction is finished (i.e. when no more bubbles of O_2 are being given off), the appearance and the mass of the black MnO_2 powder are both unchanged.

Enzymes Control Cell Reactions

1) Enzymes are biological catalysts.

2) This means that they catalyse (speed up) the chemical reactions in living cells.

3) Reactions catalysed by enzymes include respiration, photosynthesis and protein synthesis.

Catalysts are chemical stars — but success won't change them...

There's a more fun version of that H_2O_2 experiment involving washing up liquid. If you've not seen it, ask your teacher to give a demonstration of the 'elephant's toothpaste' reaction. You won't regret it.

Q1 What is a catalyst? [2 marks]

Q2 A student adds some dark brown lead dioxide (PbO_2) powder to a flask of hydrogen peroxide solution. Lead dioxide is a catalyst for the decomposition of hydrogen peroxide. With reference to the catalyst, describe what you would expect to see in the flask after the decomposition reaction had finished. [1 mark]

Dynamic Equilibrium

Reversible reactions — products forming from reactants and reactants forming from products. I can't keep up...

Reversible Reactions can go Forwards and Backwards

A reversible reaction is one where the products can react with each other to produce the original reactants. In other words, it can go both ways.

$$A + B \rightleftharpoons C + D$$

The '$\rightleftharpoons$' shows the reaction goes both ways.

Reversible Reactions Will Reach Equilibrium

1) As the reactants (A and B) react, their concentrations fall — so the forward reaction will slow down. But as more and more of the products (C and D) are made and their concentrations rise, the backward reaction will speed up.

2) After a while the forward reaction will be going at exactly the same rate as the backward one — this is equilibrium.

3) At equilibrium both reactions are still happening, but there's no overall effect — it's a dynamic equilibrium. This means the concentrations of reactants and products have reached a balance and won't change.

4) Equilibrium can only be reached if the reversible reaction takes place in a 'closed system'. A closed system just means that none of the reactants or products can escape.

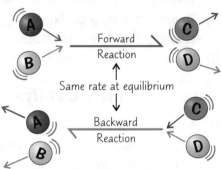

Forward Reaction

Same rate at equilibrium

Backward Reaction

The Position of Equilibrium Can be on the Right or the Left

When a reaction's at equilibrium it doesn't mean the amounts of reactants and products are equal.

1) Sometimes the equilibrium will lie to the right — this basically means 'lots of the products and not much of the reactants' (i.e. the concentration of products is greater than the concentration of reactants).

2) Sometimes the equilibrium will lie to the left — this basically means 'lots of the reactants but not much of the products' (the concentration of reactants is greater than the concentration of products).

3) The exact position of equilibrium depends on the conditions (as well as the reaction itself).

Three Things Can Change the Position of Equilibrium

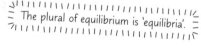

The plural of equilibrium is 'equilibria'.

These three things can change the position of equilibrium (which changes the amounts of products and reactants present at equilibrium):

1) Temperature
2) Pressure
   (only affects equilibria involving gases)
3) Concentration

Dynamic equilibrium — lots of activity, but not to any great effect*...

Keep an eagle eye out for that arrow that shows you that a reaction is reversible. I'd hate you to miss it.

Q1 Explain what is meant by the term 'reversible reaction'. [1 mark]

Q2 What is dynamic equilibrium? [1 mark]

Q3 Name three things which can affect the position of equilibrium. [3 marks]

*Much like the England football team...

Le Chatelier's Principle

This stuff might feel a bit complicated to start with, but it all comes down to one simple rule — whatever you do to a <u>reversible reaction</u>, the <u>equilibrium position</u> will <u>move</u> to try to <u>undo</u> your change. How contrary...

The Equilibrium Position Moves to Minimise Any Changes You Make

<u>Le Chatelier's principle</u> states that if there's a <u>change</u> in concentration, pressure or temperature in a reversible reaction, the <u>equilibrium position will move</u> to help <u>counteract</u> that change.

TEMPERATURE All reactions are <u>exothermic</u> in one direction and <u>endothermic</u> in the other (see page 111).

1) If you <u>decrease the temperature</u>, the equilibrium will move in the <u>exothermic direction</u> to produce more heat.

2) If you <u>increase the temperature</u>, the equilibrium will move in the <u>endothermic direction</u> to absorb the extra heat.

> For example: $N_2 + 3H_2 \rightleftharpoons 2NH_3$
> This reaction is exothermic in the forward direction.
> If you decrease the temperature, the equilibrium will shift to the right (so you'll make more product).

PRESSURE Changing this only affects equilibria involving <u>gases</u>.

1) If you <u>increase the pressure</u>, the equilibrium will move towards the side that has <u>fewer moles of gas</u> to <u>reduce</u> pressure.

2) If you <u>decrease the pressure</u>, the equilibrium will move towards the side that has <u>more moles of gas</u> to <u>increase</u> pressure.

> For example:
> $N_2 + 3H_2 \rightleftharpoons 2NH_3$
> This reaction has 4 moles of gas on the left and 2 on the right. If you increase the pressure, the equilibrium will shift to the right (so you'll make more product).

CONCENTRATION

1) If you <u>increase the concentration</u> of the <u>reactants</u>, the equilibrium will move to the <u>right</u> to <u>use up the reactants</u> (making <u>more products</u>).

2) If you <u>increase the concentration</u> of the <u>products</u>, the equilibrium will move to the <u>left</u> to <u>use up the products</u> (making <u>more reactants</u>).

3) <u>Decreasing</u> the concentrations will have the <u>opposite effect</u>.

> For example:
> $N_2 + 3H_2 \rightleftharpoons 2NH_3$
> If you increase the concentration of N_2 or H_2, the equilibrium will shift to the right to use up the extra reactants (so you'll make more product).

You Can Predict How the Position of Equilibrium Will Change

You can apply the rules above to any reversible reaction to work out how <u>changing the conditions</u> will affect the <u>equilibrium position</u>. This has useful applications in <u>industry</u> — you can <u>increase yield</u> (how much product is made during a reaction) by changing the conditions to shift the equilibrium position to the <u>right</u> (towards the <u>products</u>).

The compound PCl_5 can be made using this reaction: $PCl_{3\,(g)} + Cl_{2\,(g)} \rightleftharpoons PCl_{5\,(g)}$
Explain what would happen to the equilibrium position and to the yield of PCl_5 if you increased the pressure that the reaction was being performed at.

According to Le Chatelier's Principle, if you increase the pressure, the position of equilibrium will move towards the side with fewer moles of gas to reduce the pressure. In this reaction there are 2 moles of gas in the reactants and 1 in the products. The position of equilibrium will move to the right, since that is the side with fewer moles of gas. This shifts the equilibrium towards the products, so the yield of PCl_5 will increase.

Le Chatelier — relieving pressure since 1884...

Le Chatelier's principle may relieve the pressure in chemical systems, but it stands a chance of giving you a right headache in the exam. So, best make sure you understand it now by trying these questions...

Q1 This reaction is endothermic in the forward direction: $CH_3OH_{(g)} \rightleftharpoons CO_{(g)} + 2H_{2\,(g)}$. What will happen to the position of equilibrium if the temperature is increased? Explain your answer. [2 marks]

Q2 What would happen to the yield of SO_3 in the reaction below if the pressure was decreased? Explain your answer. $2SO_{2\,(g)} + O_{2\,(g)} \rightleftharpoons 2SO_{3\,(g)}$ [3 marks]

Revision Questions for Topic C5

Wasn't that fun? I liked the graphs best, but that might just be me... Time to test your knowledge of <u>Topic C5</u>.

• Try these questions and <u>tick off each one</u> when you <u>get it right</u>.
• When you've done <u>all the questions</u> under a heading and are <u>completely happy</u> with it, tick it off.

<u>Rates of Reactions (p.129-131)</u> ☑

1) What is the 'rate' of a reaction? ☑

2) Explain how you could follow the rate of a reaction where
two colourless solutions react to form a precipitate. ☑

3) Describe how you would set up an experiment to follow the rate
of a reaction by measuring the volume of gas that it produced. ☑

4) Describe how you would find the rate of a reaction from a straight line graph. ☑

5) Imagine you have drawn a results graph for a rate of reaction experiment. The graph is a curve.
Describe how you could find the rate of a reaction at a certain time point using the graph. ☑

<u>Collision Theory (p.132)</u> ☑

6) State how the frequency of successful collisions affects the rate of a reaction. ☑

7) What effect will raising the temperature have on the rate of a reaction? ☑

8) How does increasing the pressure of a reaction involving gases affect the rate of a reaction? ☑

<u>Catalysts (p.133)</u> ☐

9) What effect does a catalyst have on the activation energy needed for a reaction to take place? ☑

10) Sketch a reaction profile showing an uncatalysed reaction
and the same reaction with a catalyst added. ☑

11) What is an enzyme? ☑

<u>Dynamic Equilibrium (p.134)</u> ☐

12) Draw the symbol which shows that a reaction is reversible. ☑

13) What is a closed system? ☑

14) If the position of equilibrium for a reversible reaction lies to the right,
what does that tell you about the relative amounts of reactants and products present? ☑

<u>Le Chatelier's Principle (p.135)</u> ☐

15) State Le Chatelier's principle. ☑

16) Describe what would happen to the equilibrium position of a reversible reaction
if you increased the concentration of the reactants. ☑

Extracting Metals from their Ores

A few unreactive metals, like gold, are found in the Earth as the metal itself, rather than as a compound. The rest of the metals we get by extracting them from rocks — and I bet you're just itching to find out how...

Ores Contain Enough Metal to Make Extraction Worthwhile

A metal ore is a rock which contains enough metal to make it economically worthwhile extracting the metal from it. In many cases the ore is an oxide of the metal.

For example, the main aluminium ore is called bauxite — it's aluminium oxide (Al_2O_3).

Metals Are Extracted From their Ores Chemically

1) A metal can be extracted from its ore chemically — by reduction (see below) or by electrolysis (splitting with electricity, see pages 117-119).

2) Some ores may have to be concentrated before the metal is extracted — this just involves getting rid of the unwanted rocky material.

3) Electrolysis can also be used to purify the extracted metal (see next page).

4) There are other ways to extract metals though. Some metals are extracted from their ores using displacement reactions (see page 127), or by using biological methods (see the next page).

Row faster men!

We can't — it's these cursed metal oars.

Some Metals can be Extracted by Reduction with Carbon

1) A metal can be extracted from its ore chemically by reduction using carbon.

2) When an ore is reduced, oxygen is removed from it, e.g.

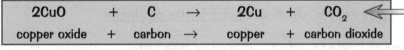

2CuO	+	C	→	2Cu	+	CO_2
copper oxide	+	carbon	→	copper	+	carbon dioxide

You can do this in the lab by heating copper oxide with charcoal (a fine powder of carbon) in a test tube over a Bunsen burner.

3) The position of the metal in the reactivity series determines whether it can be extracted by reduction with carbon.

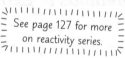

See page 127 for more on reactivity series.

- Metals higher than carbon in the reactivity series have to be extracted using electrolysis (see next page) which is expensive.

- Metals below carbon in the reactivity series can be extracted by reduction using carbon.
  For example, iron oxide is reduced in a blast furnace to make iron.

- This is because carbon can only take the oxygen away from metals which are less reactive than carbon itself is.

Extracted using electrolysis

Extracted by reduction using carbon

The Reactivity Series		
Potassium	K	more reactive
Sodium	Na	
Calcium	Ca	
Magnesium	Mg	
Aluminium	Al	
CARBON	C	
Zinc	Zn	
Iron	Fe	
Tin	Sn	
Copper	Cu	less reactive

[Please insert ore-ful pun here]...

Make sure you've got that reactivity series sorted in your head. If a metal's below carbon in the reactivity series, then it's less reactive than carbon and can be extracted from its ore by reduction using carbon. Phew... got it?

Q1   How would you extract tin from its metal ore? Explain your answer.   [2 marks]

Q2   Write a balanced chemical equation to describe the reaction that occurs
when carbon is used to extract zinc from its ore, zinc oxide (ZnO).   [2 marks]

Extracting Metals with Electrolysis

Electrolysis is an expensive process, but like many pricey things it's really rather good...

Some Metals have to be Extracted by Electrolysis

1) Metals that are more reactive than carbon (see previous page) are extracted using electrolysis of molten compounds (see page 118 for more on this).

2) Once the metal is melted, an electric current is passed through it. The metal is discharged at the cathode and the non-metal at the anode.

3) Electricity is expensive so this process is much more expensive than reduction with carbon.

> The compounds have to be molten (i.e. liquid) so that the electrons and ions are free to move.

> Example: When aluminium is extracted from its ore, aluminium oxide, the ore is first dissolved in molten cryolite (an aluminium compound) so the ions in the ore are free to move. During the electrolysis, aluminium is formed at the cathode where it sinks to the bottom of the cell and is siphoned off. Oxygen forms at the anode.

Copper is Purified by Electrolysis

1) Copper can be easily extracted by reduction with carbon (see previous page). The ore is heated in a furnace — this is called smelting.

2) However, the copper produced this way is impure — and impure copper doesn't conduct electricity very well. This isn't very useful because a lot of copper is used to make electrical wiring.

3) So electrolysis is also used to purify it, even though it's quite expensive.

4) This produces very pure copper, which is a much better conductor.

The negative electrode (cathode) starts as a thin piece of pure copper and more pure copper adds to it.

The positive electrode (anode) is just a big lump of impure copper, which will dissolve.

The electrolyte is copper sulfate solution containing Cu^{2+} ions.

sludge

There are Biological Methods to Extract Metals

1) The supply of some metal rich ores, e.g. copper ore, is limited.

2) The demand for lots of metals is growing and this may lead to shortages in the future.

3) Scientists are looking into new ways of extracting metals from low-grade ores (ores that only contain small amounts of the metal) or from the waste that is currently produced when metals are extracted.

4) Examples of new methods to extract metals from their ores are bioleaching and phytoextraction. These are biological methods as they use living organisms.

> We can also recycle metals to save resources (see page 140).

> Bioleaching: This uses bacteria to separate metals from their ores, e.g. copper can be separated from copper sulfide this way. The bacteria get energy from the bonds between the atoms in the ore, separating out the metal from the ore in the process. The leachate (the solution produced by the process) contains metal ions, which can be extracted, e.g. by electrolysis (see p.117-119) or displacement (see p.127) with a more reactive metal.

> Phytoextraction: This involves growing plants in soil that contains metal compounds. The plants can't use or get rid of the metals so they gradually build up in the leaves. The plants can be harvested, dried and burned in a furnace. The ash contains metal compounds from which the metal can be extracted by electrolysis or displacement reactions.

5) Traditional methods of mining are pretty damaging to the environment (see page 140). These new methods of extraction have a much smaller impact, but the disadvantage is that they're slow.

A policeman failed his maths test — he's a low-grade copper...

More electrolysis? It's just cropping up everywhere. That means there's no excuse not to know it.

Q1 Draw and label a diagram to show how copper is purified using electrolysis. [3 marks]

Q2 Name and describe two ways copper can be extracted from low-grade ores. [4 marks]

Life-Cycle Assessments

If a company wants to manufacture a new product, it will carry out a life-cycle assessment (LCA).
This looks at every stage of the product's life to assess the impact it would have on the environment.

Life-cycle Assessments Show Total Environmental Costs

A life-cycle assessment (LCA) looks at each stage of the life of a product — from making the material from natural raw materials, making the product from the material, using the product and disposing of the product. It works out the potential environmental impact of each stage.

Choice of material
1) Metals have to be mined and extracted from their ores. These processes need a lot of energy and cause a lot of pollution.
2) Raw materials for chemical manufacture often come from crude oil. Crude oil is a non-renewable resource, and supplies are decreasing. Also, obtaining crude oil from the ground and refining it into useful raw materials requires a lot of energy and generates pollution.

Manufacture
1) Manufacturing products uses a lot of energy and other resources.
2) It can also cause a lot of pollution, e.g. harmful gases such as CO or HCl.
3) You also need to think about any waste products and how to dispose of them.
4) Some waste can be recycled and turned into other useful chemicals, reducing the amount that ends up polluting the environment.
5) Most chemical manufacture needs water. Businesses have to make sure they don't put polluted water back into the environment at the end of the process.

Product Use
Using the product can also damage the environment. For example:
1) Paint gives off toxic fumes.
2) Burning fuels releases greenhouse gases and other harmful substances.
3) Fertilisers can leach into streams and rivers and cause damage to ecosystems.

Disposal
1) Products are often disposed of in a landfill site at the end of their life.
2) This takes up space and can pollute land and water.
3) Products might be incinerated (burnt), which causes air pollution.

Some products can be disposed of by being recycled (see next page).

EXAMPLE: A company is carrying out a life-cycle assessment to work out which car, A, B or C, it should make. Using the data in the table, explain which car the company should produce to minimise the environmental impact.

Car	CO₂ emissions (tonnes)	Waste solid produced (kg)	Water used (m³)	Expected lifespan of product (years)
A	17	10 720	8.2	11
B	21	5900	6.0	17
C	34	15 010	9.5	12

- Car A produces the least CO_2, but produces the second highest amount of waste solids and uses the second highest amount of water. It also has the shortest life span.
- Car B produces more CO_2 than car A, but produces by far the least waste solid, uses the least water and also has the longest life span. On balance, this looks a better choice than car A.
- Car C produces the most CO_2, the most waste solid, uses the most water, and has almost as short a life span as car A. This looks like the worst choice.
- So, on balance, car B looks like the one that will have the least environmental impact.

My cycle assessment — two wheels, a bell, an uncomfortable seat...

Don't get your bike-cycle and life-cycle assessments confused. Life-cycle assessments are the ones you'll need.

Q1 For the example above, suggest four further things (that aren't outlined in the table) that the company should consider when forming a life-cycle assessment for the cars. [4 marks]

Recycling Materials

Recycling's a hot topic. We don't have an infinite amount of materials, e.g. metals, to keep on making things from, so recycling's really important to make sure we don't run out of lots of important raw materials.

Extracting Raw Materials Requires Energy

1) Extracting raw materials can take large amounts of energy, lots of which comes from burning fossil fuels.

2) Fossil fuels are running out so it's important to conserve them. Not only this, but burning them contributes to acid rain and climate change (see pages 146-147).

3) Recycling materials often only uses a small fraction of the energy needed to extract and refine the material from scratch.

4) Energy doesn't come cheap, so recycling saves money too.

5) As there's a finite amount of many raw materials, e.g. metals, on Earth, recycling conserves these resources.

6) Recycling metal cuts down on the amount of rubbish that gets sent to landfill. Landfill takes up space and pollutes the surroundings.

Example: Recycling Aluminium

1) If you didn't recycle aluminium, you'd have to mine more aluminium ore — 4 tonnes for every 1 tonne of aluminium you need. But mining makes a mess of the landscape (and these mines are often in rainforests). The ore then needs to be transported, and the aluminium extracted (which uses loads of electricity). And don't forget the cost of sending your used aluminium to landfill.

2) So it's a complex calculation, but for every 1 kg of aluminium cans you recycle, you save:

- 95% or so of the energy needed to mine and extract 'fresh' aluminium,

- 4 kg of aluminium ore,

- a lot of waste.

In fact, aluminium's about the most cost-effective metal to recycle.

Sometimes Recycling isn't Straightforward

1) Recycling isn't an energy-free process. You need energy to reprocess the materials into new forms.

2) Often, items will need sorting to separate out different materials. Glass, for example, sometimes needs to be sorted into different colours, and different plastics need to be separated too.

Alloys (see page 93) can be difficult to sort for recycling as they're chemical mixtures.

3) Weighing up whether recycling a material is better than just disposing of it and starting from scratch, therefore requires you to compare how much energy is used for both these different processes.

4) Generally, you want to go for the option which has the lowest energy cost, but you also need to think about the consequences of putting materials in landfill, and whether the material you're considering recycling comes from a non-renewable or a renewable source.

5) You can also only recycle materials a finite number of times. Often, the recycled material is a lower quality than the original one, so has to be used differently. For example, paper can only usually be recycled a few times before it becomes useless. Recycled paper is often only used for toilet paper or cardboard, rather than high-quality printing paper.

A policeman failed his maths test — he's a low-grade copper...

Cracking jokes like the ones you find in this book grow on trees you know. So to save trees and reduce the environmental costs of this book, I thought I'd recycle that hilarious pun from page 138. Aren't I good?

Q1 Material X is a metal. To recycle material X you need 110% of the energy used to extract and refine it. Explain why it might still be better to recycle material X than dispose of it in landfill. [2 marks]

Crude Oil

Fossil fuels like coal, oil and gas are called non-renewable fuels as they take so long to make that they're being used up much faster than they're being formed. They're finite resources — one day they'll run out.

Crude Oil is Separated into Different Hydrocarbon Fractions

1) Crude oil is formed from the buried remains of plants and animals — it's a fossil fuel. Over millions of years, with high temperature and pressure, the remains turn to crude oil, which can be drilled up.

2) Crude oil is a mixture of lots of different hydrocarbons. It's mainly made up of fractions with the general formula C_nH_{2n+2}, i.e. alkanes.

3) Crude oil is our main source of hydrocarbons and is used as a raw material (or feedstock) to create lots of petrochemicals, for example, petrol or natural gas.

4) The different compounds in crude oil are separated by fractional distillation. The oil is heated until most of it has turned into gas. The gases enter a fractionating column (and the liquid bit, bitumen, is drained off at the bottom). In the column there's a temperature gradient (i.e. it's hot at the bottom and gets gradually cooler as you go up).

5) The longer hydrocarbons have high boiling points. They turn back into liquids and drain out of the column early on, when they're near the bottom. The shorter hydrocarbons have lower boiling points. They turn to liquid and drain out much later on, near to the top of the column where it's cooler.

6) You end up with the crude oil mixture separated out into different fractions. Each fraction contains a mixture of hydrocarbons, mostly alkanes, with similar boiling points.

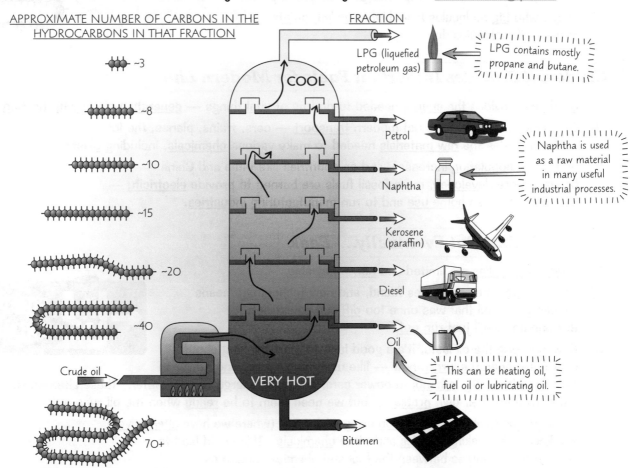

APPROXIMATE NUMBER OF CARBONS IN THE HYDROCARBONS IN THAT FRACTION

FRACTION

~3

~8

~10

~15

~20

~40

Crude oil

70+

COOL

VERY HOT

LPG (liquefied petroleum gas)

LPG contains mostly propane and butane.

Petrol

Naphtha

Naphtha is used as a raw material in many useful industrial processes.

Kerosene (paraffin)

Diesel

Oil

This can be heating oil, fuel oil or lubricating oil.

Bitumen

How much petrol is there in crude oil? Just a fraction...

Crude oil is pretty useful, so it's worth having a good read of this page to make sure you know all about it. You need to know it all for your exams, even the names of all the fractions. Yep, all of them.

Q1 Name the fractions in crude oil, in order of chain length, starting with the shortest, that are produced when crude oil is separated using fractional distillation. [5 marks]

Q2 What are the main components of LPG (liquid petroleum gas)? [1 mark]

Hydrocarbons

Fractional distillation (see last page) relies on the fact the different hydrocarbons have different boiling points. Time to find out why they do, and a bit more about crude oil besides. You lucky thing.

Crude Oil Separates Because of Different Intermolecular Forces

1) There are two important types of bond in crude oil:
   a) The strong covalent bonds between the atoms within each hydrocarbon molecule.
   b) The intermolecular forces of attraction between different hydrocarbon molecules in the mixture.

2) When the crude oil mixture is heated, the molecules are supplied with extra energy.

3) This makes the molecules move about more. Eventually a molecule might have enough energy to overcome the intermolecular forces that keep it with the other molecules. It can now go whizzing off as a gas.

4) The covalent bonds holding each molecule together are much stronger than the intermolecular forces, so they don't break. That's why you don't end up with lots of little molecules.

5) The intermolecular forces of attraction break a lot more easily in small molecules than they do in bigger molecules. That's because they are much stronger between big molecules than they are between small molecules.

6) It makes sense if you think about it — even if a big molecule can overcome the forces attracting it to another molecule at a few points along its length, it's still got lots of other places where the force is still strong enough to hold it in place.

7) That's why big molecules have higher boiling points than small molecules do.

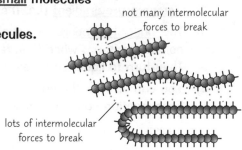

not many intermolecular forces to break

lots of intermolecular forces to break

Crude Oil Provides Important Fuels for Modern Life

1) Crude oil provides the energy needed to do lots of vital things — generating electricity, heating homes...

2) Oil provides the fuel for most modern transport — cars, trains, planes, the lot. It also provides the raw materials needed to make various chemicals, including plastics.

3) As Earth's population increases, and as countries like India and China become more developed, more fossil fuels are burned to provide electricity — both for increased home use and to run manufacturing industries.

But It Will Run Out Eventually... Eeek

1) Crude oil supplies are limited and non-renewable.

2) New reserves are sometimes found, and new technology means we can get to oil that was once too difficult to extract. But one day we'll just run out.

3) However long the oil lasts, it's a good idea to start thinking about alternative energy sources now — like using nuclear or wind power to generate electricity, ethanol to power cars, and solar energy to heat water. These alternatives aren't without their own problems, but we need them to be ready when the oil runs out.

4) Some people think we should stop using oil for fuel (where we have alternatives) and keep it for making plastics and other chemicals. This could lead to conflict for resources between the fuel and chemical industries.

I'd make a joke about oil, but it's too crude for a family product...

Crude oil's dead useful, but burning it isn't without it's problems though. Not only will it run out eventually, but burning crude oil churns loads of CO_2 into the air, which has its own issues (see pages 145-146).

Q1   Two straight-chain alkanes, A and B, have the chemical formulas C_5H_{12} and $C_{50}H_{102}$ respectively.
Explain which alkane, A or B, you would expect to have a higher boiling point.   [2 marks]

Q2   Give three ways in which we use products derived from crude oil.   [3 marks]

Cracking

Crude oil fractions from fractional distillation are split into <u>smaller molecules</u> — this is called <u>cracking</u>.
It's dead important — otherwise we might not have enough fuel for cars and planes and things.

Cracking is Splitting Up Long-Chain Hydrocarbons

1) <u>Cracking</u> turns long alkane molecules into <u>smaller alkane</u> and <u>alkene</u> molecules (which are much more <u>useful</u>).

2) It's a form of <u>thermal decomposition</u>, which is when one substance <u>breaks down</u> into at least two new ones when you <u>heat it</u>. This means breaking <u>strong covalent bonds</u>, so you need <u>lots of heat</u>. A <u>catalyst</u> is often added to speed things up.

3) A lot of the longer molecules produced from <u>fractional distillation</u> are <u>cracked</u> into smaller ones because there's <u>more demand</u> for products like <u>petrol</u> and <u>diesel</u> than for bitumen or lubricating oil.

4) Cracking also produces lots of <u>alkene</u> molecules, which can be used to make <u>polymers</u> (mostly plastics).

Cracking Involves Heat, Moderate Pressures and a Catalyst

1) <u>Vaporised hydrocarbons</u> are passed over <u>powdered catalyst</u> at about <u>400 °C – 700 °C</u> and <u>70 atm</u>.

2) <u>Aluminium oxide</u> is the <u>catalyst</u> used. The <u>long-chain</u> molecules <u>split apart</u> or 'crack' on the <u>surface</u> of the bits of catalyst.

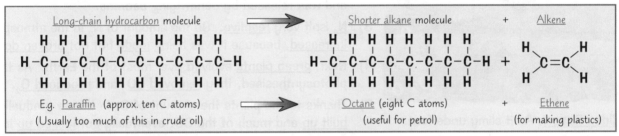

3) You can use the apparatus shown below to crack <u>liquid paraffin</u> in the lab:

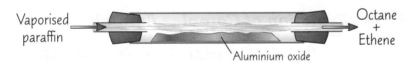

You'll probably get other products too — it all depends on what exactly is in your paraffin.

Cracking Helps Match Supply and Demand

The examiner might give you a <u>table</u> like the one below to show the <u>supply</u> and <u>demand</u> for various fractions obtained from crude oil. You could be asked which fraction is <u>more likely to be cracked</u> to provide us with petrol and diesel (demand for petrol and diesel is greater than the amount in crude oil).

Fraction	Approx % in crude oil	Approx % demand
LPG	2	4
Petrol and Naphtha	16	27
Kerosene	13	8
Diesel	19	23
Oil and Bitumen	50	38

OK, you could use the <u>kerosene fraction</u> to supply the extra <u>petrol</u> and the <u>oil and bitumen fraction</u> to supply the extra <u>diesel</u>.

Or you could crack the <u>oil and bitumen</u> to supply <u>both</u> the extra <u>petrol</u> and the extra <u>diesel</u>. This might be cleverer, as there's a lot more oil/bitumen.

Don't crack up — it's not that bad...

My incredible jokes crack me up all the time. Have you heard the one about the alkane and the chicken?

Q1 What conditions are used to crack hydrocarbons in industry? [2 marks]

Q2 When a molecule of $C_{12}H_{26}$ is cracked under certain conditions, 2 molecules are made.
If one of the product molecules is C_3H_8, what is the other product? [1 mark]

The Atmosphere

Scientists have looked at <u>evidence</u> from rocks, air bubbles in ice and fossils to see how our <u>atmosphere</u> has <u>changed</u> over many, many years. Here's one theory about how our atmosphere might have evolved.

Phase 1 — Volcanoes Gave Out Steam and CO₂

The First Billion Years

<u>Holiday report</u>: Not nice. Take strong walking boots and a coat.

1) The Earth's surface was originally <u>molten</u> for many millions of years. There was almost no atmosphere.

2) Eventually the Earth's surface cooled and a <u>thin crust</u> formed, but <u>volcanoes</u> kept erupting, releasing gases from <u>inside the Earth</u>. This '<u>degassing</u>' released mainly <u>carbon dioxide</u>, but also <u>steam</u>, <u>methane</u> and <u>ammonia</u>.

3) When things eventually settled down, the early atmosphere was <u>mostly CO₂</u> and water vapour (the water vapour later <u>condensed</u> to form the <u>oceans</u>). There was very little oxygen.

Phase 2 — Green Plants Evolved and Produced Oxygen

The Next Two Billion Years

<u>Holiday Report</u>: A bit slimy underfoot. Take wellies and a lot of suncream.

1) A lot of the early CO_2 <u>dissolved</u> into the oceans.

2) <u>Nitrogen gas</u> (N_2) was then put into the atmosphere in two ways — it was formed by ammonia reacting with oxygen, and was released by denitrifying bacteria.

3) N_2 isn't very <u>reactive</u>. So the amount of N_2 in the atmosphere <u>increased</u>, because it was being <u>made</u> but not <u>broken down</u>.

4) Next, <u>green plants</u> evolved over most of the Earth. As they photosynthesised, they <u>removed CO₂</u> and <u>produced O₂</u>.

5) Thanks to the plants the amount of O_2 in the air gradually <u>built up</u> and much of the CO_2 eventually got <u>locked up</u> in <u>fossil fuels</u> and <u>sedimentary rocks</u>.

Phase 3 — Ozone Layer Allows Evolution of Complex Animals

The Last Billion Years or so

OZONE layer, O₃

1) The build-up of <u>oxygen</u> in the atmosphere <u>killed off</u> early organisms that couldn't tolerate it.

2) But it did allow the <u>evolution</u> of more <u>complex</u> organisms that <u>made use</u> of the oxygen.

3) The oxygen also created the <u>ozone layer</u> (O_3), which <u>blocked</u> harmful rays from the Sun and <u>enabled</u> even <u>more complex</u> organisms to evolve.

4) There is virtually <u>no CO₂</u> left now.

<u>Holiday report</u>: A nice place to be. Get there before the crowds ruin it.

Today's Atmosphere is Just Right for Us

The <u>present composition</u> of Earth's atmosphere is: | **78% nitrogen and 21% oxygen**

There are also noble gases (mainly argon) and varying amounts of water vapour. About 0.04% of the atmosphere is carbon dioxide.

I went to a restaurant on the moon — nice view, no atmosphere...

We can breathe easy knowing that our atmosphere has developed into a lovely oxygen rich one. Aaaahh.

Q1　The atmosphere of Earth originally contained little or no nitrogen gas. Explain how and why the proportion of nitrogen gas in the atmosphere increased over time. [3 marks]

The Greenhouse Effect

The greenhouse effect isn't a bumper crop of tomatoes and a prize winning marrow...

Human Activity Affects the Composition of Air

1) The human population is increasing, so there are more people respiring, giving out more carbon dioxide.

2) More people means that more energy is needed for lighting, heating, cooking, transport and so on. People's lifestyles are changing too. More and more countries are becoming industrialised and well-off. This means the average energy demand per person is also increasing (since people have more electrical gadgets, more people have cars or travel on planes, etc.). This increased energy consumption comes mainly from the burning of fossil fuels, which releases more CO_2.

So, as the consumption of fossil fuels increases, as does the concentration of CO_2 in the atmosphere.

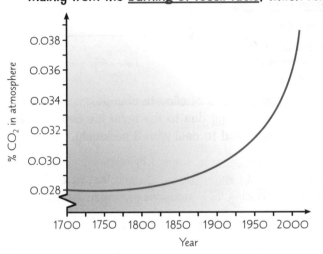

3) More people also means more land is needed to build houses and grow food. This space is often made by chopping down trees — this is called deforestation. But plants are the main things taking carbon dioxide out of the atmosphere (as they photosynthesise) — so fewer plants means less carbon dioxide is taken out of the atmosphere.

4) The graph shows how CO_2 levels in the atmosphere have risen over the last 300 years.

The Greenhouse Effect Helps to Keep the Earth Warm

The greenhouse effect is very important — it's what keeps the Earth warm enough for us to live on.

1) The Sun gives out electromagnetic radiation.

2) Some electromagnetic radiation, at most wavelengths, passes through the atmosphere.

3) The electromagnetic radiation with short wavelengths is absorbed by the Earth — warming our planet.

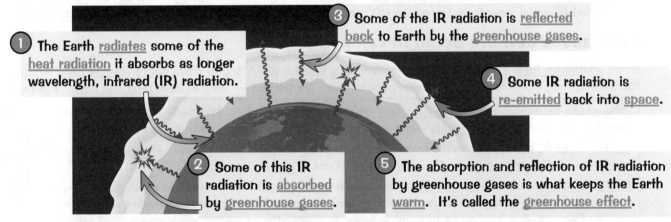

1 The Earth radiates some of the heat radiation it absorbs as longer wavelength, infrared (IR) radiation.

3 Some of the IR radiation is reflected back to Earth by the greenhouse gases.

4 Some IR radiation is re-emitted back into space.

2 Some of this IR radiation is absorbed by greenhouse gases.

5 The absorption and reflection of IR radiation by greenhouse gases is what keeps the Earth warm. It's called the greenhouse effect.

Greenhouse gases are the gases in the atmosphere that can absorb and reflect heat radiation. They're only present in small amounts. Carbon dioxide, water vapour and methane are three greenhouse gases.

4) If the concentration of greenhouse gases in the atmosphere increases, you get an enhanced greenhouse effect. This is where more heat radiation from the earth is absorbed and less is re-emitted back into space. This causes the atmosphere to heat up (see next page).

The White House effect — heated political debates...

Is all this hot air isn't making you a bit hot and bothered? If so, here are some questions to cheer you up.

Q1   Outline how the greenhouse effect works to keep our planet warm.   [3 marks]

Q2   Name three greenhouse gases.   [3 marks]

Topic C6 — Global Challenges

Global Warming

Is it me, or is it getting <u>hot</u> in here...?

Increasing Greenhouse Gases Causes Climate Change

1) You saw on the last page that the level of <u>carbon dioxide</u> in the atmosphere is <u>increasing</u>, but that's not the whole story...

2) The greenhouse gas methane is also causing problems. The concentration of <u>methane</u> has risen lots in recent years. Though it's currently only present in <u>tiny amounts</u> in our atmosphere, the increasing concentration of methane is an issue as it's a super effective <u>greenhouse gas</u>.

3) There's a <u>scientific consensus</u> that extra greenhouse gases from <u>human activity</u> have caused the average <u>temperature</u> of the Earth to <u>increase</u>, due to the enhanced greenhouse effect — see previous page. This effect is known as global warming.

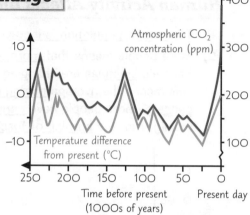

4) Global warming is a type of <u>climate change</u> and causes other types of climate change, e.g. changing rainfall patterns. It could also cause severe <u>flooding</u> due to the polar ice caps melting. It's a BIG problem that could affect the whole world, so we need to deal with it seriously.

Most of the scientific community agree that global warming is <u>anthropogenic</u> (caused by humans). But some scientists believe that the current rises in global temperature are just <u>natural fluctuations</u> and that we don't have <u>enough data</u> to prove that global warming is caused by increasing CO_2 emissions or human activity.

We Can Try To Use Less Fossil Fuels

1) In order to prevent or <u>slow down climate change</u>, we need to <u>cut down</u> on the amount of greenhouse gases we're releasing into the atmosphere.

2) To <u>reduce carbon dioxide emissions</u>, we can try to limit our own use of fossil fuels. This could be doing things on a personal level, like <u>walking</u> or <u>cycling</u> instead of driving or <u>turning your central heating down</u>.

3) On a larger scale, the UK government has formed plans to encourage the public and industry to become more <u>energy efficient</u> and use more renewable energy. The government has also created financial incentives to reduce CO_2 emissions and increased research into new energy sources.

Alternative Fuels are Being Developed

Some <u>alternative fuels</u> have already been, or are being developed. Many of them are <u>renewable</u> fuels so, unlike fossil fuels, they won't run out. However, none of them are perfect — they all have <u>pros and cons</u>. For example:

<u>Ethanol</u> can be produced from <u>plant material</u> so is known as a <u>biofuel</u>. It's made by <u>fermentation</u> of plants and is used to power <u>cars</u> in some places. It's often mixed with petrol to make a better fuel.

<u>PROS:</u> The CO_2 released when it's burnt was taken in by the plant as it grew, so it's 'carbon neutral'. The only other product is <u>water</u>.

<u>CONS:</u> <u>Engines</u> need to be <u>converted</u> before they'll work with ethanol fuels. And ethanol fuel <u>isn't widely available</u>. There are worries that as demand for it increases farmers will switch from growing food crops to growing crops to make ethanol — this will <u>increase food prices</u>.

<u>Biodiesel</u> is another type of <u>biofuel</u>. It can be produced from <u>vegetable oils</u> such as rapeseed oil and soybean oil. Biodiesel can be mixed with ordinary diesel fuel and used to run a <u>diesel engine</u>.

<u>PROS:</u> Biodiesel is '<u>carbon neutral</u>'. <u>Engines don't</u> need to be <u>converted</u>. It produces much <u>less sulfur dioxide</u> and <u>other pollutants</u> than regular diesel or petrol.

<u>CONS:</u> We <u>can't make enough</u> to completely replace diesel. It's <u>expensive</u> to make. It could <u>increase food prices</u> like using more ethanol could (see above).

Another clean, alternative fuel is hydrogen gas. Its only waste product is water, which makes it very clean, but it's expensive and tricky to produce and store.

Give the climate some privacy — it's changing...

It's not all depressing news. There are steps we can take to cut our carbon dioxide emissions, so chin up.

Q1   What is global warming and how is it caused?   [2 marks]

Pollutants

You get loads of nasties like oxides of nitrogen, sulfur dioxide and carbon monoxide when you burn fossil fuels.

Acid Rain is Caused by Sulfur Dioxide and Oxides of Nitrogen

1) When fossil fuels are burned they release mostly CO_2 (a big cause of global warming).

2) But they also release other harmful gases — especially sulfur dioxide and various nitrogen oxides.

3) The sulfur dioxide (SO_2) comes from sulfur impurities in the fossil fuels.

4) The nitrogen oxides are created from a reaction between the nitrogen and oxygen in the air, caused by the heat of the burning. (This can happen in the internal combustion engines of cars.)

5) When these gases mix with clouds they form dilute sulfuric acid and dilute nitric acid.

6) This then falls as acid rain.

7) Power stations and internal combustion engines in cars are the main causes of acid rain.

Acid Rain Kills Fish, Trees and Statues

1) Acid rain causes lakes to become acidic and many plants and animals die as a result.

2) Acid rain kills trees and damages limestone buildings and ruins some stone statues. It also makes metal corrode.

Oxides of Nitrogen Also Cause Photochemical Smog

1) Photochemical smog is a type of air pollution caused by sunlight acting on oxides of nitrogen. These oxides combine with oxygen in the air to produce ozone (O_3).

2) Ozone can cause breathing difficulties, headaches and tiredness. (Don't confuse ground-level ozone with the useful ozone layer high up in the atmosphere.)

Carbon Monoxide is a Poisonous Gas

1) Carbon monoxide (CO) can stop your blood doing its proper job of carrying oxygen around the body.

2) A lack of oxygen in the blood can lead to fainting, a coma or even death.

3) Carbon monoxide is formed when carbon compounds are burnt without enough oxygen — this is incomplete combustion.

4) One way carbon monoxide is produced is by incomplete combustion in petrol or diesel car engines.

Particulate Carbon is Caused by Incomplete Combustion

1) During incomplete combustion, small pieces of solids, called particulates, can be released into the atmosphere. These are mainly pieces of carbon, called particulate carbon.

2) If they escape into the atmosphere, which they often do, they just float around.

3) Eventually they fall back to the ground and deposit themselves as the horrible black dust we call soot.

4) Particulates also reduce air quality and can cause or worsen respiratory problems.

King Nitrogen Oxide had a long, prosperous acid reign...

Acid rain's bad news for sculptors, fish and trees alike. It's bad news for you too, as you need to know it...

Q1   How does acid rain form?   [2 marks]

Q2   Name two pollutants formed by incomplete combustion.   [2 marks]

Water Treatment

Water, water, everywhere... well, there is if you live in a submarine.

There are a Variety of Limited Water Resources in the UK

1) As well as for drinking, we need water for loads of <u>domestic</u> uses (mainly washing things).

2) <u>Industrially</u>, water is important as a <u>cheap raw material</u>, a <u>coolant</u> (especially in power stations) and a <u>solvent</u>. Between half and two thirds of all the fresh water used in the UK goes into industry.

> In the UK, we get our water from:
> 1) <u>SURFACE WATER</u>: <u>lakes</u>, <u>rivers</u> and <u>reservoirs</u>. In much of England and Wales, these sources start to run dry during the summer months.
> 2) <u>GROUNDWATER</u>: <u>aquifers</u> (rocks that trap water underground). In parts of the south-east where surface water is very limited, as much as 70% of the domestic water supply comes from groundwater.

You can also get clean water by treating wastewater (water that's been contaminated by a human process). This is preferable to disposing of the water, which can be polluting. How easy wastewater is to treat depends on the levels of contaminants in it.

All these resources are <u>limited</u>, depending on <u>annual rainfall</u>, and demand for water increases every year. Experts worry that, unless we limit our water use, by 2025 we might not have enough water to supply everybody's needs. So it's important to <u>conserve water</u>.

Water is Purified in Water Treatment Plants

How much purification the water needs depends on the source. <u>Groundwater</u> from aquifers is usually quite pure, but <u>surface water</u> needs a lot of treatment. Before we can use it, most water will be purified using the following processes:

1) <u>Filtration</u> — a wire mesh screens out large twigs etc., and then gravel and sand beds filter out any other solid bits.

2) <u>Sedimentation</u> — iron sulfate or aluminium sulfate is added to the water, which makes fine particles clump together and settle at the bottom.

3) <u>Chlorination</u> — chlorine gas is bubbled through to kill <u>harmful bacteria</u> and other <u>microbes</u>.

mesh
sand/gravel filtration
sedimentation
chlorination

Some soluble impurities that are <u>dissolved</u> in the water are not removed — because they <u>can't</u> be <u>filtered</u> out. These include minerals which cause <u>water hardness</u> and some <u>harmful chemicals</u> (see below).

Tap Water Can Still Contain Impurities

The water that comes out of our taps has to meet <u>strict safety standards</u>, but low levels of pollutants are still found. These pollutants come from various sources:

1) <u>Nitrate residues</u> from excess fertiliser 'run-off' into rivers and lakes. If too many nitrates get into drinking water it can cause serious health problems, especially for young babies. Nitrates prevent the blood from carrying oxygen properly.

Water that is fit to drink can be called potable water.

2) <u>Lead compounds</u> from old lead pipes. Lead is very poisonous, particularly in children.

3) <u>Pesticide residues</u> from spraying pesticides too near to rivers and lakes.

You Can Get Fresh Water by Distilling Sea Water

1) In some very <u>dry</u> countries, e.g. Kuwait, sea water is <u>distilled</u> to produce drinking water.

2) Distillation needs <u>loads of energy</u>, so it's really <u>expensive</u> and not practical for producing large quantities of fresh water.

If water from the ground is groundwater, why isn't rain sky water?

My huge congratulations on finishing this topic. Now for a celebratory biscuit and some questions.

Q1   Outline how surface water is purified in a water treatment plant.   [3 marks]

Q2   How do nitrate residues get into tap water and why are they dangerous?   [2 marks]

Topic C6 — Global Challenges

Revision Questions for Topic C6

Topic C6 is a pretty hefty topic, but it's the last chemistry topic, so that makes it a pretty good topic I think.

- Try these questions and tick off each one when you get it right.
- When you've done all the questions under a heading and are completely happy with it, tick it off.

Extracting Metals (p.137-138) ☑

1) Write a balanced equation to show how copper is extracted from copper oxide using carbon. ☑

2) Using the reactivity series, how can you use it to tell which metals
can be extracted from their ores using reduction with carbon? ☑

3) Name two biological methods that can be used to extract metals from low-grade ores. ☑

4) Give an advantage and a disadvantage of using bioleaching, rather than electrolysis, to extract metals. ☑

Life-Cycle Assessments and Recycling (p.139-140) ☑

5) What is a life-cycle assessment? ☑

6) Name four factors that should be considered when drawing up a life cycle assessment for a product. ☑

7) Give two benefits of recycling. ☑

Crude Oil (p.141-143) ☐

8) What is the purpose of fractional distillation? ☑

9) Name three fractions of crude oil. ☑

10) Do longer or shorter hydrocarbons drain out near the bottom of the fractional distillation column? ☑

11) Why do long hydrocarbons have higher boiling points than short-chain hydrocarbons? ☑

12) What happens to an alkane when it's cracked? ☑

13) What types of molecules are produced by cracking? ☑

The Atmosphere and Air Pollution (p.144) ☑

14) Name the gases given out by volcanoes millions of years ago. ☑

15) How was nitrogen gas originally put into the atmosphere? ☑

16) What change in the early atmosphere allowed the complex organisms to evolve? ☐

The Greenhouse Effect and Climate Change (p.145-146) ☐

17) What causes the enhanced greenhouse effect? ☑

18) Give three ways that we can combat global warming. ☑

Pollutants (p.147) ☑

19) Name a gas that contributes to the production of acid rain. ☑

20) Give three problems associated with acid rain. ☑

21) Why is carbon monoxide bad for human health? ☑

Water Treatment (p.148) ☐

22) Name three different sources of water that can be made potable. ☑

23) Name three processes that are used to make water potable. ☑

24) Name three impurities that could be present in tap water and where they come from. ☑

The History of the Atom and Atomic Structure

Atoms are the tiny particles of matter (stuff that has a mass) which make up everything. We used to think they were solid little spheres (like mini ball-bearings), then some clever clogs did some experiments...

The Theory of Atomic Structure Has Changed Over Time

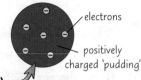
electrons

positively charged 'pudding'

1) In 1897 J J Thomson figured out that atoms weren't solid spheres. His measurements of charge and mass showed that an atom must contain smaller, negatively charged particles — electrons. From his results, he made a model of the atom known as the 'plum pudding model' (or the 'Thomson model') where negative electrons were spread through the positive 'pudding' that made up most of the atom.

2) In 1909 Ernest Rutherford, working with Hans Geiger and Ernest Marsden, conducted the famous gold foil experiment. They fired positively charged alpha particles at an extremely thin sheet of gold.

3) From the plum pudding model, they expected the particles to pass straight through the gold sheet, or only be slightly deflected. But although most of the particles did go straight through the sheet, some were deflected more than they had expected, and a few were deflected back the way they had come — something the plum-pudding model couldn't explain.

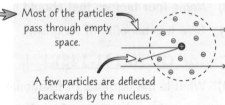
Most of the particles pass through empty space.

A few particles are deflected backwards by the nucleus.

4) Rutherford came up with the theory of the nuclear atom to explain this new evidence. In his model, most of the mass of an atom is concentrated in a tiny, positively charged nucleus at the centre, surrounded by a 'cloud' of negative electrons — most of the atom is empty space.

5) Scientists realised that electrons in a 'cloud' around the nucleus of an atom like this would be attracted to the nucleus, causing the atom to collapse.

6) Niels Bohr got round this a few years later by proposing a new model where the electrons are in shells. He suggested that electrons can only exist in these shells (or fixed orbits), and not anywhere in-between. Each shell has a fixed energy. His theory was pretty close to the model of the atom shown below.

The Atom is Made Up of Protons, Neutrons and Electrons

Protons, neutrons and electrons are all subatomic particles — particles that are smaller than atoms.

The quantities to do with atoms are really tiny, so they're written in standard form:

A is always a number between 1 and 10.

$$A \times 10^n$$

n is the number of places the decimal point would move if you wrote the number out in decimal form. It's negative for numbers less than 1, and positive for numbers greater than 1.

1) The nucleus contains protons (which are positively charged) and neutrons (which are neutral) — which gives it an overall positive charge. The nucleus is tiny — the nuclear radius is about 1×10^{-15} m. Almost the whole mass of the atom (about 1×10^{-23} g, depending on the element) is concentrated in the nucleus.

2) The rest of the atom is mostly empty space. The negative electrons whizz round outside the nucleus really quickly, in electron shells. They give the atom its overall size — the diameter of an atom is around 1×10^{-10} m — so the nuclear radius is around 10 000 times smaller than the atomic radius.

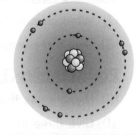

3) Atoms can join together to form molecules — e.g. molecules in oxygen gas are made up of two atoms of oxygen bonded together. Small molecules like this have a typical size of 10^{-10} m — they're roughly the same size as an atom.

Particle	Relative mass	Relative charge
Proton	1	+1
Neutron	1	0
Electron	0.0005	−1

I prefer the chocolate pudding model myself...

Scientists, eh? As soon as they've worked out one theory, they're off to find another. It's almost like they haven't thought about the people who have to revise them at all.

Q1   Describe the Thomson model of the atom.   [1 mark]

Q2   Describe the current model of the structure of an atom.   [3 marks]

Density

Time for some <u>maths</u> I'm afraid. But at least it comes with a fun experiment, so it's not all bad....

Density is Mass per Unit Volume

<u>Density</u> is a measure of the '<u>compactness</u>' (for want of a better word) of a substance. It relates the <u>mass</u> of a substance to how much <u>space</u> it <u>takes up</u>.

$$\text{Density} = \frac{\text{mass}}{\text{volume}}$$

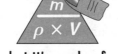

The units of density are g/cm³ or kg/m³.

The symbol for density is a Greek letter rho (ρ) — it looks like a p but it isn't.

1) The density of an object depends on what it's made of. Density <u>doesn't vary</u> with <u>size</u> or <u>shape</u>.

2) The average <u>density</u> of an object determines whether it <u>floats</u> or <u>sinks</u> — a solid object will <u>float</u> on a fluid if it has a <u>lower average density</u> than the fluid.

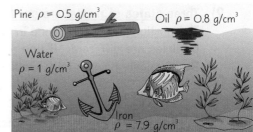

Pine $\rho = 0.5$ g/cm³   Oil $\rho = 0.8$ g/cm³
Water $\rho = 1$ g/cm³
Iron $\rho = 7.9$ g/cm³

You Can Measure the Density of Solids and Liquids

PRACTICAL

1) To <u>measure</u> the density of a substance, measure the <u>mass</u> and <u>volume</u> of a sample of the substance and use the formula above.

2) You can measure the <u>mass</u> of a solid or liquid using a <u>mass balance</u>.

3) To measure the volume of a <u>liquid</u>, you can just pour it into a <u>measuring cylinder</u>.

4) <u>1 ml = 1 cm³</u>. If you need to convert a volume into other units, e.g. m³, remember you need to <u>cube the scaling factor</u> for converting <u>distance units</u> to get the scaling factor for converting <u>volume units</u>. For example, to convert 50 cm³ into m³, you need to divide by $100^3 = 1\,000\,000$ (as there are 100 cm in 1 m). So <u>50 cm³</u> = 50 ÷ 1 000 000 = $\underline{5 \times 10^{-5}}$ m³.

The volume of any prism is the area of its base multiplied by its height.

5) If you want to measure the volume of a <u>solid cuboid</u>, measure its <u>length</u>, <u>width</u>, and <u>height</u>, then <u>multiply</u> them together. To find the volume of a <u>solid cylinder</u>, measure the diameter of one of the circles at the base, then <u>halve</u> this to give a radius. Then measure the cylinder's height, and use the formula <u>volume = $\pi \times$ radius² × height</u>.

6) An object <u>submerged</u> in water will displace a volume of water <u>equal</u> to its <u>own volume</u>. You can use this to find the volume of <u>any object</u>, for example using a <u>eureka</u> (Archimedes) <u>can</u>:

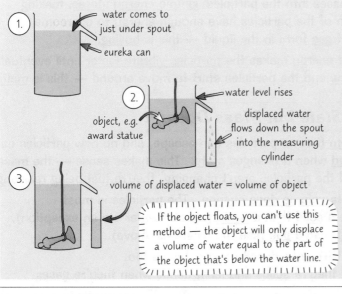

1. water comes to just under spout — eureka can

2. water level rises — object, e.g. award statue — displaced water flows down the spout into the measuring cylinder

3. volume of displaced water = volume of object

If the object floats, you can't use this method — the object will only displace a volume of water equal to the part of the object that's below the water line.

1) You need the eureka can to be filled so that the water level is <u>just under</u> the spout. The best way to do this is to <u>slightly over-fill</u> the can then let the extra water <u>drain away</u>.

2) Place a measuring cylinder under the spout, then <u>gently lower</u> your object in the can, e.g. using a <u>thin</u>, <u>strong thread</u>. The displaced water will start to <u>come out</u> of the spout.

3) Wait for the spout to <u>stop dripping</u>, then measure the <u>volume</u> of water collected in the <u>cylinder</u>. This is the volume of water displaced by the object, which is equal to the <u>volume of the object</u>.

4) Repeat three times and calculate a <u>mean</u>.

I'm feeling a bit dense after that lot...

Converting between units with volumes catches people out all the time, so be careful.

Q1   Describe an experiment to calculate the density of an irregular solid object.   [4 marks]

Q2   An object has a mass of 4.5×10^{-2} kg and a volume of 75 cm³. Calculate its density in kg/m³.   [3 marks]

Particle Theory and States of Matter

According to particle theory, everything's made of tiny little balls. The table, this book, your Gran...

Particle Theory is a Way of Explaining Matter

1) In particle theory, you can think of the particles that make up matter as tiny balls. You can explain the ways that matter behaves in terms of how these tiny balls move, and the forces between them.

2) Three states of matter are solid (e.g. ice), liquid (e.g. water) and gas (e.g. water vapour). The particles of a substance in each state are the same — only the arrangement and energy of the particles are different. If you reverse a change of state, the particles go back to how they were before. So physical changes (e.g. melting or boiling) are different from chemical reactions.

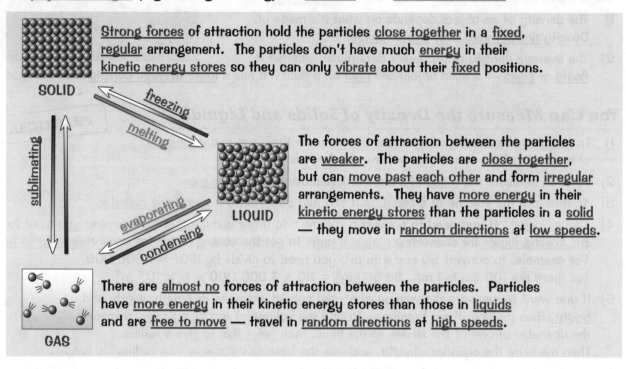

SOLID — Strong forces of attraction hold the particles close together in a fixed, regular arrangement. The particles don't have much energy in their kinetic energy stores so they can only vibrate about their fixed positions.

LIQUID — The forces of attraction between the particles are weaker. The particles are close together, but can move past each other and form irregular arrangements. They have more energy in their kinetic energy stores than the particles in a solid — they move in random directions at low speeds.

GAS — There are almost no forces of attraction between the particles. Particles have more energy in their kinetic energy stores than those in liquids and are free to move — travel in random directions at high speeds.

3) The energy in a substance's thermal energy store is held by its particles in their kinetic energy stores — this is what the thermal energy store actually is.

4) When you heat a liquid, the extra energy passes into the particles' kinetic energy stores, making them move faster. Eventually, when enough of the particles have enough energy to overcome their attraction to each other, big bubbles of gas form in the liquid — this is boiling.

5) It's similar when you heat a solid. The extra energy makes the particles vibrate faster until eventually the forces between them are partly overcome and the particles start to move around — this is melting.

Density of a Substance Varies with State but Mass Doesn't

1) Provided you're working with a closed system (i.e. no particles can escape, and no new particles can get in) the mass of a substance isn't affected when it changes state. This makes sense — the mass of a substance is the mass of its particles, and the particles aren't changing, they're just being rearranged.

2) However, when a substance changes state its volume does change. The particles in most substances are closer together when they're a solid than a liquid (ice and water are an exception), and are closer together when they're a liquid than a gas (see the diagrams above).

3) Since density = mass ÷ volume (see page 151), then density must change too. Generally, substances are most dense when they're solids and least dense when they're gases.

Physics — it's really about state of mind...

Remember, the mass of a substance just comes from the particles, not the spaces between them. So as something expands or contracts, its volume changes but its mass stays the same.

Q1 Explain how the density of a typical substance changes as it changes from solid, to liquid to gas. [4 marks]

Specific Heat Capacity

The <u>temperature</u> of something <u>isn't quite the same</u> thing as the <u>energy</u> stored in the substance's thermal energy store. That's where <u>specific heat capacity</u> comes in...

Specific Heat Capacity Relates Temperature and Energy

1) <u>Heating</u> a substance <u>increases</u> the <u>energy</u> in its <u>thermal energy store</u> (or the kinetic energy stores of its particles, see page 152). You may sometimes see this referred to as the <u>internal energy</u> of a substance.

2) In kinetic theory, <u>temperature</u> is a way of measuring the <u>average internal energy</u> of a substance.

3) However, it takes <u>more energy</u> to <u>increase the temperature</u> of some materials than others. E.g. you need <u>4200 J</u> to warm 1 kg of <u>water</u> by 1 °C, but only <u>139 J</u> to warm 1 kg of <u>mercury</u> by 1 °C. Materials which need to <u>gain</u> lots of energy to <u>warm up</u> also <u>release</u> loads of energy when they <u>cool down</u> again. They <u>store</u> a lot of energy for a given change in temperature.

4) The <u>change in the energy</u> stored in a substance when you heat it is related to the change in its <u>temperature</u> by its <u>specific heat capacity</u>. The <u>specific heat capacity</u> of a substance is the <u>change in energy</u> in the substance's thermal store needed to raise the temperature of <u>1 kg</u> of that substance by <u>1 °C</u>. E.g. water has a specific heat capacity of <u>4200 J/kg°C</u> (that's pretty high).

5) You need to know how to use the <u>equation</u> relating temperature, energy, mass and specific heat capacity:

$$\text{Change in Thermal Energy (J)} = \text{Mass (kg)} \times \text{Specific Heat Capacity (J/kg°C)} \times \text{Change in Temperature (°C)}$$

You can Find the Specific Heat Capacity of a Substance

PRACTICAL

You can use this experiment to find the specific heat capacity of a <u>liquid</u>, e.g. water, or a <u>solid</u>, e.g. a metal cylinder.

1) Use a <u>mass balance</u> to measure the <u>mass</u> of your substance.

2) Set up the experiment shown below. Make sure the <u>joulemeter</u> reads <u>zero</u>.

Add a conducting gel between the heater and the metal cylinder to improve conduction and make your results more accurate.

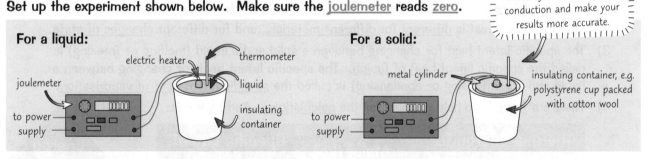

For a liquid: joulemeter, to power supply, electric heater, thermometer, liquid, insulating container

For a solid: to power supply, metal cylinder, insulating container, e.g. polystyrene cup packed with cotton wool

3) Measure the <u>temperature</u> of the substance you're investigating, then turn on the power.

4) Keep an eye on the <u>thermometer</u>. When the temperature has increased by e.g. <u>ten degrees</u>, stop the experiment and record the <u>energy</u> on the joulemeter, and the <u>increase in temperature</u>.

5) You can then calculate the specific heat capacity of your substance by <u>rearranging</u> the equation above and plugging in your measurements.

6) <u>Repeat</u> the whole experiment at least three times, then calculate the <u>mean</u> (see page 6) specific heat capacity of your substance.

You could also use a voltmeter and ammeter instead of a joulemeter, time how long the heater was on for, then calculate the energy supplied (see p.176).

7) You need to watch out for <u>systematic errors</u> due to <u>energy escaping</u> from your experiment. The <u>insulating container</u> helps by reducing the amount of energy that escapes from the <u>sides</u> and the <u>bottom</u> of the substance you're investigating. You could reduce these energy losses further by adding a <u>lid</u> to the container.

I wish I had a high specific fact capacity...

Make sure you learn that equation — it's a bit of a tricky one.

Q1   If a metal has a specific heat capacity of 420 J/kg°C, calculate how much the temperature of a 0.20 kg block of the metal will increase by if 1680 J of energy are supplied to it.   [3 marks]

Specific Latent Heat

If you heat up a pan of water on the stove, the water never gets any hotter than 100 °C. You can <u>carry on heating it up</u>, but the <u>temperature won't rise</u>. How come, you say? It's all to do with <u>latent heat</u>...

You Need to Put In Energy to Break Intermolecular Bonds

1) Remember, when you <u>heat</u> a solid or liquid, you're transferring <u>energy</u> to the kinetic energy stores of the particles in the substance, making the particles <u>vibrate</u> or <u>move faster</u>.

2) When a substance is <u>melting</u> or <u>boiling</u>, you're still putting in <u>energy</u>, but the energy's used for <u>breaking intermolecular bonds</u> rather than raising the temperature — there are <u>flat spots</u> on the heating graph.

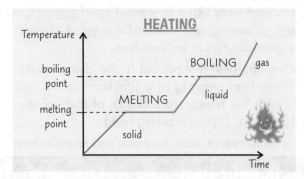
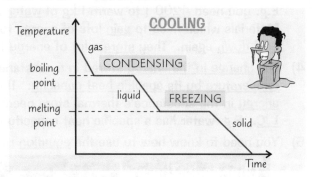

3) When a substance is <u>condensing</u> or <u>freezing</u>, bonds are <u>forming</u> between particles, which <u>releases</u> energy. This means the <u>temperature doesn't go down</u> until all the substance has turned into a liquid (condensing) or a solid (freezing).

Specific Latent Heat is the Energy Needed to Change State

1) The <u>specific latent heat</u> of a <u>change of state</u> for a substance is the <u>change of energy</u> in its <u>thermal energy store</u> when <u>1 kg</u> of the substance <u>changes state without changing its temperature</u> (i.e. the substance has got to be at the right temperature already).

2) Specific latent heat is <u>different</u> for <u>different materials</u>, and for different <u>changes of state</u>.

3) The specific latent heat for changing between a solid and a liquid (melting or freezing) is called the <u>specific latent heat of fusion</u>. The specific latent heat for changing between a liquid and a gas (boiling or condensing) is called the <u>specific latent heat of vaporisation</u>.

4) There's a <u>formula</u> to help you with all the <u>calculations</u>. And here it is:

> **Thermal Energy for a Change in State (J)** = Mass (kg) × **Specific Latent Heat (J/kg)**

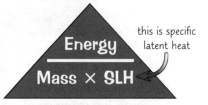

this is specific latent heat

EXAMPLE:

The specific latent heat of vaporisation for water is 2.26×10^6 J/kg. 2.825×10^6 J of energy is used to boil dry a pan of water at 100 °C. What was the mass of water in the pan?

Thermal energy of change of state = mass × specific latent heat,
so mass = thermal energy of change of state ÷ specific latent heat
= $2.825 \times 10^6 ÷ 2.26 \times 10^6$ = **1.25 kg**

> You came across standard form on page 150,
> e.g. $2.26 \times 10^6 = 2\,260\,000$.

Breaking Bonds — Blofeld never quite manages it...

Fun fact: this stuff explains how sweating cools you down — the energy that builds up in your body when you exercise is used to change liquid sweat into gas, rather than increasing your temperature. Nice...

Q1 Sketch a graph showing how the temperature of a sample of water will change over time as it's constantly heated from –5 °C to 105 °C.

[3 marks]

Pressure of Gases

Gas particles fly around, bump into things and exert forces on them. This is happening to you right now — the air around you is exerting pressure on you (unless you're somehow reading this in space).

Colliding Gas Particles Create Pressure

1) According to particle theory, matter is made up of very small, constantly moving particles. The warmer something is, the more these particles are moving.

2) In a gas, these particles are free to move around in completely random directions.

3) As gas particles move about, they randomly bang into each other and whatever else gets in the way, like the walls of their container.

4) Gas particles are very small, but they still have a mass. When they collide with something, they exert a force on it.

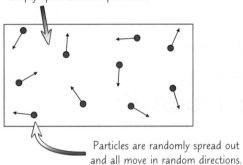

Empty space between particles.

Particles are randomly spread out and all move in random directions.

5) All these collisions cause a net force on the inside surface of the container. The force acting per unit area is the pressure.

6) The more particles there are in a given volume, the more often they'll collide with the walls of the container, and with each other, so the higher the pressure will be.

Since the particles themselves hardly take up any space, most of the gas is empty space.

Changing the Temperature Changes the Pressure

1) The pressure a gas exerts on its container also depends on how fast the particles are going and how often they hit the walls.

2) If you hold a gas in a sealed container with a fixed volume and heat it, energy is transferred to the kinetic energy stores of the gas particles and they move faster. This means the particles hit the container walls harder and more often, creating more pressure.

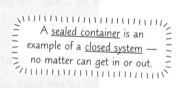

A sealed container is an example of a closed system — no matter can get in or out.

3) If the gas is cooled, the particles have less energy and move less quickly. The particles hit the walls with less force and less often, so the pressure is reduced.

EXAMPLE:

A sealed box contains argon gas at atmospheric pressure. The box is then heated. Explain what will happen to the pressure of the argon gas.

As the temperature of the gas increases, energy is transferred to the kinetic energy stores of the argon gas particles.

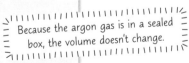

Because the argon gas is in a sealed box, the volume doesn't change.

The particles therefore hit the walls with more force and more often.

As pressure is defined as the force per unit area, the pressure of the gas will **increase**.

Gas particles need to watch where they're going...

Remember, the more gas particles there are, and the faster they travel, the higher the pressure. Simple...

Q1 Explain how a gas exerts pressure on its container. [2 marks]

Q2 Explain what happens to the pressure of a gas in a sealed container when its temperature decreases. [4 marks]

Revision Questions for Topic P1

Well, that wraps up <u>P1</u> — time to put yourself to the test and find out <u>how much you really know</u>.

- Try these questions and <u>tick off each one</u> when you <u>get it right</u>.
- When you've done <u>all the questions</u> under a heading and are <u>completely happy</u> with it, tick it off.

The Structure of the Atom (p.150) ☐

1) a) Describe Rutherford's gold foil experiment.

   b) How did the results of this experiment disagree with the Thomson model of the atom? ☑

2) How did Bohr's model of the atom differ from Rutherford's? ☑

3) Roughly how big is an atom? ☑

Density and States of Matter (p.151-152) ☐

4) What is density? ☑

5) How is density calculated? ☑

6) Describe solids, liquids, and gases in terms of the movements of their particles. ☑

7) Explain what happens to the mass of a substance when it changes state. ☑

Specific Heat Capacity and Specific Latent Heat (p.153-154) ☐

8) What is the relationship between temperature and the energy
   in the kinetic store of the particles in a substance? ☑

9) What is the specific heat capacity of a substance? ☑

10) Describe an experiment to find the specific heat capacity of water. ☑

11) A gas is cooled, until it becomes a liquid and eventually turns into a solid.
    Sketch a graph showing how the temperature of the substance changes over time.
    Include labels to show the boiling point and the melting point.
    Label the changes of state. ☑

12) What is meant by:
    a) the specific latent heat of fusion?
    b) the specific latent heat of vaporisation? ☑

Pressure of Gases (p.155) ☐

13) What happens to the pressure of a gas in a sealed container of fixed volume when it is heated? ☑

Speed and Velocity

This page will set you up for the rest of the topic. <u>Learn it</u>, don't forget it, and <u>do the questions</u> at the end.

Scalars are Just Numbers, but Vectors Have Direction Too

1) <u>Distance</u> and <u>displacement</u> are different things. They both measure how <u>far</u> something has travelled, but <u>displacement</u> also says which <u>direction</u> something has travelled in. For example, you could say a car has travelled a <u>distance</u> of <u>10 m</u>, but it has a <u>displacement</u> of <u>10 m north</u>.

2) To measure the <u>speed</u> of an object, you only need to measure <u>how fast</u> it's going — the <u>direction</u> is <u>not important</u>. E.g. <u>speed = 30 mph</u>.

3) <u>Velocity</u> is a <u>more useful</u> measure of <u>motion</u>, because it describes both the <u>speed and direction</u>. E.g. <u>velocity = 30 mph due north</u>.

4) Quantities like <u>speed</u> and <u>distance</u>, that are only <u>numbers</u>, are called <u>scalar</u> quantities.

<u>Scalar quantities</u>: speed, distance, mass, time, etc.

5) Quantities like <u>velocity</u> and <u>displacement</u>, that have a <u>direction as well</u>, are <u>vector</u> quantities.

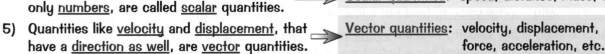

<u>Vector quantities</u>: velocity, displacement, force, acceleration, etc.

> When we use <u>vectors</u>, we often talk about there being a <u>positive</u> and a <u>negative direction</u>. E.g. a <u>car</u> moving in one direction could have a <u>velocity</u> of <u>3 m/s</u>, but moving in the <u>opposite direction</u> it will have a velocity of <u>–3 m/s</u>. In this example, the car has a <u>speed</u> of <u>3 m/s</u> in <u>both directions</u>. You can often <u>pick</u> a positive direction that makes the <u>calculations easier</u>.

Speed, Distance and Time — the Formula

You really ought to get <u>pretty slick</u> with this <u>equation</u>, it pops up a lot...

distance travelled (m) = speed (m/s) × time (s)

The equation for calculating displacement is: displacement (m) = velocity (m/s) × time (s).

EXAMPLE: A cat skulks 20 m in 50 s. Find: a) its speed, b) how long it takes to skulk 32 m.

1) <u>Rearrange</u> the equation above for speed, s.

2) Now that the speed has been calculated, you can find the time, t, taken to travel a different distance at the <u>same speed</u>.

$s = \dfrac{d}{t} = 20 \div 50 = 0.4 \text{ m/s}$

$t = \dfrac{d}{s} = 32 \div 0.4 = 80 \text{ s}$

You Need to be Able to Convert Between Units

When using any <u>equation</u>, it's important to have your quantities in the <u>right units</u>. E.g. in the speed equation above, the <u>speed</u> must be in <u>m/s</u> (metres per second), the <u>distance</u> must be in <u>m</u> (metres) and the <u>time</u> must be in <u>s</u> (seconds). You may need to convert e.g. between <u>ms</u> (milliseconds) and <u>s</u>, between <u>km</u> (kilometres) and <u>m</u> (metres).

To convert from miles to km, you multiply by 1.6.

> To convert <u>16 km</u> into <u>m</u>: <u>multiply</u> by <u>1000</u> — 16 × 1000 = 16 000 m
> To convert <u>22 ms</u> into <u>s</u>: <u>divide</u> by <u>1000</u> — 22 ÷ 1000 = 0.022 s

You can convert e.g. kilowatts to watts or milliamps to amps in the same way.

Getting <u>hours</u> and <u>minutes</u> into <u>seconds</u> is a little trickier:

> To convert <u>8 hr</u> (hours) into <u>s</u>:
> <u>Multiply</u> 8 by <u>60</u> to find the number of <u>minutes</u> — 8 × 60 = 480 minutes
> Then <u>multiply</u> 480 minutes by <u>60</u> to find the number of <u>seconds</u> — 480 × 60 = 28 800 s

A fairly easy way to start the section... — wait, whose cat is this?

Know the difference between vectors and scalars — scalars have a size, vectors have a size AND a direction.

Q1 A cyclist has a constant speed. Calculate their speed if they cycle 660 m in 2.0 minutes. [2 marks]

Q2 Find the distance travelled in 24 s by a car with a constant speed of 54 km/hr. [2 marks]

Acceleration

If an object is accelerating, its velocity is changing.

Acceleration is the Rate of Change of Velocity

1) Acceleration is how quickly the velocity is changing.

2) This change in velocity can be a CHANGE IN SPEED or a CHANGE IN DIRECTION or both.

3) You need to learn this equation for calculating acceleration:

$$\text{acceleration (m/s}^2) = \frac{\text{change in velocity (m/s)}}{\text{time (s)}}$$

4) To calculate the change in velocity, you must always do final velocity – initial velocity (and not initial velocity – final velocity).

5) Acceleration is like velocity — it's a vector and so can have a positive or negative value. If an object has a negative acceleration, it is either slowing down (decelerating), or speeding up in the negative direction.

An object travelling in a circle at a constant speed has a changing velocity (because it's always changing direction), so it's always accelerating.

EXAMPLE: A cyclist is in a race. As she approaches the finish line, she increases her speed from 11 m/s to 15 m/s in 25 s. Calculate her acceleration.

1) First find the change in velocity. change in velocity = final velocity – initial velocity = 15 – 11 = 4 m/s

2) Then substitute this into the acceleration equation. acceleration = change in velocity ÷ time
= 4 ÷ 25 = 0.16 m/s²

When the cyclist crosses the finish line, she immediately applies her brakes, and comes to a stop after 3 s. Calculate her acceleration after she crosses the finish line.

1) First find the change in velocity. change in velocity = final velocity – initial velocity = 0 – 15 = -15 m/s

2) Then substitute this into the acceleration equation. acceleration = change in velocity ÷ time
= -15 ÷ 3 = -5 m/s²

Calculating Distance or Velocity for Uniform Acceleration

For any object that is travelling with uniform acceleration (that's just a fancy way of saying its acceleration is constant), you can use the following equation:

This equation is really handy, so make sure you're comfortable with rearranging it and using it.

$$\text{(final velocity)}^2 - \text{(initial velocity)}^2 = 2 \times \text{acceleration} \times \text{distance}$$
$$\text{(m/s)}^2 \qquad \text{(m/s)}^2 \qquad \text{(m/s}^2) \qquad \text{(m)}$$

It might help you to remember the equation as $v^2 - u^2 = 2 \times a \times d$ (which is a bit shorter).

EXAMPLE: A horse is running with a constant acceleration of 0.45 m/s². It has an initial velocity of 8.0 m/s and runs a distance of 180 m. What is the horse's final velocity? Give your answer to 2 s.f.

1) Rearrange the equation for (final velocity)². (final velocity)² – (initial velocity)² = 2 × acceleration × distance
(final velocity)² = (2 × acceleration × distance) + (initial velocity)²
= (2 × 0.45 × 180) + 8.0² = 226

2) Take the square root of the answer. final velocity = √226 = 15.03... = 15 m/s (to 2 s.f.)

My dog's acceleration is negative when she gets closer to a bath...

Acceleration is odd — remember it's a measure of how fast an object's velocity is changing, and you'll be fine.

Q1 A cheetah with an acceleration of 8.25 m/s² takes 4.0 seconds to reach its maximum speed from rest. Calculate its maximum speed and the distance covered in this time. [4 marks]

Investigating Motion

Here's a simple <u>experiment</u> you can try out to investigate the relation between <u>distance</u>, <u>speed</u> and <u>acceleration</u>.

You can Investigate the Motion of a Trolley on a Ramp

1) Set up your <u>apparatus</u> as shown in the diagram below, and mark a <u>line</u> on the ramp just before the first <u>light gate</u> (see page 224) — this is to make sure the trolley starts from the <u>same point</u> each time.

2) Measure the <u>distances</u> between light gates 1 and 2, and 2 and 3.

3) Hold the trolley <u>still</u> at the start line, and then <u>let go</u> of it so that it starts to roll down the slope.

4) As it rolls down the <u>ramp</u> it will <u>accelerate</u>. When it reaches the <u>runway</u>, it will travel at a <u>constant speed</u> (ignoring any friction).

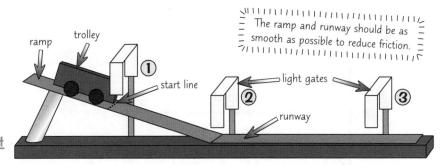

The ramp and runway should be as smooth as possible to reduce friction.

5) Each <u>light gate</u> will record the <u>time</u> when the trolley passes through it.

6) The time it takes to travel between <u>gates 1 and 2</u> can be used to find the <u>average speed</u> on the ramp, and between <u>gates 2 and 3</u> gives the <u>speed</u> on the <u>runway</u> (using <u>speed = distance ÷ time</u>).

7) The <u>acceleration</u> of the trolley on the ramp can be found using <u>acceleration = change in speed ÷ time</u>, with the following values:

You can also measure speed at a point using one light gate.

- the <u>initial speed</u> of the trolley (= 0 m/s),
- the <u>final speed</u> of the trolley, which equals the speed of the trolley on the <u>runway</u> (ignoring <u>friction</u>),
- the <u>time</u> it takes the trolley to travel between light gates 1 and 2.

The trolley's <u>acceleration</u> on the ramp and its final <u>speed</u> on the runway will <u>increase</u> when the <u>angle</u> of the ramp increases, or the amount of <u>friction</u> between the ramp and the trolley <u>decreases</u>. Increasing the <u>distance</u> between the <u>bottom</u> of the ramp and where the <u>trolley</u> is <u>released</u> will also increase the final speed of the trolley.

Try varying these things in your experiment to see the results for yourself.

You can use Different Equipment to Measure Distance and Time

Generally, you measure <u>speed</u> by <u>measuring distance</u> and <u>time</u>, and then <u>calculating</u> speed. You might need to use <u>different methods</u> for measuring distance and time depending on what you're investigating.

1) If possible, your <u>measuring instrument</u> should always be <u>longer</u> than the <u>distance</u> you're measuring with it — e.g. you shouldn't use a 30 cm ruler to measure something that's 45 cm long.

2) For experiments in the lab like the one above, the distances involved will generally be <u>less than a metre</u>, so you'll be able to measure them with a <u>ruler</u> or a <u>metre stick</u>.

3) If you're investigating e.g. how fast someone <u>walks</u>, you'll want to measure their speed over <u>many metres</u>, so you'll need a <u>long tape measure</u>, or a <u>rolling tape measure</u> (one of those clicky wheel things).

4) To measure time intervals longer than about e.g. <u>5 seconds</u>, you can use a <u>stopwatch</u>.

5) To measure <u>short intervals</u>, like in the experiment above it's best to use e.g. <u>light gates</u> connected to a <u>computer</u>. Using a stopwatch involves <u>human error</u>, due to, for example, <u>reaction times</u>. This is more of a problem the shorter the interval you're timing, as the reaction time makes up a <u>larger proportion</u> of the interval.

If you want to investigate motion you'll need to invest in gates...

Think about it this way — say you were measuring the height of an elephant, you wouldn't use a 30 cm ruler, that would be daft. You'd be there forever. What experiment are you doing with an elephant anyway?

Q1 Explain how the speed of an object can be found using two light gates. [3 marks]

Q2 Explain why using light gates to measure short time intervals is more accurate than a stopwatch. [2 marks]

Distance-Time Graphs

A graph speaks a thousand words, so drawing one can be better than writing 'An object starts at rest, then moves at a steady speed of 10 m/s for 2 s until it reaches a distance of 20 m, then remains stationary for 5 s before increasing its velocity with a constant acceleration for 2.5 s.'

Distance-Time (d-t) Graphs Tell You How Far Something has Travelled

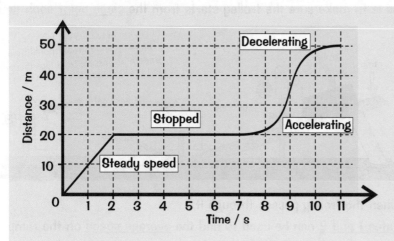

The different parts of a *d-t* graph describe the motion of an object:

- The gradient (slope) at any point gives the speed of the object.
- Flat sections are where it's stopped.
- A steeper graph means it's going faster.
- Curves represent acceleration.
- A steepening curve means it's speeding up (increasing gradient).
- A levelling off curve means it's slowing down (decreasing gradient).

The Speed of an Object can be Found From a Distance-Time Graph

1) The gradient of a distance-time graph at any point is equal to the speed of the object at that time.

2) If the graph is a straight line, the gradient at any point along the line is equal to $\dfrac{\text{change in the vertical}}{\text{change in the horizontal}}$.

> **Example:** In the graph above, the speed at any time between 0 s and 2 s is:
>
> $$\text{Speed} = \text{gradient} = \frac{\text{change in the vertical}}{\text{change in the horizontal}} = \frac{20}{2} = \underline{10 \text{ m/s}}$$

3) If the graph is curved, to find the speed at a certain time you need to draw a tangent to the curve at that point, and then find the gradient of the tangent.

A tangent is a line that is parallel to the curve at that point.

4) You can also calculate the average speed of an object when it has non-uniform motion (i.e. it's accelerating) by dividing the total distance travelled by the time it takes to travel that distance.

> **Example:** The graph shows the distance-time graph for a bike accelerating for 30 seconds and then travelling at a steady speed for 5 s. The speed of the bike at 25 s can be found by drawing a tangent to the curve (red line) at 25 s and then finding the gradient of the tangent:
>
> $$\text{gradient} = \frac{\text{change in the vertical}}{\text{change in the horizontal}} = \frac{170}{20} = \underline{8.5 \text{ m/s}}$$
>
> The average speed of the bike between 0 s and 30 s can also be calculated as:
>
> $$\text{average speed} = \frac{\text{total distance travelled}}{\text{time taken to travel}} = \frac{150}{30} = \underline{5 \text{ m/s}}$$

Tangent — a man who's just come back from holiday...

For practice, try sketching *d-t* graphs for different scenarios. Like cycling up a hill or running from a bear.

Q1   Sketch a distance-time graph for an object that initially accelerates, then travels at a constant speed, then decelerates to a stop.

[2 marks]

Velocity-Time Graphs

Huzzah, more graphs. And they're <u>velocity-time graphs</u> too, you lucky thing. Keep an eye out for those <u>negative gradients</u> — they're not too tricky really, it just means the object has a <u>negative acceleration</u>.

Velocity-Time (v-t) Graphs can Be Used to Find Acceleration

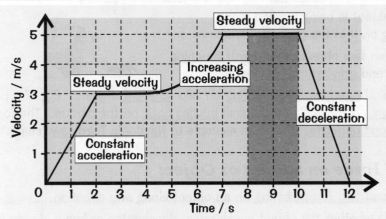

- <u>Gradient = acceleration</u>.
- <u>Flat</u> sections represent <u>steady</u> velocity.
- The <u>steeper</u> the graph, the <u>greater</u> the <u>acceleration</u> or deceleration.
- <u>Uphill</u> sections (/) are <u>acceleration</u>.
- <u>Downhill</u> sections (\) are <u>deceleration</u>.
- A <u>curve</u> means <u>changing acceleration</u>.
- The <u>area</u> under any section of the graph (or all of it) is equal to the <u>distance</u> travelled in that <u>time</u> interval.

You can find the <u>acceleration</u>, <u>velocity</u> and <u>distance</u> travelled from a velocity-time graph:

> To find the acceleration at any point on a curved velocity-time graph, you draw a tangent to the curve and then find the gradient of the tangent (see page 160).

1) The <u>acceleration</u> represented between 0 s and 2 s on the graph is:

$$\text{Acceleration} = \text{gradient} = \frac{\text{change in the vertical}}{\text{change in the horizontal}} = \frac{3}{2} = 1.5 \text{ m/s}^2$$

2) The <u>velocity</u> at any time is simply found by <u>reading the value</u> off the <u>velocity axis</u>.

3) The <u>distance travelled</u> in any time interval is equal to the <u>area</u> under the graph. For example, the distance travelled between $t = 8$ s and $t = 10$ s is equal to the <u>shaded area</u>, which is <u>10 m</u> (5 m/s × 2 s).

You can Use the Counting Squares Method To Find the Area Under the Graph

1) If an object has an <u>increasing</u> or <u>decreasing acceleration</u> (or deceleration), the graph is <u>curved</u>. You can estimate the <u>distance travelled</u> from the <u>area under the graph</u> by <u>counting squares</u>.

2) First you need to find out how much distance <u>one square</u> of the graph paper <u>represents</u>. To do this, multiply the <u>width</u> of square (in <u>seconds</u>) by the <u>height</u> of one square (in <u>metres per second</u>).

3) Then you just <u>multiply</u> this by the <u>number of squares</u> under the graph. If there are squares that are <u>partly</u> under the graph, you can <u>add them together</u> to make <u>whole squares</u> (see below).

The graph below is a <u>velocity-time graph</u>. You can estimate the <u>distance travelled</u> in the <u>first 10 s</u> by <u>counting</u> the number of squares <u>under</u> the graph (shown by the shaded area).

Total number of shaded squares = <u>32</u>

Distance represented by one square
= width of square × height of square
= 1 s × 0.2 m/s = <u>0.2 m</u>

So total distance travelled in 10 s
= 32 × 0.2 = <u>6.4 m</u>

> As you go through and count the squares, it helps to put a dot in the square once it's been counted. That way you don't lose track of what's been counted and what hasn't.

These two partially shaded squares add up to make one square.

Anyone up for a game of squares?

Remember — the acceleration of an object on a velocity-time graph is the gradient of the curve at that time. And the total distance travelled within a time interval is the area under the graph for that time interval.

Q1 Sketch a velocity-time graph for a car that initially travels at a steady speed and then decelerates constantly to a stop. It is then stationary for a short time before accelerating with increasing acceleration. [3 marks]

Forces and Free Body Force Diagrams

Forces are everywhere, so it only makes sense that you should learn about them. Read on...

Forces can be Contact or Non-Contact

1) To exert a contact force, two objects must be touching, for example pushing or pulling an object.

2) Friction is a contact force — as an object is being pushed along a surface, there will be friction acting on it in the opposite direction.

3) Non-contact forces are forces between two objects that aren't touching. For example, electrostatic, magnetic and gravitational forces.

4) An interaction pair is a pair of equal and opposite forces acting on two different objects. E.g. if a person leans against a wall, the person pushes on the wall and the wall pushes back on the person. The forces on the person and the wall are equal and opposite. This is an example of Newton's Third Law (see p.166).

Resultant Force is the Overall Force on a Point or Object

1) In most real situations there are at least two forces acting on an object along any direction.

2) The overall effect of the forces decide whether the object accelerates, decelerates or has a steady speed.

3) If a number of forces act at a single point, you can replace them with a single force called the resultant force. The resultant force has the same effect on the motion as the original forces acting altogether.

4) If the forces all act along the same line (they're all parallel and act in the same or the opposite direction), the resultant force is found by just adding or subtracting them.

> The diagram on the right shows a ball falling. Weight and air resistance are acting along the same line, so the resultant force acting on the ball = weight – air resistance = 8 – 3 = 5 N in the downwards direction.
>
> Air resistance = 3 N
>
> Weight = 8 N

Free Body Force Diagrams Show All the Forces Acting on a Body

Forces are vectors (see page 157) so they have a size and direction. A free body force diagram is a diagram of an object with arrows drawn to show the direction and size of the forces acting on the object.

A Resultant Force of Zero Means all the Forces are Balanced

An object with a zero resultant force will either be stationary or moving at a steady speed.

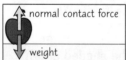

normal contact force

weight

This diagram shows an apple sat on a table. The force due to gravity (its weight, see p.169) is acting downwards. The apple isn't moving because there's another force of the same size acting in the opposite direction to balance the weight. This is the normal contact force from the table top pushing up on the apple.

A Non-Zero Resultant Force Means the Forces are Unbalanced

If there's a non-zero resultant force on an object, then it will either accelerate or decelerate. This is because the forces are unbalanced. In the example of the car on the right, the thrust is greater than the drag, so the car is accelerating. If the drag was greater than the thrust, the car would decelerate. The normal contact force and the weight acting on the car balance each other (otherwise the car would go flying off or sink through the road).

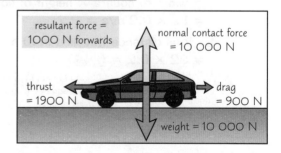

resultant force = 1000 N forwards

normal contact force = 10 000 N

thrust = 1900 N

drag = 900 N

weight = 10 000 N

Drag yourself away from the TV and force yourself to revise...

The resultant force acting on an object will decide the motion of the object. If the resultant force is zero, the object is stationary or moving at a steady speed. If the resultant force is non-zero, it's accelerating. Easy.

Q1   Draw a free body diagram for: a) a book on a table   b) an accelerating falling ball.   [4 marks]

Scale Diagrams and Forces

You saw on the page 162 how to find the resultant force of two forces acting along the same line. Now here's what to do if they're at an angle to each other.

Use Scale Drawings to Find the Resultant Force

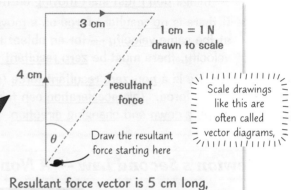

Resultant force can also be called the net force.

You can find the size and direction of the resultant force on an object using scale drawings. Draw the forces acting on the object to scale and 'tip-to-tail', then measure the length of the resultant force on the diagram. This is the line drawn from the start of the first force to the end of the last force.

A man is on an electric bicycle that pushes him with a force of 4 N north. However, the wind is pushing him with a force of 3 N east. Find the magnitude of the resultant force.

1) Start by drawing a scale diagram to illustrate the forces acting on the man. Make sure you choose a sensible scale (e.g. 1 cm = 1 N).

2) Then just measure the missing side with a ruler.

If you were asked to find direction as well, you would just measure the angle θ with a protractor.

Scale drawings like this are often called vector diagrams.

Resultant force vector is 5 cm long, so the resultant force is 5 N.

An Object is in Equilibrium if all the Forces on it are Balanced

When an object has a zero resultant force, it is in equilibrium. All the forces on the object cancel each other out. You can use scale drawings to demonstrate this.

For example, look at the scale drawing of the three forces that are acting on the object on the right. If you draw all the forces tip-to-tail, you can see that they create a loop, so the resultant force is zero. The object is in equilibrium.

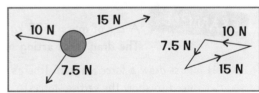

You May Need to Resolve Vectors

1) When you resolve a force, you split the force into two forces that are at right angles to each other. The two forces have the same overall effect as the original force.

2) You can resolve a force using a scale drawing — just draw two lines so that the original force becomes the longest side of a right-angled triangle (see example below).

3) Resolving forces is useful when you need to see the effect of a force along a particular line.

A toy train is being pulled along a track by a rope at an angle to the track. The scale drawing shows this force and the direction the train is moving.

The force can be resolved into a force acting horizontally and a force acting vertically. You just need to draw a right-angled triangle as shown on the scale drawing. The size of the vertical force is found by measuring the length of the vertical part of the triangle. Vertical length = 1.5 cm = 1.5 N.

The size of the force acting horizontally can also be found by measuring the length of the horizontal part of the triangle. Horizontal length = 2 cm = 2 N. So 2 N is the size of the force that's pulling the train in its direction of movement.

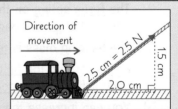

Force yourself to revise this...oh wait, I've already done that pun...

If you're making a scale drawing, choose a sensible scale. It'll be no good if you need A0 paper to draw a triangle.

Q1 A boat is being pushed by its propeller with a driving force of 600 N south, and by the wind with a force of 450 N east. Use a scale drawing to find the size of the resultant force acting on the boat. [2 marks]

Newton's First and Second Laws of Motion

Clever chap <u>Isaac Newton</u> — he came up with <u>three</u> handy laws about motion. This page covers the first two.

Newton's First Law — No Resultant Force Means No Change in Velocity

1) <u>Newton's First Law</u> says that:

> An object will remain <u>stationary</u> or at a <u>constant</u> <u>velocity</u> unless acted upon by an <u>external force</u>.

2) As you saw on p.162, if the <u>resultant force</u> on a <u>stationary</u> object is <u>zero</u>, the object <u>remains stationary</u> — things <u>don't just start moving</u> on their own, there has to be a <u>resultant force</u> to get them started.

3) If there is <u>no resultant force</u> on a <u>moving</u> object it'll just carry on moving at the <u>same velocity</u> — for an object to travel with a <u>uniform</u> (constant) velocity, there must be <u>zero resultant force</u>.

4) If there is a <u>non-zero resultant force</u> (see below), then the object will <u>accelerate</u> in the direction of the force. This <u>acceleration</u> can take <u>five</u> different forms: <u>starting</u>, <u>stopping</u>, <u>speeding up</u>, <u>slowing down</u> and <u>changing direction</u>.

Newton's Second Law — A Non-Zero Resultant Force Causes an Acceleration

<u>Newton's Second Law</u> says: The force acting on an object is equal to its rate of change of momentum.

See page 167 for more on momentum.

But don't panic, this is roughly translated to — any <u>resultant force</u> will produce an <u>acceleration</u>, and the <u>formula</u> for it is:

> force (N) = mass (kg) × acceleration (m/s²)

Remember that the *F* is always the <u>resultant force</u> — that's pretty important.   or $F = ma$

EXAMPLE: A car of mass 1625 kg has an engine which provides a driving force of 5650 N. The drag force acting on the car is 450 N. Find its acceleration.

1) First draw a force diagram (there's no need to show the vertical forces).

    5650 N   450 N

2) Work out the resultant force.   Resultant force = 5650 − 450 = 5200 N

3) Rearrange $F = ma$ to calculate the acceleration. $a = F \div m = 5200 \div 1625 = 3.2$ m/s²

A Simple Experiment Demonstrates Newton's Second Law

1) The <u>acceleration</u> of a <u>trolley</u> on an air track can be used to investigate <u>Newton's Second Law</u>.

2) The <u>force</u> acting on the trolley is equal to the <u>weight</u> ($W = M \times g$, see page 169) of the <u>hanging mass</u>.

3) The hanging mass is <u>released</u>, pulling the trolley along the track.

4) By measuring the <u>time</u> and <u>speed</u> at which the trolley passes each <u>light gate</u>, its <u>acceleration</u> can be <u>calculated</u>.

5) You can <u>increase</u> the <u>force</u> acting on the trolley by moving one of the masses from the <u>trolley</u> to the <u>hanging mass</u>, and <u>repeating</u> the experiment.

6) If you plot your results on a graph of <u>force</u> against <u>acceleration</u>, you should get a <u>straight line</u>, showing that $F = ma$.

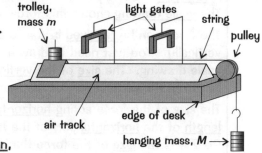

trolley, mass m   *light gates*   *string*   *pulley*   *air track*   *edge of desk*   *hanging mass, M* →

Air tracks and light gates — sounds like a band from the 80s...

Newton's First Law means that an object at a steady speed doesn't need a net force to keep moving. Remember that.

Q1   Calculate the resultant force acting on a 26 000 kg lorry with an acceleration of 1.5 m/s².   [1 mark]

Topic P2 — Forces

Friction and Terminal Velocity

Imagine a world without <u>friction</u> — you'd be sliding around all over the place. Weeeeeeeeee.... Ouch.

Friction Will Slow Things Down

1) When an object is <u>moving</u> (or trying to move), <u>friction</u> acts in the direction that <u>opposes movement</u>.

2) <u>Friction</u> makes things <u>slow down and stop</u>, so you need a <u>driving force</u> to keep moving (e.g. thrust).

3) If the <u>driving force</u> is <u>equal</u> to the <u>friction force</u>, the object will move at a <u>steady speed</u>.
   If the <u>driving force</u> is <u>greater than (>)</u> the <u>friction force</u>, the object will <u>accelerate</u>.
   If the <u>driving force</u> is <u>less than (<)</u> the <u>friction force</u>, the object will <u>decelerate</u>.

4) <u>Friction</u> occurs between <u>two</u> surfaces in <u>contact</u> (e.g. tyres and the road), and <u>drag</u> occurs when an object <u>passes</u> through a <u>fluid</u> (e.g. a boat through water). <u>Air resistance</u> is a type of drag.

Moving Vehicles and Falling Objects Can Reach a Terminal Velocity

When objects <u>first set off</u> they have <u>more</u> <u>driving force</u> than <u>friction force</u> (resistance), so they accelerate. But the <u>resistance</u> is <u>directly proportional</u> to the <u>velocity</u> of the object — resistance ∝ velocity. So as the <u>velocity</u> increases, the resistance <u>increases</u> as well. This gradually <u>reduces</u> the <u>acceleration</u> until the <u>friction force</u> is <u>equal</u> to the <u>driving force</u> so it doesn't accelerate any more. The forces are <u>balanced</u> (there's <u>no resultant force</u>). The object will have reached its maximum velocity or <u>terminal velocity</u>.

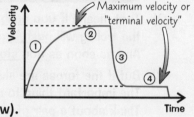

1) A <u>skydiver</u> <u>accelerates</u> as <u>weight due to gravity > air resistance</u>.

2) But air resistance <u>increases</u> as velocity increases until <u>weight = air resistance</u>, and they reach <u>terminal velocity</u>.

3) The <u>parachute opens</u> and <u>weight < air resistance</u>, so they <u>decelerate</u>.

4) As velocity <u>decreases</u>, the air resistance also decreases until <u>weight = air resistance</u> — they reach a <u>new terminal velocity</u> (see below).

Terminal Velocity of Moving Objects Depends on Their Drag

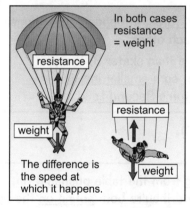

In both cases resistance = weight

The difference is the speed at which it happens.

1) The <u>greater the drag</u> (or air resistance or friction), the <u>lower the terminal velocity</u> of an object, and drag depends on the object's <u>shape and area</u>.

2) For example, the <u>driving force</u> for a <u>skydiver</u> is his <u>weight</u> due to <u>gravity</u> and the <u>drag</u> (air resistance) depends on the skydiver's shape and area.

3) <u>Without</u> his <u>parachute</u> open, a <u>skydiver's</u> area is quite <u>small</u>. His <u>terminal velocity</u> is about <u>120 mph</u>.

4) With the <u>parachute open</u>, there's <u>more air resistance</u> (at any given speed) because the skydiver's <u>area is larger</u>, but the <u>driving force</u> (his weight) is the <u>same</u>. This means his <u>terminal velocity</u> is much <u>smaller</u> (~<u>15 mph</u>), which is a <u>safe speed</u> to hit the ground at.

5) <u>Decreasing drag</u> makes things <u>faster</u> — <u>streamlined cars</u> have less drag.

To find the <u>terminal velocity</u> of a <u>toy parachute</u> — drop it from a <u>sensible height</u> in front of an object with regular <u>vertical markings</u> at set heights (e.g. 0.5 m markings on a wall), and measure the <u>time</u> at which it falls past <u>each marking</u>. Use the differences between times to find its <u>average velocity</u> between each pair of markings and plot your results on a <u>graph</u> of <u>velocity against time</u>. It should have a <u>curved shape</u>, like the graph above between points 1 and 2.

To measure the times accurately, you could film the parachute falling, then replay the video at a slower speed, and read the time the parachute passes each marking from the video.

Air resistance — it can be a real drag...

Make sure you can explain how an object reaches its terminal velocity in terms of forces. Then go skydiving.

Q1   A boat sets off with a constant thrust moving it forwards. After some time the boat reaches a terminal velocity. Explain the boat's motion in terms of the forces acting on the boat.   [4 marks]

Inertia and Newton's Third Law of Motion

Another law eh? Isaac probably wasn't thinking about anyone having to revise them back in the 17th century.

Inertia Explains Why it's Harder to Move a Hammer Than a Feather

1) Inertia is the measure of how difficult it is to change an object's velocity.

2) It is dependent on the mass of the object — the larger the mass, the larger the inertia, and the harder it is to change the velocity of the object.

3) Imagine that a bowling ball and a golf ball roll towards you with the same velocity. It would require a larger force to stop the bowling ball than the golf ball in the same time. This is because the bowling ball has a larger mass and a larger inertia.

4) By rearranging the equation for Newton's Second Law (see page 164) you can show that mass is defined as the ratio of the force over acceleration: $\Rightarrow$ $mass = \dfrac{force}{acceleration}$ So a larger mass requires a larger force to accelerate by a certain amount — i.e. it has a larger inertia.

Newton's Third Law — Reaction Forces are Equal and Opposite

1) Newton's Third Law says that:

> When two objects interact, the forces they exert on each other are equal and opposite.

2) That means if you push something, say a shopping trolley, the trolley will push back against you, just as hard. And as soon as you stop pushing, so does the trolley. Kinda clever really.

3) But if the forces are always equal, how does anything ever go anywhere? The important thing to remember is that the two forces are acting on different objects. Think about a pair of ice skaters:

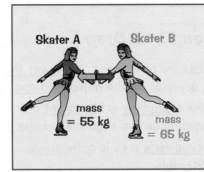

Skater A   Skater B

mass = 55 kg   mass = 65 kg

- When skater A pushes on skater B (the 'action' force), she feels an equal and opposite force from skater B's hand (the 'reaction' force).
- Both skaters feel the same sized force, in opposite directions, and so accelerate away from each other.
- Skater A will be accelerated more than skater B, though, because she has a smaller mass, so a smaller inertia — $a = F/m$ (from rearranging Newton's Second Law).

4) It's a bit more complicated for an object in equilibrium (see page 163). Imagine a book sat on a table:

> The weight of the book pulls it down, and the normal reaction force from the table pushes it up. This is NOT Newton's Third Law. These forces are different types and they're both acting on the book.
>
> The pairs of forces due to Newton's Third Law in this case are:
> - The weight of book is pulled down by gravity from Earth (W_B) and the book also pulls back up on the Earth (W_E).
> - The normal contact force from the table pushing up on the book (R_B) and the normal contact force from the book pushing down on the table (R_T).

R_B
R_T
$\downarrow W_B$
$\uparrow W_E$

Newton's fourth law — revision must be done with cake...

Mmm... cake. A couple of tricky concepts here — inertia and Newton's Third Law. You can't say I don't spoil you.

Q1   A full shopping trolley and an empty one are moving at the same speed. Explain why it is easier to stop the empty trolley than the full trolley over the same amount of time.   [1 mark]

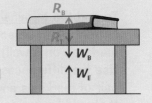

Momentum

All moving objects have momentum. Like this book when I throw it across the room.

Momentum = Mass × Velocity

The greater the mass of an object and the greater its velocity, the more momentum the object has. They're linked by this equation:

$$\text{momentum (kg m/s)} = \text{mass (kg)} \times \text{velocity (m/s)} \quad \text{or:} \quad p = m \times v$$

Momentum is a vector — it has size and direction.

A 65 kg kangaroo is moving in a straight line at 12 m/s. Calculate its momentum.

Momentum = mass × velocity = 65 × 12 = **780 kg m/s**

Forces Cause Changes in Momentum

1) When a resultant force acts on an object for a certain amount of time, it causes a change in momentum. Newton's 2nd Law can explain this:

- A resultant force on an object causes it to accelerate: force = mass × acceleration.

- Acceleration is just change in velocity over time, so: $\text{force} = \dfrac{\text{mass} \times \text{change in velocity}}{\text{time}}$.
  This means a force applied to an object over any time interval will change the object's velocity.

- Mass × change in velocity is equal to change in momentum, so you end up with the equation:

$$\text{force (N)} = \frac{\text{change in momentum (kg m/s)}}{\text{time (s)}} \quad \text{or} \quad F = \frac{p}{t}$$

EXAMPLE: A rock of mass 1.0 kg is travelling through space at 15 m/s. A comet hits the rock, applying a force of 2500 N for 0.60 seconds. Calculate:
a) the rock's initial momentum
b) the change in the rock's momentum resulting from the impact.

a) Substitute into the equation for momentum: momentum = mass × velocity = 1.0 × 15 = **15 kg m/s**

b) Use the equation for force and momentum to find what happens when the comet hits the rock. $\text{force} = \dfrac{\text{change in momentum}}{\text{time}}$ so:
change of momentum = force × time = 2500 × 0.60 = **1500 kg m/s**

2) The faster a given change in momentum happens, the bigger the force causing the change must be (i.e. if t gets smaller in the equation above, F gets bigger).

3) So if someone's momentum changes very quickly, like in a car crash, the forces on the body will be very large, and more likely to cause injury. There's more about this on page 209.

4) You can also think of changes in momentum in collisions in terms of acceleration — a change in momentum normally involves a change in velocity, which is what acceleration is.

5) As you know, force = mass × acceleration, so the larger the acceleration (or deceleration), the larger the force needed to produce it.

Learn this stuff — it'll only take a moment... um...

Momentum is a pretty fundamental bit of physics — learn it well. Know the equations and know how to use them.

Q1   Calculate the momentum of a 220 000 kg aeroplane that is travelling at 250 m/s.   [1 mark]

Q2   Calculate the force a tennis racket needs to apply to a 58 g tennis ball to accelerate it from rest to 34 m/s in 11.6 ms.   [4 marks]

Conservation of Momentum

Momentum is always <u>conserved</u>. Easy peasy. Go squeeze some lemons.

Momentum Before = Momentum After

Make sure you learn the <u>law of conservation of momentum</u>:

> In a collision when no other external forces act, momentum is conserved
> — i.e. the total momentum <u>after</u> the collision is the <u>same</u> as it was <u>before</u> it.

1) Imagine a <u>red</u> snooker ball rolls towards a <u>stationary yellow</u> snooker ball with the <u>same mass</u>. If after the collision, the red ball <u>stops</u> and the yellow ball <u>moves off</u>, then the yellow ball will have the <u>same velocity</u> as the original velocity of the red ball (assuming there's no friction).

2) Conservation of momentum also explains <u>rocket propulsion</u>:

> When a rocket is <u>stationary</u>, it has <u>zero velocity</u> and so <u>zero momentum</u>. If the rocket's engines then fire, it'll chuck a load of <u>exhaust gases</u> out <u>backwards</u> (negative momentum). Since <u>momentum is always conserved</u>, this means the rocket has to <u>move forwards</u> (positive momentum), in order to keep the <u>combined</u> momentum of the gases and the rocket at <u>zero</u>.

3) You can use the idea of conservation of momentum to find the <u>velocity</u> of an object <u>after</u> a <u>collision</u>:

EXAMPLE: Ball A (mass = 0.08 kg) is moving at 9 m/s towards ball B (mass = 0.36 kg). Ball B is moving at 3 m/s in the same direction as ball A. The two balls collide. After the collision, ball A is stationary and ball B moves away. Calculate the velocity of ball B after the collision.

Before

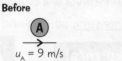
u_A = 9 m/s u_B = 3 m/s

After

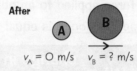
v_A = 0 m/s v_B = ? m/s

1) First, calculate the <u>total momentum</u> before the collision.

2) The total momentum <u>before</u> the collision is <u>equal</u> to the total momentum <u>after</u> the collision.

3) Write out the equation for the total momentum <u>after</u> the collision, and substitute in the values you know.

4) Rearrange and <u>solve</u> the equation.

total momentum before = ball A's momentum + ball B's momentum
$= (m_A \times u_A) + (m_B \times u_B)$
$= (0.08 \times 9) + (0.36 \times 3) = 1.8$ kg m/s

total momentum after = total momentum before = 1.8 kg m/s

total momentum after = $(m_A \times v_A) + (m_B \times v_B)$
$1.8 = (0.08 \times 0) + (0.36 \times v_B)$
$1.8 = 0 + (0.36 \times v_B)$

$v_B = 1.8 \div 0.36 = 5$ m/s

4) If two objects collide and <u>join together</u>, then the total momentum of <u>both</u> objects <u>before</u> the collision = momentum of the <u>combined</u> object <u>after</u> the collision. So in the example above, if the balls had joined together and moved away at a <u>steady speed</u>, you would have ended up with:
total momentum after = $(m_A + m_B) \times v$.

Collisions can be Elastic or Inelastic

Momentum is conserved in both elastic and inelastic collisions.

1) An <u>elastic</u> collision is where the <u>total energy</u> in the <u>kinetic energy stores</u> of the objects colliding is the <u>same before</u> and <u>after</u> the collision — i.e. the energy in the kinetic energy stores is <u>conserved</u>.

2) An <u>inelastic</u> collision is where some of the <u>energy</u> in the kinetic energy stores is <u>transferred</u> to <u>other stores</u>. For example, energy can be transferred away <u>by heating</u> or <u>by sound</u>.

Homework this week — build a rocket to investigate momentum...

...*sigh* if only. It's probably to practise questions instead. Won't get you to the moon, but it'll help you in exams.

Q1   A 2.0 kg trolley travelling at 1.5 m/s collides with a 3.0 kg stationary trolley. They then move off together at a constant speed. Find the final velocity of the two trolleys.   [3 marks]

Mass, Weight and Gravity

Gravity attracts everything with <u>mass</u>, but you only notice it when one of the masses is <u>huge</u>, like a <u>planet</u>.

Gravity is the Force of Attraction Between All Masses

1) <u>Everything</u> that is made of <u>matter</u> has a <u>gravitational field</u> around it. <u>Everything</u>. And a gravitational field <u>attracts</u> other masses.

2) The more <u>massive the object</u> is, the <u>greater the strength</u> of its gravitational field.

3) <u>Earth</u> has got a gravitational field that <u>pulls</u> us and everything else <u>towards it</u>.

4) The <u>Moon</u> is big enough that its gravitational field creates the <u>tides</u> on Earth.

5) Even <u>you</u> have a gravitational field, but it's so <u>teeny tiny</u> that it doesn't have any noticeable effect.

The Force due to Gravity is Called Weight

1) A planet's <u>gravitational field</u> makes all things <u>accelerate</u> towards the <u>planet's surface</u>, all with the <u>same</u> acceleration, g.

2) g is called the <u>gravitational field strength</u>. It's also known as the <u>acceleration due to gravity</u> (i.e. it's the acceleration an object will have when falling to Earth).

3) It has a value of about <u>10 N/kg</u> (or 10 m/s²) near the Earth's surface. This means that anything that <u>falls</u> or is <u>dropped</u> on Earth (i.e. an object in <u>free fall</u>) will have an acceleration of <u>10 m/s²</u>. The value of g is <u>different</u> on <u>other planets</u>, so an object in free fall on another planet will have a <u>different acceleration</u>.

4) The <u>force acting</u> on an object when it's in a <u>gravitational field</u> is called the <u>weight</u>, or <u>gravity force</u>. It's measured in <u>newtons</u> (N). You can calculate this <u>force</u> using the equation:

> gravity force (N) = mass (kg) × gravitational field strength, g (N/kg)

5) Or in <u>symbols</u>, where W is the <u>weight</u> in N (i.e. the gravity force) and m is the <u>mass</u> in kg:

$$W = m \times g$$

You'll need to remember that g = 10 N/kg on Earth for your exam.

6) Remember, <u>mass</u> is <u>not the same</u> as weight. Mass is just the <u>amount of 'stuff'</u> in an object. For any given object this will have the same value <u>anywhere</u> in the Universe.

7) The <u>more massive</u> an object is, the <u>larger its weight</u>. Similarly, the <u>stronger</u> the gravitational field an object is in (e.g. the more massive the planet it is on), the <u>higher</u> the <u>gravitational field strength</u> and so the <u>larger the object's weight</u>.

EXAMPLE: What is the weight, in newtons, of a 2.0 kg chicken, both on Earth (g = 10 N/kg) and on the Moon (g = 1.6 N/kg).

Weight is the same as gravity force.

1) Calculate the weight on <u>Earth</u> using the equation given above.
   weight = $m \times g$ = 2.0 × 10 = **20 N**

2) Calculate the weight on the moon using its <u>value of g</u>.
   weight = $m \times g$ = 2.0 × 1.6 = **3.2 N**

The chicken has a weight of 34 N on a mystery planet. What is the gravitational field strength of the planet?

1) <u>Rearrange</u> the equation for g. $g = w \div m$
2) <u>Substitute</u> the values in.   = 34 ÷ 2.0 = **17 N/kg**

Remember — the mass of the chicken is the same on every planet, it's the weight of the chicken that changes.

I'm always attracted to a shop with a sale on...

A common mistake is thinking that mass and weight are the same thing. They are not. Learn the difference.

Q1   Calculate the weight of a 67 kg mass on Earth.   [1 mark]

Q2   A person has a weight of 820 N on Earth. Calculate their mass.   [2 marks]

Mechanical Energy Stores

Take a sneaky peek at page 202 for more about energy stores. This page covers two types of energy stores and how to calculate how much energy is in them.

An Object at a Height has Energy in its Gravitational Potential Energy Store

1) When an object is at any height above the Earth's surface, it will have energy in its gravitational potential energy store.

2) You can calculate the amount of energy in the gravitational potential energy store using the equation:

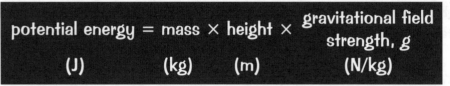

potential energy = mass × height × gravitational field strength, g

(J)   (kg)   (m)   (N/kg)

or $PE = m \times h \times g$

EXAMPLE: Calculate the energy in the gravitational potential energy store of a 1.2 kg book when it is 4.25 m above the ground.

potential energy = mass × height × g
= 1.2 × 4.25 × 10
= 51 J

Don't forget, on Earth, g = 10 N/kg.

A Moving Object has Energy in its Kinetic Energy Store

1) When an object is moving, it has energy in its kinetic energy store.

2) This energy depends on both the object's mass and velocity.

3) The greater its mass and the faster it's going, the more energy it has in its kinetic energy store.

4) For example, a high-speed train will have a lot more energy in its kinetic energy store than you running.

5) You need to know how to use the formula:

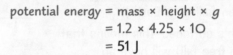

kinetic energy = 0.5 × mass × (speed)²
(J)   (kg)   (m/s)²

or $KE = \frac{1}{2} \times m \times v^2$

6) If you double the mass, the energy in the kinetic energy store doubles. If you double the speed, though, the energy in the kinetic energy store quadruples (increases by a factor of 4) — it's because of the '(speed)²' in the formula.

EXAMPLE: A car of mass 1450 kg is travelling at 28 m/s. Calculate the energy in its kinetic energy store, giving your answer to 2 s.f.

kinetic energy = 0.5 × mass × (speed)²
= 0.5 × 1450 × 28²
= 568 400 = 570 000 J (to 2 s.f.)

Watch out for the (speed)², that's where people tend to make mistakes and lose marks.

There's potential for a joke here somewhere...

More equations to learn here. Look on the bright side, at least you don't have to learn something like

$-\dfrac{\hbar^2}{2m}\dfrac{d^2\Psi(x)}{dx^2} + U(x)\Psi(x) = E\Psi(x)$. And we all know what that equation is — altogether now, it's... erm...*

Q1   Calculate the energy in the gravitational potential energy store of a 0.80 kg ball at a height of 1.5 m above the Earth's surface.   [1 mark]

Q2   An otter is swimming with a speed of 2.0 m/s. It has a mass of 4.9 kg. Calculate the energy in the otter's kinetic energy store.   [1 mark]

             *don't panic, you really don't need to know what this is.

Work Done and Power

Whenever I think of <u>power</u>, I have to stop myself from plotting world domination whilst stroking a cat.

Work is Done When a Force Moves an Object

> When a <u>FORCE</u> makes an object <u>MOVE</u>, <u>ENERGY IS TRANSFERRED</u> and <u>WORK IS DONE</u>.

1) Whenever something <u>moves</u>, something else is providing some sort of <u>effort</u> to move it.
2) The thing putting the <u>effort</u> in needs a <u>supply</u> of energy (from <u>fuel</u> or <u>food</u> or <u>electricity</u> etc.).
3) It then does <u>work</u> by <u>moving</u> the object, and <u>transfers</u> the energy it receives (from fuel) to <u>other stores</u>.
4) Whether this energy is <u>transferred usefully</u> (e.g. by <u>lifting a load</u>) or <u>wasted</u> (e.g. dissipated by <u>heating</u> from <u>friction</u>), you still say that '<u>work is done</u>'. '<u>Work done</u>' and '<u>energy transferred</u>' are <u>the same</u>.
5) The <u>formula</u> to calculate the <u>amount of work done</u> is:

> work done (J) = force (N) × distance (m) or $W = F \times d$

The <u>distance</u> here is the distance moved <u>along</u> the <u>line of action</u> of the <u>force</u> (i.e. the distance moved in the <u>direction</u> of the force).

> **EXAMPLE:** Find the energy transferred when a tyre is dragged 5.0 m with a constant force of 340 N.
> work done = force × distance = 340 × 5.0 = 1700 J

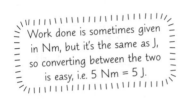
Work done is sometimes given in Nm, but it's the same as J, so converting between the two is easy, i.e. 5 Nm = 5 J.

6) If a force is applied to <u>move an object</u>, the <u>work done</u> on the object will be equal to the <u>energy transferred</u> to the <u>kinetic energy store</u> of the object <u>if there's no friction</u>.
7) If an object is <u>already moving</u> and then a force (such as friction) <u>slows it down</u>, the energy transferred from the object's <u>kinetic energy store</u> is equal to the <u>work done</u> against the <u>object's motion</u>.
8) <u>Work done</u> on an object can also be transferred to <u>other energy stores</u>. E.g. the work done on <u>lifting</u> an object off the ground will be equal to the energy <u>transferred</u> to its <u>gravitational potential energy store</u>.

Power is the 'Rate of Doing Work' — i.e. How Much per Second

1) <u>Power</u> is a measure of <u>how quickly work</u> is being <u>done</u>. As <u>work done</u> = <u>energy transferred</u>, you can <u>define</u> power like this:

> <u>Power</u> is the <u>rate</u> at which <u>energy is transferred</u>.

2) So, the power of a <u>machine</u> is the <u>rate</u> at which it <u>transfers energy</u>. For example, if an <u>electric drill</u> has a power of <u>700 W</u> this means it can transfer <u>700 J</u> of energy <u>every second</u>.
3) This is the <u>very easy formula</u> for power:
4) The proper unit of power is the <u>watt</u> (<u>W</u>). <u>1 W = 1 J</u> of energy <u>transferred per second</u> (J/s).

> power (W) = $\dfrac{\text{work done (J)}}{\text{time (s)}}$ or $P = \dfrac{W}{t}$

> **EXAMPLE:** A motor transfers 4.8 kJ of useful energy in 2 minutes. Find its power output.
> 1) <u>Convert</u> the values to the <u>correct units</u> first.   4.8 kJ = 4800 J and 2 mins = 120 s
> 2) <u>Substitute</u> the values into the power equation.
> power = $\dfrac{\text{work done}}{\text{time}} = \dfrac{4800}{120} = 40$ W

Watt's power? Power's watts...

Make sure you're happy with using both the equations on this page before you move on.

Q1   A book sliding across a table has 1.25 J of energy in its kinetic energy store. Friction from the table provides a constant force of 5.0 N. Calculate the distance travelled by the book before it stops.   [2 marks]

Forces and Elasticity

Elasticity involves lots of physics and pinging elastic bands at people. OK, maybe not that last one.

A Deformation can be Elastic or Plastic

1) When you apply forces to an object it can be stretched, compressed or bent — this is deformation.
2) To deform an object, you need at least two forces. Think of a spring — if you just pull one end of it, and there's no force at the other end, you'll just pull the spring along rather than stretching it.
3) If an object returns to its original shape after the forces are removed, it's an elastic deformation.
4) If the object doesn't return to its original shape when you remove the forces, it's a plastic deformation.

Extension is Directly Proportional to Force for an Elastic Deformation...

1) Imagine you have a vertical spring that is fixed at the top end and has a mass attached to the bottom.
2) When the spring and mass are in equilibrium (i.e. the spring isn't stretching any further), the downwards force on the mass (its weight) is equal in size to the upwards force that the spring exerts on the mass.
3) The extension of a spring (or any object that's deforming elastically) is directly proportional to the force that the spring exerts on the mass (up to a point, see below).
4) How much an elastically deforming object stretches for a given force depends on its spring constant. The spring constant depends on the material that you're stretching — the stiffer the material, the larger the spring constant.
5) The relationship between the extension of a spring and the force is called Hooke's law:

| force exerted by a spring = extension × spring constant |
| (N)   (m)   (N/m) |

or $F = x \times k$

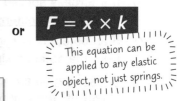

This equation can be applied to any elastic object, not just springs.

...but this Stops Working when the Force is Great Enough

1) There's a limit to the amount of force you can apply to an object for the extension to keep on increasing proportionally.
2) The graph shows force against extension for an object being stretched.
3) For small forces, force and extension have a linear relationship. So the first part of the graph shows a straight-line (up to point P). This is where Hooke's law (see above) applies to the object.
4) The gradient of the straight line is equal to the spring constant of the object — the larger the spring constant, the steeper the gradient.
5) Beyond point P, the object no longer obeys Hooke's law.
6) Most objects still deform elastically for a little bit after you reach the limit of proportionality. But if you continue to increase the deforming force, you'll reach a point where its elasticity 'runs out' and it starts to deform plastically — the object won't spring back to its original shape after the stretching force has been removed.
7) The maximum force that can be applied to a material before this happens is called its elastic limit. For the graph here it'll be somewhere after point P (P is just where a material stops obeying Hooke's law).
8) For some objects, the elastic limit is so low that you'll never normally see them deforming elastically — you might see these called plastic materials. The relationship between force and extension for these materials is non-linear, so the force-extension graphs of these materials are curved.

I hope this stuff isn't stretching you too much...

The gradient of a force-extension graph for a material obeying Hooke's law is equal to its spring constant. Super.

Q1   A spring has a natural length of 0.16 m. When a force of 3.0 N is applied to the spring, its length becomes 0.20 m. Calculate the spring constant of the spring.   [2 marks]

Investigating Hooke's Law

More springs here, but now you actually get to do some experiments with them. Hip hip hooray.

You can Investigate the Extension of a Spring | PRACTICAL

1) Hang your spring from a clamp stand, as shown in the diagram (without the masses, but with the hook the masses hang from), then measure the spring's length using the ruler — this is the spring's original length.

2) Weigh your masses and add them one at a time to the hook hanging from the spring, so the force on the spring increases.

3) After each mass is added, measure the new length of the spring, then calculate the extension: extension = new length − original length

4) Plot a graph of force (weight) against extension using your results and draw a line of best fit.

5) A straight line of best fit is where the spring obeys Hooke's law and the gradient = spring constant (see page 172). If you've loaded the spring with enough masses, the graph will start to curve.

6) Make sure you carry out the experiment safely. You should be standing up so you can get out of the way quickly if the masses fall, and wearing safety goggles to protect your eyes in case the spring snaps.

When measuring the length of the spring, you should move yourself so the pointer on the hook is at eye level. Otherwise it could look like it is next to a different marking on the ruler. You also need to make sure the ruler is exactly vertical to get an accurate measurement, and that the spring isn't moving.

Work is Done to Deform an Object

1) When a force deforms an object, work is done to stretch, compress or bend the object.

2) If the deformation is elastic, this transfers energy to the object's elastic potential energy store.

3) The equation for the energy stored in an object's elastic potential energy store is:

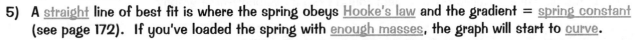

energy transferred in stretching = 0.5 × spring constant × (extension)^2
(J)   (N/m)   (m)^2

4) You can also write this in symbols. It's: $E = 0.5 \times k \times x^2$

5) This also works for objects that are being compressed elastically. Just use the compression instead of extension.

> The compression of an object is how much shorter it gets when it's squashed.

EXAMPLE: A spring has a spring constant of 32 N/m. Calculate the work done on the spring if it is stretched elastically from 0.40 m to 0.45 m.

extension = new length − original length = 0.45 − 0.40 = 0.05 m

energy transferred in stretching = 0.5 × spring constant × (extension)^2 = 0.5 × 32 × 0.05^2 = 0.04 J

> Remember: work done = energy transferred.

6) You can also find the energy transferred when an object deforms elastically from its force-extension graph. The energy transferred is equal to the area under the graph up to its current extension.

7) You can find this area by counting squares, or if the graph is linear, by finding the area of the triangle.

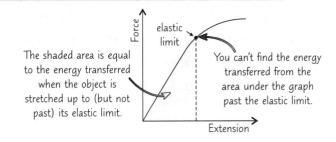

The shaded area is equal to the energy transferred when the object is stretched up to (but not past) its elastic limit.

You can't find the energy transferred from the area under the graph past the elastic limit.

Tell your parents you need to buy a trampoline for your revision...

More energy transfers — you'd better get used to them, there's more of them coming up later on in the book.

Q1   A 1.2 m long spring (k = 54 N/m) extends elastically to 1.3 m. Calculate the work done.   [2 marks]

Revision Questions for Topic P2

Phew that was a lot of information — time to see what you've learnt and what needs revisiting.
- Try these questions and <u>tick off each one</u> when you <u>get it right</u>.
- When you've done <u>all the questions</u> under a heading and are <u>completely happy</u> with it, tick it off.

Motion (p.157-161) ☑

1) What is the difference between a scalar and a vector quantity? Give two examples of each. ☑
2) Define acceleration in terms of velocity. ☑
3) Explain why an object travelling in a circle at a constant speed is accelerating. ☑
4) Describe an experiment to investigate the acceleration of a trolley down a ramp. ☑
5) How is the speed of an object found from its distance-time graph? ☑
6) What does a flat section on a velocity-time graph represent? ☑
7) How is the distance travelled by an object found from its velocity-time graph? ☑

Forces, Newton's Laws and Momentum (p.162-169) ☐

8) What is meant by the 'resultant force' acting on an object? ☑
9) What will happen to an object that has a zero resultant force? ☑
10) What will happen to an object that has a non-zero resultant force? ☑
11) What is Newton's First Law of motion? ☑
12) Give the equation for Newton's Second Law. ☑
13) Explain how a car moving with a constant driving force will reach terminal velocity. ☑
14) What is inertia? ☑
15) What is Newton's Third Law of motion? Give an example of it in action. ☑
16) Give the equation for momentum in terms of mass and velocity. ☑
17) What is an elastic collision? ☑
18) What is the difference between mass and weight and how can weight be calculated? ☑

Energy and Elasticity (p.170-173) ☑

19) Give the equation for the energy in an object's gravitational potential energy store. ☑
20) Give the equation for the energy in the kinetic energy store of a moving object. ☑
21) Give the equation for the work done on an object when it's moved a certain distance by a force. ☑
22) What is meant by power? How is power calculated? ☑
23) What is the minimum number of forces needed to stretch, compress or bend an object? ☑
24) Give the equation that is known as Hooke's law. ☑
25) What constant can be found from calculating the gradient of
    a force-extension graph for a material obeying Hooke's law? ☑
26) What is the difference between an elastic deformation and a plastic deformation? ☑
27) Describe a simple experiment to investigate Hooke's law. ☑
28) Give the equation for calculating the energy transferred to a spring when it's stretched. ☑

Static Electricity

Static electricity builds up when <u>electrons</u> are transferred between things that <u>rub together</u>.

Build-up of Static is Caused by Transferring Electrons

<u>All matter</u> contains charge — <u>atoms</u> contain <u>positive protons</u> and <u>negative electrons</u>. Most matter contains an <u>equal number</u> of positive and negative charges, so their effects <u>cancel each other out</u> (the matter has <u>zero net charge</u> and is <u>neutral</u>). But in some situations charge can <u>build up</u> on objects — this is <u>static electricity</u>:

1) When two materials are <u>rubbed together</u>, <u>electrons</u> are <u>transferred</u> from one to the other.

2) If the materials are <u>conductors</u>, the electrons will <u>flow back into or out of</u> them, so they <u>stay neutral</u>.
    But if the materials are <u>insulators</u>, electrons <u>can't</u> flow, so a <u>positive static charge</u> is left on the object that <u>lost electrons</u> and a <u>negative static charge</u> is left on the object that <u>gained electrons</u>.

3) It's always <u>negative charges</u> (electrons) that move.
    The <u>direction</u> of electron transfer depends on the <u>materials</u>:

4) If <u>enough</u> charge builds up, it can <u>suddenly move</u>, causing <u>sparks</u> or <u>shocks</u>.

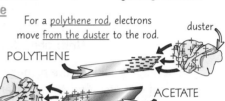

For a <u>polythene rod</u>, electrons move <u>from the duster</u> to the rod.

POLYTHENE

duster

ACETATE

For an <u>acetate rod</u>, electrons move <u>from the rod</u> to the duster.

Like Charges Repel, Opposite Charges Attract

1) Electrically charged objects <u>exert a force</u> on one another.

2) These forces get <u>weaker</u> the <u>further apart</u> the two objects are.

3) Things with <u>opposite</u> electric charges <u>attract</u> each other, things with the <u>same</u> electric charge <u>repel</u>.

4) The force between two charged objects is known as <u>electrostatic attraction</u> (if they attract each other), or <u>electrostatic repulsion</u> (if they repel). It's a <u>non-contact</u> force — the objects don't need to touch.

5) If you <u>hang</u> a charged <u>rod</u> from a string and put an object with the <u>same charge</u> near the rod, the rod will <u>move away</u> from the object. An <u>oppositely-charged</u> object will <u>attract</u> the rod towards it.

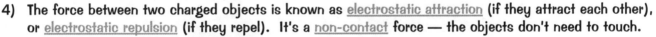

You Need to Know How to Test Whether an Object is Charged

1) Electrically charged objects <u>attract</u> small neutral objects placed near them. E.g. if you hold a charged rod above some <u>small scraps of paper</u> the scraps will 'jump' towards it.

2) This happens because the charged rod <u>induces a charge</u> in the paper — if the rod is <u>positively charged</u>, it <u>attracts the electrons</u> in the paper towards it, and if it's <u>negatively charged</u> it <u>repels the electrons</u>. This gives the <u>surface of the paper</u> near the rod an <u>opposite charge</u> to the rod, so the rod and the paper are <u>attracted</u> together.

Negative charges in the paper are repelled by the negatively charged rod...

...this means the parts of the paper nearest the rod have a positive charge. They're attracted to the rod.

3) You can also test if a rod is charged by holding it near a <u>stream of water</u> from a tap. The rod will induce a charge in the water, so the stream will be attracted to the rod and <u>bend</u> towards it.

You can also test for charge using a <u>gold leaf electroscope</u>:

• If a <u>negatively charged</u> insulator touches the <u>zinc plate</u>, some of its charge is <u>transferred</u> to the electroscope, and <u>conducted</u> down to the metal <u>stem</u> and <u>gold leaf</u>. This <u>negatively charges</u> both the stem and the gold leaf, which <u>repel</u> each other. This makes the gold leaf <u>rise</u>.

• If you touch the plate with a <u>positively charged</u> insulator, <u>electrons flow into it</u> from the plate, stem and leaf. Again, the stem and leaf will have the <u>same charge</u> and the leaf will <u>rise</u>.

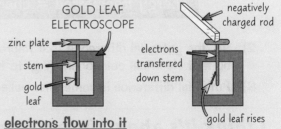

GOLD LEAF ELECTROSCOPE

negatively charged rod

zinc plate

stem

gold leaf

electrons transferred down stem

gold leaf rises

Come on, think positive...

The methods above are just a couple of ways of testing if an object is charged — you might see another in the exams.

Q1   Describe one way of demonstrating that an insulating object is carrying a static charge.   [2 marks]

Current and Potential Difference

When charge moves, you get a <u>current</u>. Currents <u>transfer energy</u> around a circuit.

A Potential Difference Pushes a Current Through a Resistance

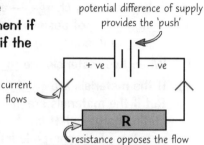

potential difference of supply provides the 'push'

current flows

resistance opposes the flow

1) <u>Current</u> is the <u>rate of flow</u> of electric charge (electrons) around the circuit. Current will <u>only flow</u> through an electrical component if there is a <u>potential difference</u> across that component, and if the circuit is <u>complete</u> (closed). Unit: ampere, A.

2) <u>Potential Difference</u> is the <u>driving force</u> that pushes the current round. Unit: volt, V.

3) <u>Resistance</u> is a measure of how easily charge can flow. Unit: ohm, Ω.

Generally speaking, the <u>higher the potential difference</u> across a given component, the <u>higher the current</u> will be. And the <u>greater the resistance</u> of a component, the <u>smaller the current</u> that flows (for a given potential difference across the component). There's more on resistance on page 178.

In a <u>single closed loop</u> (like the one in the diagram above) the current will have the <u>same value</u> at any point.

Total Charge Through a Circuit Depends on Current and Time

1) <u>Current</u> is the <u>rate of flow</u> of <u>charge</u>. If a <u>current</u> (I) flows past a point in a circuit for a length of <u>time</u> (t), then the <u>charge</u> (Q) that has passed this point is given by this formula:

$$\text{charge} = \text{current} \times \text{time}$$

$$\frac{Q}{I \times t}$$

More charge passes around the circuit in a given time when a greater current flows.

2) To use this formula, you need <u>current</u> in <u>amperes</u>, <u>A</u>, <u>charge</u> in <u>coulombs</u>, <u>C</u> and <u>time</u> in <u>seconds</u>, s.

EXAMPLE:

A battery passes a current of 0.25 A through a light bulb over a period of 4 hours. How much charge does the battery transfer through the bulb altogether?

charge = current × time = 0.25 × (4 × 60 × 60) = 3600 C

Watch out for units — your time needs to be in seconds if you're calculating charge.

Potential Difference is the Energy Transferred Per Unit Charge

1) The <u>potential difference</u> (V) is the <u>energy transferred</u> (E) <u>per coulomb of charge</u> (Q) that passes between <u>two points</u> in an electrical circuit. You can calculate energy transferred, in joules, J, from potential difference, in V, and charge, in C, using <u>this formula</u>:

$$\text{energy transferred} = \text{charge} \times \text{potential difference}$$

$$\frac{E}{V \times Q}$$

2) So, the <u>potential difference</u> (p.d.) across an electrical component is the <u>amount of energy</u> transferred by that electrical component (e.g. to the kinetic energy store of a motor) <u>per unit of charge</u>.

3) Potential difference is sometimes called <u>voltage</u>. They're the same thing.

I think it's about time you took charge...

Electrons in circuits actually move from –ve to +ve, but it's conventional to draw current as though it's flowing from +ve to –ve. It's what early physicists thought (before they found out about the electrons), and it's stuck.

Q1 Calculate how long it takes a current of 2.5 A to transfer a charge of 120 C. [2 marks]

Q2 A current flowing through a resistor transfers 360 J of energy when 75 C of charge are passed through it. Calculate the potential difference across the resistor. [2 marks]

Circuits — the Basics

That's enough theory for a minute, time to get practical...

Circuit Symbols You Should Know

there's more about a.c. and d.c. on p.214.

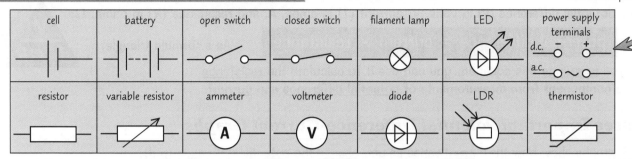

| cell | battery | open switch | closed switch | filament lamp | LED | power supply terminals |
| resistor | variable resistor | ammeter | voltmeter | diode | LDR | thermistor |

Some resistors have a fixed resistance, but for other resistors their resistance varies depending on the current that's flowing through them.

The Standard Test Circuit

You can use this circuit to investigate components — e.g. how their resistance changes with current and potential difference.

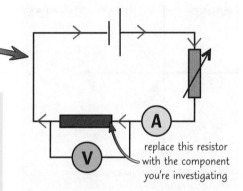

replace this resistor with the component you're investigating

1) The AMMETER measures the current (in amps) flowing through the component.

2) Must be placed in series (in line with) the component.

3) Can be put anywhere in series in the main circuit, but never in parallel like the voltmeter.

1) The VOLTMETER measures the potential difference across the component.

2) Must be placed in parallel with the component under test, NOT the variable resistor or battery (so it can compare the energy the charge has before and after passing through the component).

You can use this circuit to produce I-V graphs (see p.178) for different components.

PRACTICAL

1) Connect the circuit as shown above. The component, the ammeter and the variable resistor are all in series, which means they can be put in any order in the main circuit. (Remember the voltmeter must be in parallel around the component under test.)

2) Begin to vary the resistance of the variable resistor. This alters the current flowing through the circuit and the potential difference across the component.

3) Take several pairs of readings from the ammeter and voltmeter to see how the potential difference across the component varies as the current changes.

4) Plot the current against the potential difference to get I-V graphs like the ones on page 178.

5) You can use this data to work out the resistance for each measurement of I and V, using the formula on page 178 — so you can see if the resistance of the component changes as I and V change.

6) Make sure the circuit doesn't get too hot over the course of your experiment, as this will mess up your results. If the circuit starts to warm up, disconnect it for a while between readings so it can cool down. And, like any experiment, you should do repeats and calculate averages.

Measure gymnastics — use a vaultmeter...

Learn all those circuit symbols — you could be asked to draw a circuit using one or more of them in your exams.

Q1   Draw the circuit symbol for an LED.   [1 mark]

Q2   Draw a circuit you could use to create an I-V graph for a thermistor.   [2 marks]

Topic P3 — Electricity and Magnetism

Resistance and $V = I \times R$

With your current and your potential difference measured, you can now make some <u>sweet</u> graphs...

Resistance, Potential Difference and Current: $V = I \times R$

For potential difference (*V*) in volts, V, current (*I*) in amps, A, and resistance (*R*) in ohms, Ω:

> **potential difference = current × resistance**

As a formula triangle:

If you <u>rearrange</u> this equation, you can use it to calculate the <u>resistance</u> of a component from measurements of <u>potential difference</u> and <u>current</u>.

Three Important Potential Difference-Current Graphs

I-V graphs show how the <u>current</u> varies as you <u>change</u> the <u>potential difference</u> (p.d). Here are three examples, plotted from experiments like the one on page 177:

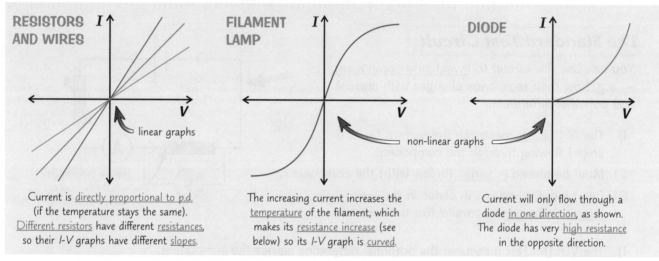

RESISTORS AND WIRES

Current is <u>directly proportional to p.d.</u> (if the temperature stays the same). <u>Different resistors</u> have different <u>resistances</u>, so their *I-V* graphs have different <u>slopes</u>.

FILAMENT LAMP

The increasing current increases the <u>temperature</u> of the filament, which makes its <u>resistance increase</u> (see below) so its *I-V* graph is <u>curved</u>.

DIODE

Current will only flow through a diode <u>in one direction</u>, as shown. The diode has very <u>high resistance</u> in the opposite direction.

linear graphs

non-linear graphs

1) You can find the <u>resistance</u> for <u>any point</u> on any *I-V* graph by reading the p.d. and <u>current</u> at that point and sticking them in the formula above.

2) A resistor or wire has a <u>constant resistance</u> (i.e. it doesn't change with current or p.d.), so its *I-V* graph is <u>linear</u>. If the line goes through <u>the origin</u>, the resistance of the component equals the <u>inverse</u> of the <u>gradient</u> of the line, or "<u>1/gradient</u>". The <u>steeper</u> the graph, the <u>lower</u> the resistance.

3) For some components, the <u>resistance changes</u> as the current and p.d. change — the *I-V* graph <u>curves</u>.

Resistance Increases with Temperature (Usually)

1) When an electron flows through a resistor, some of its energy is <u>transferred to the thermal energy store</u> of the resistor, <u>heating it up</u>.

2) As you know from p.152, the <u>thermal energy store</u> of a substance is really just the <u>kinetic energy store</u> of its particles. So as the resistor heats up its particles start to <u>vibrate more</u>. With the particles jiggling around it's <u>more difficult</u> for the charge-carrying electrons to get through the resistor — the <u>current can't flow</u> as easily and the <u>resistance increases</u>.

3) For most resistors there's a <u>limit</u> to the current that can flow. More current means an <u>increase</u> in <u>temperature</u>, which means an <u>increase</u> in <u>resistance</u>, which means the <u>current decreases</u> again.

> Thermistors (see page 179) are different — their resistance decreases with increasing temperature.

4) This is why the graph for the filament lamp <u>levels off</u> at high currents.

In the end you'll have to learn this — resistance is futile...

You may get given an *I-V* graph in your exam that you haven't seen before. Make sure you understand why these graphs have the shape they do, and you'll be ready for anything they throw at you.

Q1 A potential difference of 4.25 V is applied across a resistor, causing a current of 0.25 A to flow. Calculate the resistance, in ohms, of the resistor.

[1 mark]

Circuit Devices

Lamps and resistors are all very well and good, but <u>diodes</u>, <u>LDRs</u> and <u>thermistors</u> are where the fun's really at.

Current Only Flows in One Direction through a Diode

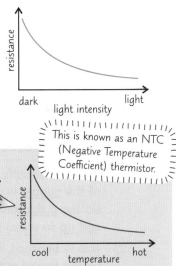

current flows this way

1) A diode is a special device made from <u>semiconductor</u> material such as <u>silicon</u>.

2) It lets current flow freely through it in <u>one direction</u>, but <u>not</u> in the other (i.e. there's a very high resistance in the <u>reverse</u> direction).

3) This turns out to be really useful in various <u>electronic circuits</u>, e.g. in <u>radio receivers</u>. Diodes can also be used to get direct current from an alternating supply (see page 214).

A Light-Dependent Resistor or "LDR" to You

1) An LDR is a resistor that's <u>dependent</u> on the <u>intensity</u> of <u>light</u>.

2) In <u>darkness</u>, the resistance is <u>highest</u>. As light levels <u>increase</u> the resistance <u>falls</u> so (for a given p.d.) the <u>current</u> through the LDR <u>increases</u>.

3) They have lots of applications including <u>automatic night lights</u>, <u>outdoor lighting</u> and <u>burglar detectors</u>.

resistance vs *light intensity* (dark → light) — graph showing resistance falling as light increases.

A Thermistor is a Temperature-Dependent Resistor

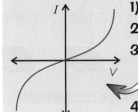

1) In <u>hot</u> conditions, the resistance of a thermistor <u>drops</u>.

2) In <u>cool</u> conditions, the resistance goes <u>up</u>.

3) In constant conditions, their *I-V* graphs are <u>curved</u> — as the <u>current increases</u>, the thermistor <u>warms up</u>, so the <u>resistance decreases</u>.

4) They're used as <u>temperature detectors</u>, in e.g. <u>thermostats</u>, <u>irons</u> and <u>car engines</u>.

This is known as an NTC (Negative Temperature Coefficient) thermistor.

resistance vs *temperature* (cool → hot) — graph showing resistance falling as temperature increases.

You Can Use LDRs and Thermistors in Sensing Circuits

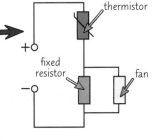

thermistor
fixed resistor
fan

1) <u>Sensing circuits</u> can be used to <u>turn on</u> or <u>increase the power</u> to components depending on the <u>conditions</u> that they are in.

2) The circuit on the right is a <u>sensing circuit</u>.

3) The fixed resistor and the fan will always have the <u>same potential difference</u> across them (because they're connected in parallel — see page 180).

4) The <u>p.d.</u> of the power supply is <u>shared out</u> between the thermistor and the loop made up of the fixed resistor and the fan according to their <u>resistances</u> — the <u>bigger</u> a component's resistance, the <u>more</u> of the p.d. it takes.

5) As the room gets hotter, the resistance of the thermistor <u>decreases</u> and it takes a <u>smaller share</u> of the p.d. from the power supply. So the p.d. across the fixed resistor and the fan <u>rises</u>, making the fan go faster.

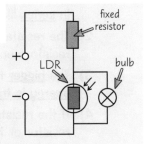

fixed resistor
LDR
bulb

You can also connect the component <u>across the variable resistor</u> instead.

For example, if you connect a <u>bulb</u> in parallel to an <u>LDR</u>, the <u>p.d.</u> across both the LDR and the bulb will be <u>high</u> when it's <u>dark</u> and the LDR's resistance is <u>high</u>. The <u>greater the p.d.</u> across a component, the <u>more energy</u> it gets. So a <u>bulb</u> connected <u>across an LDR</u> would get <u>brighter</u> as the room got <u>darker</u>.

Permistors — resistance decreases with curliness of hair...

Bonus fact — circuits like the one above are called potential dividers (because they divide up potential difference).

Q1   a) Sketch an *I-V* graph for a thermistor in constant conditions.   [1 mark]

       b) Explain the shape of the graph you drew in part a).   [2 marks]

Series and Parallel Circuits

Wiring a circuit in <u>series</u> or <u>parallel</u> can have a <u>big difference</u> on its behaviour.

Series and Parallel Circuits are Connected Differently

1) In <u>series circuits</u>, the different components are connected <u>in a line</u>, <u>end to end</u>, between the +ve and −ve terminals of the power supply. Current has to flow through <u>all</u> of the components to get round the circuit, so if you <u>remove</u> one of them it can have a <u>big effect</u> on the others.

2) In <u>parallel circuits</u> each component is <u>separately</u> connected to the +ve and −ve terminals of the <u>supply</u>. This means if you remove or disconnect <u>one</u> of them, it will <u>hardly affect</u> the others at all.

3) Parallel circuits are usually the most sensible way to connect things, for example in <u>cars</u> and in <u>household electrics</u>, where you have to be able to switch everything on and off <u>separately</u>. But you need to know all about both types of circuit I'm afraid.

4) If you add <u>more cells</u> to <u>any circuit</u>, connect them in <u>series</u>, not parallel. Connecting <u>several cells in series</u>, <u>all the same way</u> (+ to −) gives a <u>bigger total p.d.</u> — because each charge in the circuit passes through each cell and gets a 'push' from each one. So <u>two 1.5 V</u> cells <u>in series</u> would supply <u>3 V in total</u>.

Series Circuits — Everything in a Line

Potential Difference is Shared

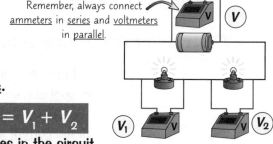

Remember, always connect <u>ammeters</u> in <u>series</u> and <u>voltmeters</u> in <u>parallel</u>.

1) In series circuits, the <u>total potential difference</u> (p.d.) of the <u>supply</u> is <u>shared</u> between the various <u>components</u>. So the <u>p.d.s</u> round a series circuit always <u>add up</u> to equal the p.d. across the <u>power supply</u>:

$$V = V_1 + V_2$$

2) This is because the total <u>energy transferred</u> to the charges in the circuit by the <u>power supply</u> equals the total <u>energy transferred</u> from the charges to the <u>components</u>.

Current is the Same Everywhere

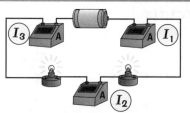

1) In series circuits the <u>same current</u> flows through <u>all parts</u> of the circuit:

$$I_1 = I_2 = I_3$$

2) The <u>size</u> of the current is determined by the <u>total p.d.</u> of the power supply and the <u>total resistance</u> of the circuit: i.e. $I = V/R$.

Resistance Adds Up

1) In series circuits, the <u>total resistance</u> is just the <u>sum</u> of the individual resistances: You can treat <u>multiple resistors</u> connected in <u>series</u> like this as a <u>single resistor</u> with <u>equivalent resistance</u> **R**.

$$R = R_1 + R_2 + R_3$$

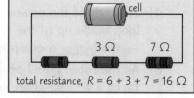

total resistance, $R = 6 + 3 + 7 = 16 \ \Omega$

2) The resistance of <u>two</u> (or more) resistors in <u>series</u> is <u>bigger</u> than the resistance of just one of the resistors on its own because the <u>battery</u> has to <u>push each charge</u> through <u>all</u> of them.

3) The <u>bigger</u> the resistance of a component, the bigger its <u>share</u> of the <u>total p.d.</u> because more <u>energy is transferred</u> from the charge when moving through a <u>large</u> resistance than a <u>small</u> one).

4) If the resistance of <u>one</u> component <u>changes</u> (e.g. if it's a variable resistor, light-dependent resistor or thermistor) then the <u>potential difference</u> across <u>all</u> the components will change too.

I like series circuits so much I bought the box set...

Series circuits are simple to make, but a real pain — if one of the bulbs in the diagrams above blew, it'd break the circuit, so they'd all go out. That's one of the reasons they're not as popular as parallel circuits.

Q1   Three identical filament bulbs are connected in series to a power supply of 3.6 V. Calculate the p.d. across each bulb.

[1 mark]

More on Series and Parallel Circuits

Parallel Circuits — Independence and Isolation

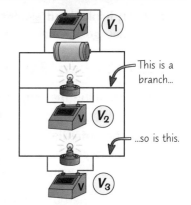

Potential Difference is the Same Across All Branches

1) In parallel circuits <u>all</u> branches get the <u>full source p.d.</u>, so the p.d. is the <u>same</u> across all branches:

$$V_1 = V_2 = V_3$$

2) This is because <u>each charge</u> can only pass down <u>one branch</u> of the circuit, so it must <u>transfer all the energy</u> supplied to it by the <u>source p.d.</u> to whatever's on that branch.

This is a branch...

...so is this.

Current is Shared Between Branches

1) In parallel circuits the <u>total current</u> flowing round the circuit equals the <u>total</u> of all the currents through the <u>separate branches</u>.

$$I = I_1 + I_2$$

2) You can find the current in a branch using <u>$I = V/R$</u>, where V is the <u>p.d. across the branch</u> (which is equal to the source p.d.) and R is the <u>resistance</u> of the <u>component on the branch</u> (or the <u>equivalent resistance</u> of the branch if there's more than one component on it).

3) In a parallel circuit, there are <u>junctions</u> where the current either <u>splits</u> or <u>rejoins</u>. The total current going <u>into</u> a junction has to equal the total current <u>leaving</u>.

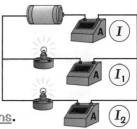

Resistance Is Tricky

1) The <u>total resistance</u> of a parallel circuit is <u>tricky to work out</u>, but it's always <u>less</u> than that of the branch with the <u>smallest</u> resistance.

2) The resistance is lower because the charge has <u>more than one</u> branch to take — only <u>some</u> of the charge will flow along each branch.

3) A circuit with two resistors in <u>parallel</u> will have a <u>lower</u> resistance than a circuit with either of the resistors <u>by themselves</u> — which means the <u>parallel</u> circuit will have a <u>higher total current</u>.

R_1 R_2

total $R < R_1$ and total $R < R_2$

You Can Investigate Series and Parallel Circuits using Bulbs

1) Set up a <u>circuit</u> consisting of a <u>power supply</u> and a <u>bulb</u>. Use a <u>voltmeter</u> to measure the <u>p.d.</u> across the bulb, and an <u>ammeter</u> to measure the <u>current</u> in the circuit.

2) Add a <u>second bulb</u> in <u>series</u> with the first. Measure the current flowing through the circuit and the p.d. across each bulb. The bulbs should both look <u>dimmer</u>.

3) Add a <u>third bulb</u> in series with the first two. All three will look <u>even dimmer</u>. Again, measure the p.d. across each bulb, and the current through the circuit.

4) You'll find that each time you <u>add a bulb</u>, the <u>p.d.</u> across each bulb <u>falls</u> — this is because the p.d.s across the bulbs in the circuit need to <u>add up</u> to the <u>source p.d.</u>

5) The <u>current</u> also <u>falls</u> each time you add a bulb, because you're increasing the <u>resistance</u> of the circuit.

6) <u>Less current</u> and <u>less p.d.</u> means the bulbs get <u>dimmer</u> (i.e. the power of each bulb is decreasing).

7) Repeat the experiment, this time adding each bulb in <u>parallel</u> on a <u>new branch</u>. You'll need to measure the <u>current</u> on <u>each branch</u> each time you add a bulb.

8) You should find that the bulbs <u>don't get dimmer</u> as you add more to the circuit.

9) The p.d. across <u>each bulb</u> is <u>equal</u> to the <u>source p.d.</u>, no matter how many bulbs there are.

10) The <u>current</u> on each branch is <u>the same</u>, and <u>doesn't change</u> when you add more bulbs, because the resistance of each branch stays the same.

Remember, you connect voltmeters in parallel, and ammeters in series.

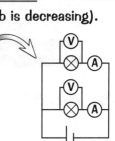

A current shared is a current halved...

Remember, in parallel circuits, each branch has the same p.d., but the total current is shared between branches.

Q1 If 3 identical bulbs are connected in parallel to a 3.5 V battery, state the p.d. across each bulb. [1 mark]

Energy and Power in Circuits

You can think about <u>electrical circuits</u> in terms of <u>energy transfer</u> — the charges travel around the circuit, and when they go through an electrical component energy is transferred to make the component work.

Think about Potential Difference in Terms of Energy and Charges

1) Anything that supplies <u>electricity</u> is <u>supplying energy</u> — an electrical <u>current transfers energy</u> from the <u>power supply</u> (e.g. cells, batteries, generators etc) to the <u>components</u> of the circuit.

2) The potential difference between two points is the energy transferred by one coulomb of charge between these points — <u>energy = charge × potential difference</u> (p.176). This gives you a useful way of thinking about how electric circuits <u>actually work</u>:

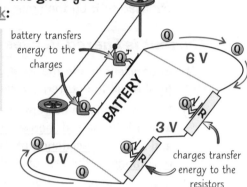

battery transfers energy to the charges

charges transfer energy to the resistors

- Energy is <u>supplied</u> to the charge at the <u>power source</u> to 'raise' it through a potential.
- The charge <u>gives up</u> this energy when it '<u>falls</u>' through a <u>potential drop</u> in any <u>components</u> elsewhere in the circuit.

3) A battery with a <u>bigger p.d.</u> will supply <u>more energy</u> to the circuit for every <u>coulomb</u> of charge which flows round it, because the charge is raised up "<u>higher</u>" at the start — and <u>more energy</u> will be <u>transferred</u> in the circuit too.

4) The greater the <u>resistance</u> of a component, the <u>more energy</u> the charge has to transfer to it to pass through, so the <u>bigger the drop</u> in p.d.

Power is the Rate of Energy Transfer

1) The <u>power</u> of a component tells you <u>how much energy it transfers per second</u>. <u>Energy</u> (*E*) and <u>power</u> (*P*) are related by the formula:

in seconds (s)

$$\text{energy transferred} = \text{power} \times \text{time}$$

in joules (J)   in watts (W)

$$\frac{E}{P \times t}$$

2) Energy is usually given in joules, but you may also see it given in <u>kilowatt-hours</u>.

3) A kilowatt-hour (kWh) is the amount of energy a device with a <u>power of 1 kW</u> (1000 W) <u>transfers</u> in <u>1 hour</u> of operation. It's <u>much bigger</u> than a joule, so it's useful for when you're dealing with <u>large amounts</u> of energy.

4) To calculate the energy transferred in kWh, you need <u>power</u> in <u>kilowatts, kW</u>, and the <u>time</u> in <u>hours, h</u>.

Calculate Power from Current and Potential Difference

1) You can calculate <u>electrical power</u> of a component in watts, W, from the <u>potential difference</u> across it in volts, V, and the <u>current</u> through it in amperes, A, using the formula:

$$\text{power} = \text{potential difference} \times \text{current}$$

$$\frac{P}{V \times I}$$

2) You know that <u>potential difference = current × resistance</u>. If you substitute this into the formula above, you get <u>another</u> handy way to calculate power:

Resistance is measured in ohms, Ω.

$$\text{power} = \text{current}^2 \times \text{resistance}$$ or, in symbols: $P = I^2R$

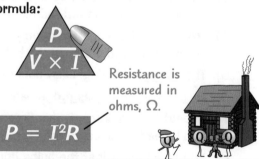

You have the power — now use your potential...

There are a lot of equations to learn here I'm afraid. You could try writing them out and sticking them to your wall to help get them firmly lodged in your brain. If not, at least you'll have some funky new wallpaper.

Q1   A 1.5×10^3 W hairdryer is turned on for 11 minutes. Calculate the energy transferred, in J.   [2 marks]

Q2   A p.d. of 2.5 V is applied across a resistor with a power of 8.5 W.
Calculate the current flowing through the resistor.   [2 marks]

Q3   A 15 Ω resistor transfers energy at a rate of 375 W. Calculate the current through the resistor.   [2 marks]

Magnets and Magnetic Fields

I think magnetism is an <u>attractive</u> subject, but don't get <u>repelled</u> by the exam — <u>revise</u>.

Magnets Have Magnetic Fields

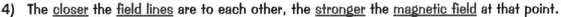

magnetic field lines

north pole

south pole

1) All magnets have <u>two poles</u> — <u>north</u> and <u>south</u>.

2) A <u>magnetic field</u> is a <u>region</u> where a <u>magnetic material</u> (<u>iron</u>, <u>nickel</u> or <u>cobalt</u>) experiences a <u>force</u>.

3) <u>Magnetic field lines</u> (or "lines of force") are used to show the <u>size</u> and <u>direction</u> of magnetic fields. They <u>always</u> point from <u>NORTH</u> to <u>SOUTH</u>.

4) The <u>closer</u> the <u>field lines</u> are to each other, the <u>stronger</u> the <u>magnetic field</u> at that point.

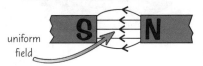

uniform field

5) The <u>strength of the magnetic field</u> is called the <u>magnetic flux density</u> and is measured in <u>teslas (T)</u>.

6) Placing the north and south poles of <u>two</u> permanent bar magnets <u>near</u> each other creates a <u>uniform field</u> between these two poles.

There Are Different Ways to See Magnetic Field Patterns

1) You can use <u>iron filings</u> to see <u>magnetic field patterns</u> of a magnet. Just put the magnet under a <u>piece of paper</u> and <u>scatter</u> the iron filings on top. The iron filings will <u>align</u> themselves with the field lines, e.g.:

2) You can also use a <u>compass</u> to plot magnetic field patterns:

- Put the magnet on a <u>piece of paper</u> and <u>place</u> the <u>compass</u> on the paper, next to the magnet. The <u>compass needle</u> will point in the <u>direction</u> of the <u>field line</u> at this position. Mark the <u>direction</u> that the compass needle is pointing in by marking <u>two dots</u> on the paper, <u>one at each end</u> of the needle.

- <u>Move</u> the compass so that the <u>tail end</u> of the needle is where the <u>tip</u> of the needle was previously. Repeat this and then <u>join up</u> the marks you've made — you will end up with a <u>drawing</u> of one <u>field line</u> around the magnet.

- <u>Repeat</u> this method at <u>different points</u> around the magnet to get <u>several field lines</u>.

3) Using a <u>compass</u> is <u>better</u> than iron filings as the <u>drawing</u> of the field will still be there after the magnet has been removed, and the drawing also shows the <u>direction</u> of the field lines. Also, iron filings are quite <u>messy</u> to work with — they're a nightmare if you <u>drop</u> them and <u>incredibly difficult</u> to <u>take off</u> a magnet if they get in contact with it.

4) Compasses will <u>always point North</u> when they aren't near a magnet. This is <u>evidence</u> that the <u>Earth</u> has a magnetic north and south pole and therefore must have a <u>magnetic core</u>.

Magnets Affect Magnetic Materials and Other Magnets

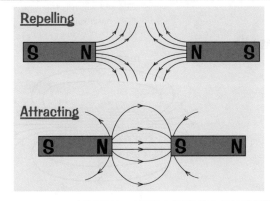

Repelling

Attracting

1) Like poles <u>repel</u> each other and unlike (opposite) poles <u>attract</u>.

2) Both poles <u>attract</u> magnetic materials (that aren't magnets).

3) When a magnet is brought <u>near</u> a magnetic material then that material acts as a <u>magnet</u>.

4) This magnetism has been <u>induced</u> by the original magnet. The <u>closer</u> the two get, the <u>stronger</u> the induced magnetism.

5) The <u>difference</u> between permanent and induced magnets is that <u>induced magnets</u> will (usually) <u>lose</u> their magnetism once the magnet has been moved away.

Magnets are like farmers — surrounded by fields...

Lots of fun diagrams here, so get arty and practise drawing field lines around and between magnets.

Q1   Describe how to plot the magnetic field lines of a bar magnet with a compass.   [4 marks]

Q2   Explain why a piece of copper is not attracted to or repelled by a magnet.   [1 mark]

Electromagnetism

It would be <u>really</u> handy if you could turn a magnetic field <u>on</u> and <u>off</u>. Entrance stage left — <u>electromagnetism</u>.

A Current-Carrying Wire has a Magnetic Effect

1) An <u>electric current</u> in a material produces a <u>magnetic field</u> around it.

2) The <u>larger</u> the electric current, the <u>stronger</u> the magnetic field.

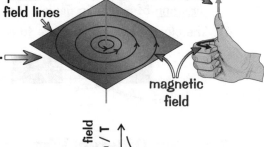
The wire that carries the current doesn't have to be a magnetic material — it can be any metal.

The Magnetic Field Around a Straight Wire

1) A magnetic field around a <u>straight</u>, <u>current-carrying wire</u> is made up of <u>concentric circles</u> with the wire in the centre. You can find the <u>direction</u> of the field with the <u>right-hand rule</u>.

2) You could <u>show</u> that there's a magnetic field around a current-carrying wire by using <u>compasses</u>. They can also be used to find the <u>direction</u> of the magnetic field.

3) The <u>further</u> away from the <u>wire</u>, the <u>weaker</u> the <u>magnetic field</u> (shown by the field lines getting further apart). A <u>graph</u> of <u>magnetic field strength</u> against <u>distance from wire</u> would look like this: It's a <u>non-linear</u> relationship — the strength <u>decreases quickly</u> at first, but this <u>slows down</u> with an <u>increasing distance</u>.

plane of field lines — current — magnetic field

magnetic field strength / T vs distance from wire / m

The Magnetic Field Around a Flat Circular Coil

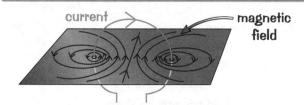
current — magnetic field

1) The magnetic field in the <u>centre</u> of a flat circular coil of wire is similar to that of a <u>bar magnet</u>.

2) There are concentric <u>ellipses</u> (stretched circles) of magnetic field lines <u>around</u> the coil.

The Magnetic Field Around a Solenoid

1) If you have lots of <u>coils</u> of wire joined together to make a <u>solenoid</u>, the magnetic effect is increased. The magnetic field <u>inside</u> a current-carrying <u>solenoid</u> is <u>strong</u> and <u>uniform</u>.

2) <u>Outside</u> the coil, the field is just like the one around a <u>bar magnet</u>.

3) This means that the <u>ends</u> of a solenoid act like the <u>north pole</u> and <u>south pole</u> of a bar magnet. This type of magnet is called an <u>electromagnet</u>.

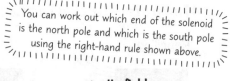
You can work out which end of the solenoid is the north pole and which is the south pole using the right-hand rule shown above.

The magnetic effect at the ends of the solenoid will <u>increase</u> if:

- the <u>current</u> in the wire is <u>increased</u>
- the <u>number of turns</u> (i.e. the number of <u>coils</u>) of wire is <u>increased</u>, but the length stays the same
- the <u>length</u> of the solenoid is <u>decreased</u> (but the number of turns stays the same)
- an <u>iron core</u> is added <u>inside</u> the solenoid.

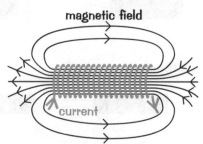
magnetic field — current

Give me one good raisin why I should make the currant joke...

Remember — the closer to the current-carrying wire or solenoid, the stronger the magnetic field.

Q1   Sketch the magnetic field lines produced by each of the following.
     Include the direction of both the current and the field lines in your answer.
     a) A straight current-carrying wire.   b) A current-carrying solenoid.   [4 marks]

Magnetic Forces

If you put a current-carrying conductor into a magnetic field, you have two magnetic fields combining.

A Current in a Magnetic Field Experiences a Force

When a current-carrying conductor (e.g. a wire) is put between magnetic poles, the two magnetic fields affect one another. The result is a force on the wire.

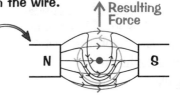

↑ Resulting Force

This is an aerial view. The red dot represents a wire carrying current "out of the page" (towards you). (If it was a cross ('×') then that would mean the current was going into the page.)

→ Normal magnetic field of wire
→ Normal magnetic field of magnets
→ Deviated magnetic field of magnets

1) To experience the full force, the wire has to be at 90° (right angles) to the magnetic field. If the wire runs along the magnetic field, it won't experience any force at all. At angles in between, it'll feel some force.

2) The force gets stronger if either the current or the magnetic field is made stronger.

The wire also exerts an equal and opposite force on the magnet, but here we're just looking at the force on the wire.

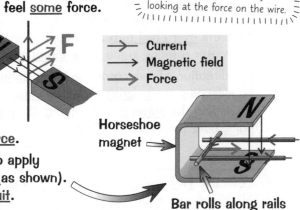

→ Current
→ Magnetic field
→ Force

3) The force always acts in the same direction relative to the magnetic field of the magnets and the direction of the current in the wire. So changing the direction of either the magnetic field or the current will change the direction of the force.

4) A good way of showing the direction of the force is to apply a current to a set of rails inside a horseshoe magnet (as shown). A bar is placed on the rails, which completes the circuit. This generates a force that rolls the bar along the rails.

Horseshoe magnet →

Bar rolls along rails when current is applied

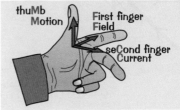

thuMb Motion
First finger Field
seCond finger Current

1) Fleming's left-hand rule is used to find the direction of the force on a current-carrying conductor.

2) Using your left hand, point your First finger in the direction of the magnetic Field and your seCond finger in the direction of the Current.

3) Your thuMb will then point in the direction of the force (Motion).

You can Calculate the Force Acting on a Current-Carrying Conductor

The equation used to calculate the force on a current-carrying conductor (e.g. a wire) when it's at right-angles to a magnetic field is:

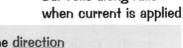

$$\text{Force on a conductor carrying a current (N)} = \text{magnetic flux density (T)} \times \text{current (A)} \times \text{length (m)} \quad \text{or} \quad F = B \times I \times L$$

Remember — 'magnetic flux density' is just a fancy term for magnetic field strength.

EXAMPLE: An iron bar of length 0.20 m is connected in a circuit so a current of 15 A flows through it. If an external magnetic field of 0.18 T is placed at right angles to the direction of the current in the bar, calculate the force acting on the iron bar due to the presence of the magnetic field.

Force on the bar = magnetic flux density × current × bar length = 0.18 × 15 × 0.20 = 0.54 N

A current-carrying conductor — a ticket inspector eating sultanas...*

Learn the left-hand rule and use it — don't be scared of looking like a muppet in the exam.

Q1 State what the thumb, first finger and second finger each represent in Fleming's left-hand rule. [3 marks]

Q2 A 35 cm long piece of wire is at 90° to an external magnetic field. The wire experiences a force of 9.8 N when a current of 5.0 A is flowing through it. Calculate the magnetic flux density of the field. [2 marks]

*OK, so I did make the currant joke. Again.

Motors

This lot might look a bit tricky, but really it's just applying the stuff you learnt on the previous page.

A Simple Electric Motor uses Magnets and a Current-Carrying Coil

1) In a simple d.c. motor, a current-carrying coil sits between two opposite poles of a magnet.

2) Because the current is flowing in different directions on each side of the coil, and each side of the coil is perpendicular to the magnetic field, each side will experience forces in opposite directions.

3) Because the coil is on a spindle, and the forces act in opposite directions on each side, it rotates.

4) The split-ring commutator is a clever way of swapping the contacts every half turn to keep the motor rotating in the same direction.

5) The direction of the motor can be reversed either by swapping the polarity of the d.c. supply (reversing the current) or swapping the magnetic poles over (reversing the field).

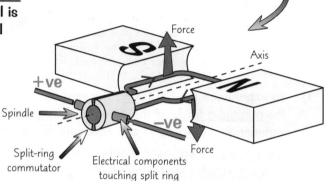

To speed up the motor, increase the current, add more turns to the coil or increase the magnetic flux density.

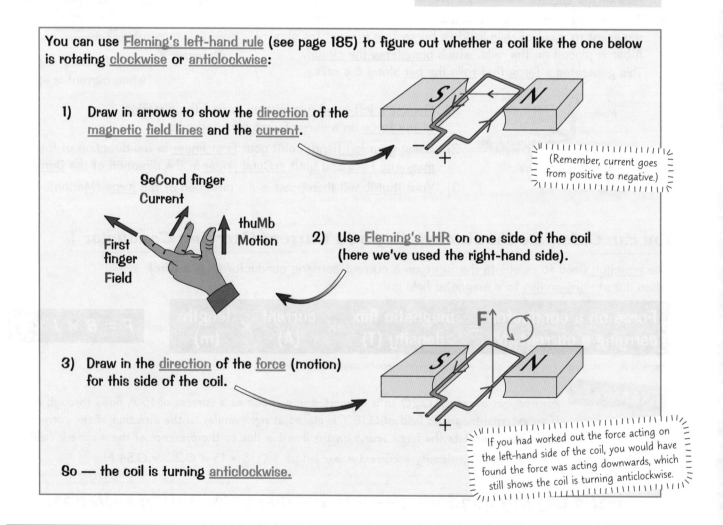

You can use Fleming's left-hand rule (see page 185) to figure out whether a coil like the one below is rotating clockwise or anticlockwise:

1) Draw in arrows to show the direction of the magnetic field lines and the current.

(Remember, current goes from positive to negative.)

SeCond finger
Current

thuMb
Motion

First finger
Field

2) Use Fleming's LHR on one side of the coil (here we've used the right-hand side).

3) Draw in the direction of the force (motion) for this side of the coil.

So — the coil is turning anticlockwise.

If you had worked out the force acting on the left-hand side of the coil, you would have found the force was acting downwards, which still shows the coil is turning anticlockwise.

What makes the world go round? Not an electric motor. Or love...

Practise using Fleming's LHR rule on coils, so you're super confident in working out which way they will turn.

Q1   State two properties that could be changed to decrease the speed of an electric motor.   [2 marks]

Topic P3 — Electricity and Magnetism

Revision Questions for Topic P3

<u>Topic P3</u> — it was a tough ride but we got through it. Now let's see how much of it stuck...
- Try these questions and <u>tick off each one</u> when you <u>get it right</u>.
- When you've done <u>all the questions</u> under a heading and are <u>completely happy</u> with it, tick it off.

<u>Static Electricity (p.175)</u> ☐

1) Explain how static electricity builds up on a polythene rod when it's rubbed with a duster. ☑
2) Explain why a charged rod will attract small pieces of paper. ☑

<u>Electricity and Circuits (p.176-179)</u> ☑

3) What conditions are needed for a current to flow in a circuit? ☑
4) What are the units of: a) current, b) charge, c) potential difference? ☑
5) What is the equation linking current, charge and time? ☑
6) Define potential difference in terms of energy and charge. ☑
7) Draw the circuit symbols for: a) a battery, b) a filament lamp, c) a thermistor, d) an LDR ☑
8) Sketch a standard test circuit. Describe how you could use it to draw an *I-V* graph for a resistor. ☑
9) Sketch the *I-V* graph of: a) a filament lamp, b) a wire, c) a diode. ☑
10) Describe how to find a component's resistance for a particular current and p.d. from an *I-V* graph. ☑
11) Describe how the resistance of an LDR changes with light-level. ☑

<u>Series and Parallel Circuits (p.180-181)</u> ☑

12) What is the rule relating the p.d.s across the components of a series circuit to the source p.d.? ☑
13) What is the rule for current in a series circuit? ☑
14) What is the total resistance of a series circuit equal to? ☑
15) State the rule relating the p.d.s across the components of a parallel circuit to the source p.d. ☑
16) What is the rule for current in a parallel circuit? ☑

<u>Energy and Power in Circuits (p.182)</u> ☐

17) What is the power of a circuit component? How is power related to energy and time? ☑
18) Explain what a kilowatt-hour is. ☑
19) Write equations linking power to: a) potential difference and current, b) current and resistance. ☑

<u>Magnets and Magnetic Fields (p.183-184)</u> ☑

20) Sketch the field lines (including their direction) around a bar magnet. ☑
21) What is the magnetic flux density and what unit is it measured in? ☑
22) What is the difference between a permanent magnet and an induced magnet? ☑
23) Describe what happens to magnetic field strength as you get further from a current-carrying wire. ☑

<u>Magnetic Forces and Motors (p.185-186)</u> ☐

24) Why could a magnet and a current-carrying conductor feel a force when they're near each other? ☑
25) At what angle must a current-carrying wire be to an external magnetic field to feel a maximum force? ☑
26) Name the rule used to find the direction of the force on a current-carrying wire in a magnetic field. ☑
27) Give the equation that relates the force on a current-carrying conductor, the magnetic flux density of an external magnetic field, the current in the conductor and the length of the conductor. ☑
28) Explain how magnetic forces are used in electric motors. ☑

Wave Basics

Waves transfer <u>energy</u> from one place to another without transferring any <u>matter</u> (stuff). Clever so and so's.

Waves Transfer Energy in the Direction they are Travelling

When waves travel through a medium, the <u>particles</u> of the medium <u>vibrate</u> and <u>transfer energy</u> between each other. BUT overall, the particles stay in the <u>same place</u> — <u>only energy</u> is transferred.

> For example, if you drop a twig into a calm pool of water, <u>ripples</u> form on the water's surface. The ripples <u>don't</u> carry the <u>water</u> (or the twig) away with them though.
> Similarly, if you strum a <u>guitar string</u> and create <u>sound waves</u>, the sound waves don't carry the <u>air</u> away from the guitar and create a <u>vacuum</u>.

1) The <u>amplitude</u> of a wave is the <u>displacement</u> from the <u>rest position</u> to a <u>crest</u> or <u>trough</u>.

2) The <u>wavelength</u> is the length of a <u>full cycle</u> of the wave, e.g. from <u>crest to crest</u> (or from <u>compression</u> to <u>compression</u> — see below).

3) <u>Frequency</u> is the <u>number of complete waves</u> or cycles passing a certain point <u>per second</u>. Frequency is measured in <u>hertz</u> (<u>Hz</u>). 1 Hz is <u>1 wave per second</u>.

4) The <u>period</u> of a wave is the <u>number of seconds</u> it takes for <u>one full cycle</u>. <u>Period = 1 ÷ frequency</u>.

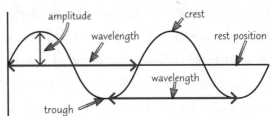

Transverse Waves Have Sideways Vibrations

In <u>transverse waves</u>, the vibrations are <u>perpendicular</u> (at 90°) to the <u>direction</u> the wave travels. <u>Transverse waves</u> can travel on the <u>surface</u> of a <u>liquid</u>, but they <u>can't travel through liquids</u>. <u>Most waves</u> are transverse, including:

1) <u>All electromagnetic waves</u> (see page 193), e.g. light.

2) <u>Ripples</u> and waves in <u>water</u>.

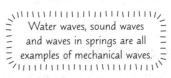

A spring wiggled <u>up and down</u> gives a <u>transverse</u> wave.

wave travels this way

vibrations go up and down

Water waves, sound waves and waves in springs are all examples of mechanical waves.

Longitudinal Waves Have Parallel Vibrations

1) In <u>longitudinal waves</u>, the vibrations are <u>parallel</u> to the <u>direction</u> the wave travels.

2) <u>Sound waves</u> are a good example.

3) Longitudinal waves <u>squash up</u> and <u>stretch out</u> the arrangement of particles in the medium they pass through, making <u>compressions</u> (<u>high pressure</u>, lots of particles) and <u>rarefactions</u> (<u>low pressure</u>, fewer particles).

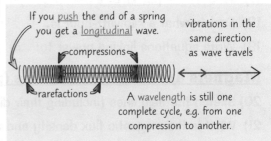

If you <u>push</u> the end of a spring you get a <u>longitudinal</u> wave.

vibrations in the same direction as wave travels

compressions

rarefactions

A wavelength is still one complete cycle, e.g. from one compression to another.

Learn the Wave Speed Equation

> wave speed (m/s) = frequency (Hz) × wavelength (m)

Wave frequencies are often given in <u>kHz</u> (kilohertz) or <u>MHz</u> (megahertz). Change them to Hz to use them in the equation.
<u>1 kHz = 1000 Hz</u> and <u>1 MHz = 1 000 000 Hz</u>.

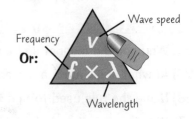

Or:

Wave speed

Frequency

Wavelength

$\dfrac{v}{f \times \lambda}$

What about Mexican waves...

You won't get far unless you understand these wave basics. Try a question to test your knowledge.

Q1   A wave has a speed of 0.15 m/s and a wavelength of 7.5 cm. Calculate its frequency.   [3 marks]

Wave Experiments

Time to _experiment_. Microphones and ripple tanks — sounds like fun, just don't mix them together...

Use an Oscilloscope to Measure the Speed of Sound

By attaching a signal generator to a speaker you can generate sounds with a specific frequency.
You can use two microphones and an oscilloscope to find the wavelength of the sound waves generated.

1) Set up the oscilloscope so the detected waves at each microphone are shown as separate waves.

2) Start with both microphones next to the speaker, then slowly move one away until the two waves are aligned on the display, but have moved exactly one wavelength apart.

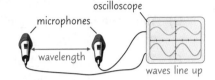

3) Measure the distance between the microphones to find one wavelength (λ).

4) You can then use the formula $v = f\lambda$ to find the speed (v) of the sound waves passing through the air — the frequency (f) is whatever you set the signal generator to in the first place.

Measure Speed, Frequency and Wavelength with a Ripple Tank | PRACTICAL

You can generate waves in a ripple tank using a motor attached to a dipper.
The motor moves the dipper up and down to create water waves at a fixed frequency.

> **To measure the frequency, you'll need a cork and a stopwatch:**

1) Float the cork in the ripple tank. It should bob up and down as the waves pass it.

2) When the cork is at the top of a 'bob', start the stopwatch.

3) Count how many times the cork bobs in, e.g. 20 seconds.

4) Divide this number by your time interval (how long you counted for) to get the number of 'bobs' per second — this is the frequency of the wave.

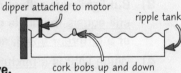

> **To measure the wavelength, use a strobe light:**

1) Place a card covered with centimetre-squared paper behind the ripple tank.

2) Turn on the strobe light and adjust its frequency until the waves appear to 'freeze'.

3) Using the squared paper, measure the distance that, e.g. five waves cover. Divide this distance by the number of waves to get an average wavelength.

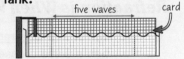

> **Use a pencil and a stopwatch to measure the wave speed:**
> (You'll need two people to do this one.)

1) Place a large piece of paper next to the tank.

2) As the waves move across the tank, one of you should track the path of one of the crests on the paper, using the pencil. Make sure your line is straight, and parallel to the direction the wave travels. You could use a ruler to help you.

3) The other should time how long the first has been drawing for. Pick a duration, e.g. 10 seconds, and stop drawing when this time has passed.

4) Calculate the speed of the wave by measuring the length of the line and plugging this into the formula distance travelled = speed × time.

> As $v = f\lambda$, you could measure two of these quantities and calculate the third.

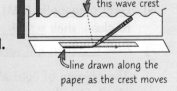

As always, for each of these experiments make sure you do at least three repeats and take an average.
Also, make sure it's a fair test — keep the equipment the same and the variables you aren't testing the same every time, e.g. the position of the dipper, the amplitude of the waves, the depth of the water...

Disco time in the physics lab...

Sound waves and ripples on water are model longitudinal and transverse waves because they're easy to work with.

Q1   Describe an experiment to measure the frequency of a water wave.   [3 marks]

Reflection and Refraction

All waves <u>reflect</u> and <u>refract</u>. 'What does that mean', you say? Read on...

Waves Are Absorbed, Transmitted and Reflected at Boundaries

When a <u>wave</u> meets a <u>boundary</u> between two materials (a <u>material interface</u>), <u>three</u> things can happen:

1) The wave may be <u>absorbed</u> by the second material, <u>transferring energy</u> to the <u>material's energy stores</u> (this is how a microwave works — see page 194).

2) The wave may be <u>transmitted</u> — it carries on <u>travelling</u> through the new material, often at a <u>different speed</u> (velocity), which can lead to <u>refraction</u> (see below)

3) The wave may <u>reflect</u> off the boundary. This is where the incoming ray is neither <u>absorbed</u> or <u>transmitted</u>, but 'sent back' away from the second material (see below).

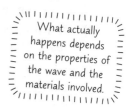

What actually happens depends on the properties of the wave and the materials involved.

Reflection of Light Lets Us See Things

There's <u>one simple rule</u> for <u>all reflected</u> waves:

Angle of Incidence = Angle of Reflection

Each angle is <u>measured from</u> the <u>normal</u> — an imaginary line that's at <u>right angles</u> to the surface at the point the light hits it (drawn with a <u>dotty</u> line).

1) The reflection of <u>visible light</u> is what let's us see things — light <u>bounces off</u> objects and into our eyes.

2) <u>Light rays</u> reflect off <u>smooth surfaces</u> (e.g. a <u>mirror</u>) all in the <u>same direction</u>, giving a <u>clear reflection</u>.

3) But light rays reflect off <u>rough surfaces</u> (e.g. paper) in <u>all different directions</u>. The angle of incidence <u>still equals</u> the angle of reflection for each ray, but the rough surface means each ray <u>hits</u> the surface at a <u>different angle</u>, and so is reflected at a different angle, <u>scattering</u> the light.

4) <u>White light</u> is a <u>mixture</u> of all the <u>different colours</u> of light, which all have a different <u>wavelength</u>.

5) <u>All the colours</u> of light in white light are reflected at the <u>same angle</u> — white light <u>doesn't split</u> into the different colours when it reflects, as all the wavelengths <u>follow the rule</u> above.

Refraction is When Waves Bend

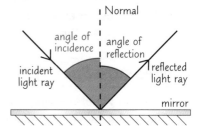

For light, when we say density we mean <u>optical density</u> — how the material affects the speed of light.

1) Waves travel at <u>different speeds</u> in materials with <u>different densities</u>. So when a wave crosses a boundary between materials, e.g. from glass to air, it <u>changes speed</u>.

2) The <u>frequency</u> of the wave <u>stays the same</u> when it crosses a boundary. As <u>$v = f\lambda$</u>, this means the wavelength changes — the wavelength <u>decreases</u> if the wave <u>slows down</u>, and <u>increases</u> if it <u>speeds up</u>.

3) If the wave hits the boundary <u>at an angle</u> to the normal, this change in speed (and wavelength) makes the wave <u>bend</u> — this is called <u>refraction</u>. The <u>greater</u> the <u>change</u> in speed, the <u>more</u> it <u>bends</u>.

   If the wave is travelling along the normal, it doesn't bend (but it still changes speed).

4) If the wave <u>slows down</u>, it will bend <u>towards the normal</u>. If it <u>speeds up</u> it will bend <u>away from</u> the normal.

5) <u>Sound</u> generally travels <u>faster</u> in <u>denser</u> material. So going to water from air, its <u>wavelength increases</u>.

6) <u>Electromagnetic</u> (EM) waves like light usually travel more <u>slowly</u> in <u>denser</u> materials. So going from air to glass, their <u>wavelength</u> would <u>decrease</u>, and they would <u>bend towards</u> the normal (if they refracted).

7) How <u>much</u> an <u>EM wave</u> refracts can be affected by its <u>wavelength</u> — <u>shorter</u> wavelengths <u>bend more</u>:

> The colours of light all have slightly <u>different wavelengths</u> — <u>shortest to longest</u> it goes violet, indigo, blue, green, yellow, orange, red.
>
> They travel at the <u>same speed in air</u>, but when they enter a <u>denser</u> substance (e.g. glass), the <u>shorter</u> wavelengths <u>slow down more</u> and so <u>refract</u> (bend) <u>more</u>.
>
> air / glass / violet (most) / red (least)

Red light bends the least — it should try yoga...

Hooray, a light mnemonic — <u>R</u>ichard <u>o</u>f <u>Y</u>ork <u>g</u>ave <u>b</u>attle <u>i</u>n <u>v</u>ain (<u>r</u>ed, <u>o</u>range, <u>y</u>ellow, <u>g</u>reen, <u>b</u>lue, <u>i</u>ndigo, <u>v</u>iolet).

Q1   A light ray enters air from water at 50° to the normal. How does it bend relative to the normal?   [1 mark]

 **PRACTICAL**

More on Reflection

Light reflects off lots of stuff. Which is pretty useful, or you wouldn't be able to read this book.

You can Investigate Reflection Using a Ray Box and a Mirror

To investigate reflection, you'll need a light source (e.g. a ray box), a plane (flat) mirror and a piece of plain white paper:

1) Take the piece of paper and draw a solid line across it using a ruler. Then draw a dotted line at 90° to the solid line (this will be the normal).

2) Place the plane (flat) mirror so it lines up with the solid line.

3) Using the ray box, shine a thin beam of white light at the mirror, so the light hits the mirror where the normal meets the mirror.

4) Your set-up should be something like this:

Do this experiment in a dark room. Keep the light levels the same throughout your experiment.

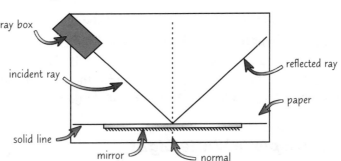

5) Trace the incident and reflected light rays.

6) Measure the angle between the incident ray and the normal (the angle of incidence) and the angle between the reflected ray and the normal (the angle of reflection) using a protractor.

7) Repeat these steps, varying the angle of incidence. You should find that no matter its value, the angle of incidence ALWAYS equals the angle of reflection.

8) If you wanted to take this investigation further, you could repeat the experiment using different colours of light by placing colour filters in front of the ray box. You should find that for any colour of light the angle of incidence still always equals the angle of reflection.

If you shine two (or more) parallel light rays at the mirror, the reflected rays will be parallel to each other too.

9) As always, keep your test fair by keeping other variables the same, e.g. use the same mirror and keep the width and brightness of the beam the same every time.

The Results of Your Experiment Will be a Ray Diagram

1) A ray diagram is just a picture that shows what path a beam of light took in a light experiment.

2) When you've done the experiment described above, you'll be left with a ray diagram on your paper.

3) Complete the ray diagram by marking on the angle of incidence and the angle of reflection, and adding arrows to your traced light rays, to show which direction the light was travelling in.

4) You can label all the lines and angles on your diagram to show what they are too.

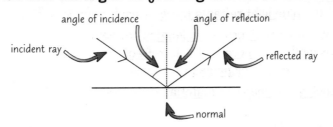

Remember, the angle of incidence should be equal the angle of reflection — if it isn't, something's gone wrong.

If you struggled with this page, take a moment to reflect on it...

That's how to do an experiment with a mirror and a ray box. For my next trick, I'll pull a question out of my hat...

Q1   A student shines a beam of white light on to a plane mirror. The angle of incidence between the light ray and the normal is 27°. State what the angle of reflection will be.   [1 mark]

Topic P4 — Waves and Radioactivity

More on Refraction

Remember refraction? Well, here's some more stuff you need to know about it...

When Light Travels From One Material Into Another it's Refracted

1) For refraction, you can draw a normal (see page 190) at any point where a ray meets a boundary between two materials.

2) If the light ray is travelling into a MORE dense material, it will slow DOWN, making it bend TOWARDS the normal.

3) If the light ray is travelling into a LESS dense material, it will speed UP, making it bend AWAY from the normal.

4) If a light ray is travelling through a rectangular block, the emerging ray and the incident ray will be parallel.

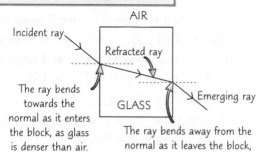

AIR

Incident ray

Refracted ray

GLASS

Emerging ray

The ray bends towards the normal as it enters the block, as glass is denser than air.

The ray bends away from the normal as it leaves the block, as air is less dense than glass.

1) The angle of incidence is between the incident ray and the normal.

2) The angle of refraction is between the refracted ray and the normal.

3) The angle of refraction varies with the angle of incidence. It also depends on the light's wavelength — the shorter the wavelength, the more it refracts. And it depends on the materials either side of the boundary, e.g. glass refracts light more than water.

angle of incidence

angle of refraction

Triangular Prisms Disperse White Light

Different wavelengths (colours) of light travel at different speeds in glass, so they refract by different amounts. So when white light passes through a triangular prism, you get a rainbow:

You don't get a rainbow with a rectangular block because it has parallel boundaries, so the different colours bend by the same amount when they leave as when they enter — so they emerge parallel.

1. The light bends towards the normal as it enters the prism, as glass is denser than air. Different wavelengths (colours) of light bend by different amounts — red bends the least, violet bends the most.

2. Light bends away from the normal as it leaves the prism. Again, different colours bend by different amounts. Because of the prism's shape, this spreads the wavelengths out even more.

3. On the far side of the prism, you see a spectrum (rainbow).

They said prism, Dave.

You can Investigate the Refraction of Light using a Prism

PRACTICAL

You'll need a light source (e.g. a ray box), coloured filters, and a triangular glass prism on a piece of paper:

1) Place a red filter in front of the ray box, then shine a thin light beam into the prism at an angle to the normal. (Some light will be reflected.)

2) Trace the incident and emerging rays onto the paper and remove the prism.

3) Draw the refracted ray by joining the ends of the other two rays with a straight line. (You could measure the angles of incidence and refraction.)

4) Repeat using a blue filter (keeping the angle of incidence the same) — you should see that the blue light refracts more at each boundary.

5) You could repeat this with more colours (wavelengths) of light — the shorter the wavelength, the more it should refract. Or without filters, so the white light disperses (as shown above).

6) You could also try changing the shape or material of the prism.

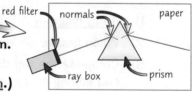

red filter

normals

paper

ray box

prism

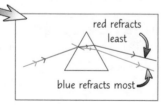

red refracts least

blue refracts most

Lights, camera, refraction...

When light goes into a denser material, it slows down and bends towards the normal. But when it goes into a less dense material, it speeds up and bends away from the normal. Get it? Got it? Good.

Q1   Sketch a diagram showing how a ray of red light would travel from the air, through a triangular glass prism and back out into the air. Label the incident ray and the emerging ray.   [3 marks]

Electromagnetic Waves

You've learned a lot about <u>light</u> so far, but light's just one <u>small part</u> of the <u>EM spectrum</u>...

There's a Continuous Spectrum of EM Waves

1) <u>Electromagnetic</u> (<u>EM</u>) <u>waves</u> are <u>transverse</u> waves (see page 188).

2) They all travel at the <u>same speed</u> (velocity) through <u>air</u> or <u>space</u> (a <u>vacuum</u>). But they travel at <u>different speeds</u> in <u>different materials</u>.

3) EM waves vary in <u>wavelength</u> from around <u>10^{-15} m</u> to more than <u>10^4 m</u>, and those with <u>shorter wavelengths</u> have <u>higher frequencies</u> (from $v = f\lambda$).

4) We <u>group</u> them based on their <u>wavelength</u> and <u>frequency</u> — there are <u>seven basic types</u>, but the different groups <u>merge</u> to form a <u>continuous spectrum</u>.

5) Our <u>eyes</u> can only detect a <u>small part</u> of this spectrum — <u>visible light</u>. <u>Different colours</u> of light have different <u>wavelengths</u>. From <u>longest</u> to <u>shortest</u> — red, orange, yellow, green, blue, indigo, violet.

> Electromagnetic waves are vibrations of electric and magnetic fields (rather than vibrations of particles). This means they can travel through a vacuum.

RADIO WAVES	MICRO WAVES	INFRA RED	VISIBLE LIGHT	ULTRA VIOLET	X-RAYS	GAMMA RAYS
1 m – 10^4 m	10^{-2} m	10^{-5} m	10^{-7} m	10^{-8} m	10^{-10} m	10^{-15} m

wavelength ↘

long wavelength, low frequency → short wavelength, high frequency

6) <u>All</u> EM waves <u>transfer energy</u> from a <u>source</u> to an <u>absorber</u>. For example, when you warm yourself by an <u>electric heater</u>, <u>infra-red</u> waves <u>transfer energy</u> from the <u>thermal energy store</u> of the <u>heater</u> (the source) to your <u>thermal energy store</u> (the absorber).

7) The <u>higher the frequency</u> of the EM wave, the <u>more energy</u> it transfers.

Different EM Waves Have Different Properties

As you saw on page 190, when EM waves meet a <u>boundary</u> they can be <u>absorbed</u>, <u>transmitted</u>, <u>refracted</u> or <u>reflected</u>. What happens depends on the materials at the <u>boundary</u> and the <u>wavelength</u> of the EM wave:

- Some materials <u>absorb</u> some wavelengths of <u>light</u> but <u>reflect</u> others. This is what causes things to be a certain <u>colour</u>).
- <u>Radio waves</u> are <u>refracted</u> by some layers of the <u>atmosphere</u> but <u>microwaves aren't</u>, making them better for <u>satellite communications</u>.

blue light will not be transmitted

Differences in how EM waves are transmitted, reflected and absorbed have implications for <u>human health</u>:

1) <u>Radio waves</u> are transmitted through the body <u>without</u> being <u>absorbed</u>.

2) Some wavelengths of <u>microwaves</u> can be <u>absorbed</u>, causing <u>heating</u> of cells, which may be dangerous.

3) <u>Infra-red</u> (<u>IR</u>) and <u>visible light</u> are mostly <u>reflected</u> or <u>absorbed</u> by the skin, causing some <u>heating</u> too. IR can cause <u>burns</u> if the skin gets <u>too hot</u>.

> The Sun produces a lot of UV radiation, but fortunately most of this is absorbed by the Earth's atmosphere.

4) <u>Ultra-violet</u> (<u>UV</u>) is also <u>absorbed</u> by the skin. But it has a <u>higher frequency</u>, so it <u>transfers more energy</u>, causing <u>more damage</u>. When it enters living cells, it <u>collides</u> with <u>atoms</u> in molecules, which may knock electrons off and cause <u>ionisation</u> — it's <u>ionising radiation</u>. This <u>damages cells</u> which may cause <u>genetic mutation</u> and <u>cancer</u>, and can lead to <u>tissue damage</u> or <u>radiation sickness</u>.

5) <u>X-rays</u> and <u>gamma rays</u> are also <u>ionising</u>, so they can cause tissue damage and cancer too. But they have <u>even higher frequencies</u>, so transfer even <u>more energy</u>, causing even <u>more damage</u>. They can also pass through the skin and be absorbed by <u>deeper tissues</u>.

Learn about the EM spectrum and wave goodbye to exam woe...

Here's a handy mnemonic for the order of EM waves: 'Rock Music Is Very Useful for eXperiments with Goats'.

Q1   Explain why gamma rays are more dangerous to humans than visible light.   [2 marks]

Uses of EM Waves

Different EM waves have different properties, which make them useful to us in different ways.

Radio Waves are used for Communications

We use radio waves to transmit information like television and radio shows from one place to another:

1) Radio waves and all EM waves are just oscillating electric and magnetic fields.

2) Alternating currents (a.c.) in electrical circuits cause charges to oscillate. This creates an oscillating electric and magnetic field — an EM wave.

3) This EM wave will have the same frequency as the current that created it, so it can create a radio wave.

4) EM waves also cause charged particles to oscillate. If the charged particles are part of a circuit, this induces an alternating current of the same frequency as the EM wave that induced it.

5) So if you've got a transmitter and a receiver, you can encode information (e.g. a TV show) in an a.c. and then transmit it as a radio wave. The wave induces an a.c. in the receiver (e.g. the aerial) and bam, you've got your information.

There's more on a.c. on p.214.

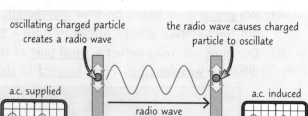

oscillating charged particle creates a radio wave

the radio wave causes charged particle to oscillate

a.c. supplied

radio wave transfers energy

a.c. induced

transmitter

receiver

> TV and FM radio transmissions use very short wavelength radio waves, and other radio transmissions (MW and LW) use medium and long-wave (funnily enough).
> Bluetooth® uses short radio waves to send data over short distances between devices.

Microwaves are Used for Communications and Cooking

1) Communication to and from satellites (including satellite TV signals and mobile phones) uses microwaves with a wavelength that can pass easily through the Earth's watery atmosphere.

2) We also use microwaves of a slightly different wavelength to cook food. These microwaves penetrate up to a few centimetres into the food before being absorbed and transferring energy to water molecules in the food, causing the water to heat up. The water molecules then transfer this energy to the rest of the molecules in the food by heating — which quickly cooks the food.

Infra-red Radiation Can be Used to Increase or Monitor Temperature

1) Infra-red (IR) radiation is given off by all objects. The hotter the object, the more it gives off.

2) Infra-red cameras can detect IR radiation and monitor temperature. They detect the IR and turn it into an electrical signal, which is displayed on a screen as a picture. The hotter an object is, the brighter it appears. E.g. IR is used in night-vision cameras.

night-vision camera

hot man hiding in the bushes

3) IR radiation is also used in medical imaging. IR cameras can detect increases in temperature caused by infections in a small area (e.g. at an infected wound) or in the whole body.

4) Absorbing IR radiation also causes objects to get hotter. Food can be cooked using IR radiation — the temperature of the food increases when it absorbs IR radiation, e.g. from a toaster's heating element.

Or you could just stream the radio over the Internet...

Microwaves are ace — without them I'd have nothing to eat and no one to talk to. Sad times.

Q1 Explain how an alternating current in a transmitter produces a radio wave. [2 marks]

Q2 Give one use of infra-red radiation. [1 mark]

More Uses of EM Waves

If you enjoyed the last page, you're in for a real treat. If not, I guess it sucks to be you...

Light Signals Can Travel Through Optical Fibres

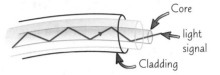
Core
light signal
Cladding

1) Light is used to look at things (and to take endless selfies and holiday snaps). But it's also used for communication using optical fibres, which carry data over long distances as pulses of light.

2) Optical fibres work by bouncing light off the sides of a very narrow core. The pulse of light enters the core at a certain angle at one end and is reflected again and again until it emerges at the other end.

3) Optical fibres are used for telephone and internet cables. They're also used for medical purposes to see inside the body — only a small hole is needed for the optical fibre (and any instruments) to enter the body, which is better than having more major surgery.

Ultra-violet is Used in Fluorescent Lamps

1) Fluorescence is a property of certain chemicals, where ultra-violet (UV) radiation is absorbed and then visible light is emitted. That's why fluorescent colours look so bright — they actually emit light.

2) Fluorescent lights use UV to emit visible light. They're energy-efficient so they're good to use when light is needed for long periods (like in your classroom).

3) Security pens can be used to mark property (e.g. laptops). Under UV light the ink will glow, but it's invisible otherwise, helping to identify stolen property.

X-rays Let Us See Inside Things

1) X-rays can be used to view the internal structure of objects and materials, including our bodies.

2) They affect photographic film in the same way as light, meaning you can take X-ray photographs. But X-ray images are usually formed electronically these days.

3) Radiographers in hospitals take X-ray images to help doctors diagnose broken bones — X-rays are transmitted by flesh but are absorbed by denser material like bones or metal.

4) To produce an X-ray image, X-ray radiation is directed through the object or body onto a detector plate. The brighter bits of the image are where fewer X-rays get through, producing a negative image (the plate starts off all white).

5) Exposure to X-rays can cause cell damage, so radiographers and patients are protected as much as possible, e.g. by lead aprons and shields, and exposure to the radiation is kept to a minimum.

Gamma Rays are Used for Sterilising Things

1) Gamma rays are used to sterilise medical instruments — they kill microbes (e.g. bacteria).

2) This is better than trying to boil plastic instruments, which might be damaged by high temperatures.

3) Food can be sterilised in the same way — again killing microbes. This keeps the food fresh for longer, without having to freeze it, cook it or preserve it some other way, and it's perfectly safe to eat.

4) Gamma radiation is used in some cancer treatments — radiation is targeted at cancer cells to kill them. Doctors have to be careful to minimise the damage to healthy cells when treating cancer like this.

5) Gamma radiation is also used in medical imaging. Patients can swallow (or be injected with) radiotracers (radioactive isotopes), which emit gamma rays as they move round the body. These rays are detected by a gamma camera outside the body and used to form an image of structures inside the body.

Phones, lights, medical images — what can't EM do?...

You've probably got the idea now that we use EM waves an awful lot. If you get asked about an example you haven't come across before, don't panic — just apply what you know about the EM spectrum and you'll be fine.

Q1   Give two uses of gamma rays.   [2 marks]

Isotopes and Radioactive Decay

Understanding what isotopes are is important for learning about radioactive decay. So let's get cracking.

Isotopes are Different Forms of the Same Element

1) Atoms consist of a nucleus (made up of protons and neutrons), surrounded by electrons.

2) The atomic/proton number is the number of protons in an atom.
The number of protons defines what the element is (e.g. a carbon atom always has 6 protons).

3) Since protons are positively charged and neutrons are neutral,
the nucleus of each element has a particular overall positive charge.

4) The mass number is the number of protons plus the number of neutrons
in an atom — it tells you the mass of the nucleus.

5) You can represent atoms using this notation:

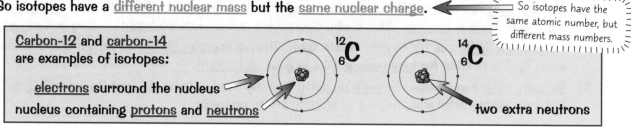

Mass number → A
Atomic number → Z **X** — Chemical symbol

6) Isotopes are atoms of the same element — they have
the same number of protons but a different number of neutrons.
So isotopes have a different nuclear mass but the same nuclear charge.

So isotopes have the same atomic number, but different mass numbers.

Carbon-12 and carbon-14
are examples of isotopes:

$^{12}_{6}C$ $^{14}_{6}C$

electrons surround the nucleus

nucleus containing protons and neutrons   two extra neutrons

7) Most elements have different isotopes, but there are usually only one or two stable ones.

8) The other isotopes tend to be unstable and radioactive, which means they
give out nuclear radiation and may decay into other elements (see below).

There are Different Ways that Nuclei can Decay

When a nucleus decays, it will spit out one or more of four types of radiation — alpha,
beta, gamma or neutron. In the process, the nucleus will often change into a new
element, as the nucleus changes its charge, its mass or both (see page 197).

- An alpha particle (α) is two neutrons and two protons — the same as a helium nucleus.
  They have a relative mass of 4 and a charge of +2.
- They are relatively big and heavy and slow moving.

- A beta particle (β) is simply an electron, with virtually no mass and a charge of –1.
- Beta particles move quite fast and are quite small.
- For every beta particle emitted, a neutron turns to a proton in the nucleus.

- After spitting out an alpha or beta particle, the nucleus might need to get rid of some
  extra energy. It does this by emitting a gamma ray — a type of electromagnetic wave.
- Gamma rays (γ) have no mass and no charge. They are just energy,
  so they don't change the element of the nucleus that emits them.

- If a nucleus contains a lot of neutrons, it may just throw out a neutron.
- The number of protons stays the same, but it now has a different
  nuclear mass, so it becomes an isotope of the same element.

Isotopes of an outfit — same dress, different accessories...

I'd learn those alpha, beta, gamma and neutron radiations if I were you. They'll be coming up again, mark my words.

Q1   Isotope A of an element has a mass number of 15 and an atomic number of 7.
Isotope B of the same element has 7 neutrons. What is the mass number of isotope B?   [1 mark]

Radiation Properties and Decay Equations

Time to learn a bit <u>more</u> about some of the types of radiation before putting them in <u>equations</u>. How thrilling.

Different Types of Radiation Have Different Penetration Properties

1) When <u>radiation</u> travels through a <u>material</u>, it can <u>collide</u> with the material's <u>atoms</u>, which <u>slows down</u> or <u>stops</u> the radiation. This means the <u>radiation</u> can only <u>penetrate</u> so far into a material before it's <u>absorbed</u>. The <u>range</u> of the radiation depends on the <u>type</u> of radiation and <u>material</u> it's travelling through.

   <u>Alpha particles don't get very far</u> before they start hitting atoms — they have the <u>shortest</u> range in a material. <u>Beta particles</u> can travel <u>quite far</u> before hitting an atom. <u>Gamma radiation</u> travels a <u>long way</u> before hitting an atom — so <u>gamma</u> radiation has the <u>longest</u> range in a material.

2) <u>Count rate</u> is the <u>number of radioactive particles</u> that reach a <u>detector</u> in a <u>given time</u>. The <u>further</u> the radiation has to travel, the <u>higher</u> the <u>chance</u> it will be <u>absorbed</u> by the material it is travelling through. This means the <u>count rate decreases</u> the <u>further</u> the <u>detector</u> is from a <u>radioactive source</u>.

3) The <u>different penetration properties</u> means each nuclear radiation can be stopped by different <u>materials</u>:

   - <u>Alpha particles</u> are blocked by e.g. <u>paper</u>.
   - <u>Beta particles</u> are blocked by e.g. thin <u>aluminium</u>.
   - <u>Gamma rays</u> are blocked by e.g. <u>thick lead</u>.

   The alpha and beta particles would also be blocked by the lead, and the alpha particles would also be blocked by the aluminium.

   Sheet of paper stops alpha   Thin aluminium stops beta   Thick lead stops gamma

You Need to be Able to Balance Nuclear Equations

You can write nuclear decays as <u>nuclear equations</u>. You need to be able to <u>balance</u> these equations for <u>alpha</u>, <u>beta</u> and <u>gamma</u> decays by balancing the total <u>masses and charges</u> on each side.

Alpha Radiation

When a nucleus emits an <u>alpha particle</u>:

- the <u>mass number decreases by 4</u> — as it <u>loses</u> two protons and two neutrons.
- the <u>atomic number decreases by 2</u> — because it has <u>two less</u> protons.

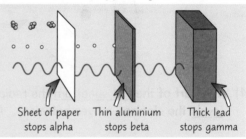

$$^{226}_{88}\text{Ra} \rightarrow \, ^{222}_{86}\text{Rn} + \, ^{4}_{2}\alpha$$

| mass number: | 226 | → | 222 | + | 4 (= 226) |
| atomic number: | 88 | → | 86 | + | 2 (= 88) |

In both alpha and beta emissions, a new element will be formed, as the number of protons changes.

Beta Radiation

When a nucleus emits a <u>beta particle</u>, a neutron changes into a proton, so:

- The <u>mass number doesn't change</u> — as it has <u>lost</u> a neutron but <u>gained</u> a proton.
- The <u>atomic number increases by 1</u> — because it has <u>one more</u> proton.

$$^{14}_{6}\text{C} \rightarrow \, ^{14}_{7}\text{N} + \, ^{0}_{-1}\beta$$

| mass number: | 14 | → | 14 | + | 0 | (= 14) |
| atomic number: | 6 | → | 7 | + | (−1) | (= 6) |

You can also write the beta particle as $^{0}_{-1}e^{-}$ in equations.

Gamma Radiation

When a nucleus emits a <u>gamma ray</u>:

- The <u>mass number</u> and the <u>atomic number don't change</u>.
- You might see gamma rays written as γ in <u>balanced equations</u>.

$$^{234}_{91}\text{Pa} \rightarrow \, ^{234}_{91}\text{Pa} + \gamma$$

I think balancing equations is more fun than anything ever...

Right? Right?? *cough* I can't see your face, but I'm going to take a wild guess and say you don't believe me.

Q1   A uranium (U) atom with 92 protons and 146 neutrons decays into a thorium (Th) atom by emitting an alpha particle. Write a balanced equation to show this decay.   [3 marks]

Electron Energy Levels

There's some quirky stuff on this page — and the best part is that you can tell everyone you've been doing a little quantum physics today. Honestly. And if you study physics to a higher level, things get even quirkier.

Electrons Can be Excited to Higher Energy Levels

1) Electrons in an atom sit in different energy levels or shells. Each energy level is a different distance from the nucleus.

2) An inner electron can move up one or more energy levels in one go if it absorbs electromagnetic (EM) radiation with the right amount of energy. When it does move up, it moves to an partially filled (or empty) shell and is said to be 'excited'.

3) The electron will then fall back to its original energy level, and in doing so will lose the same amount of energy it absorbed. The energy is carried away by EM radiation.

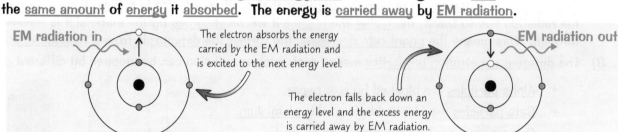

The electron absorbs the energy carried by the EM radiation and is excited to the next energy level.

The electron falls back down an energy level and the excess energy is carried away by EM radiation.

4) The part of the EM spectrum the radiation is from depends on its energy (which depends on the energy levels the electron moves between). A higher energy means a higher frequency of EM radiation.

An Atom is Ionised if it Loses an Electron

1) If an outer electron absorbs radiation with enough energy, it can move so far that it leaves the atom. It is now a free electron and the atom is said to have been ionised.

2) The atom is now a positive ion. It's positive because there are now more protons than electrons.

3) An atom can lose more than one electron. The more electrons it loses, the greater its positive charge.

Nuclear Radiation Ionises Atoms

1) Alpha, beta and gamma radiation can ionise atoms, and so can also be called ionising radiation.

2) The ionisation power is different for different ionising radiations — this is a measure of how likely it is that the radiation will ionise an atom.

3) Alpha particles have the highest ionisation power — this means that they can't travel very far through a substance without hitting an atom and ionising it. Gamma radiation has the lowest ionisation power.

Fluorescent Tubes use Excited Electrons to Produce Light

1) Fluorescent tubes contain mercury vapour. Electrons are accelerated through the mercury vapour, which ionises some of the mercury atoms, producing more free electrons.

2) When this flow of free electrons collides with electrons in other mercury atoms, the electrons in the mercury atoms are excited to higher energy levels.

3) When these excited electrons return to their original energy levels, they emit radiation in the ultraviolet range of the electromagnetic spectrum (see page 193).

4) A phosphorus coating on the inside of the tube absorbs this radiation, exciting its electrons to higher energy levels. These electrons then cascade down the energy levels, emitting many different frequencies of radiation, all in the visible part of the electromagnetic spectrum.

What's an atom's favourite chore? Ioning...

So, an electron absorbs EM radiation and moves up one or more energy levels, then falls back to its original energy level and loses the same amount of energy it absorbed, which is carried away by EM radiation. Simple...

Q1 What is a positive ion and how is one formed? [2 marks]

Half-Life

Radioactive decay is <u>totally random</u>, so how can we know how an isotope will decay? I give you, <u>half-lives</u>.

The Radioactivity of a Sample Always Decreases Over Time

1) <u>Radioactive decay</u> is a <u>random process</u>, so you <u>can't predict</u> when a particular nucleus is going to decay.

2) Instead, you can make predictions about <u>large numbers</u> of nuclei of an isotope.

3) <u>Radioactive isotopes</u> decay at <u>different rates</u>. The <u>number of unstable nuclei</u> that <u>decay</u> in a given time is called the <u>activity</u> and is measured in <u>becquerels (Bq)</u> — the number of nuclei that decay each second.

4) The <u>radiation</u> emitted from a decaying nucleus can be <u>detected</u> using a <u>Geiger Muller tube</u>, which measures the <u>count rate</u> (see page 197) in <u>counts per minute</u> (or per second).

5) As more <u>unstable nuclei</u> decay, the <u>activity</u> of the source as a whole <u>decreases</u>.

6) <u>How quickly</u> the activity <u>decreases</u> is given by the <u>half-life</u>:

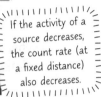
If the activity of a source decreases, the count rate (at a fixed distance) also decreases.

> The half-life of a source is the average time taken for its activity (or count rate) to halve.

7) It can also be thought of as the <u>average time taken</u> for <u>half</u> of the remaining <u>unstable nuclei</u> to <u>decay</u>.

8) A <u>short half-life</u> means the <u>activity falls quickly</u>, because <u>lots</u> of the nuclei decay in a <u>short time</u>.

9) A <u>long half-life</u> means the activity <u>falls more slowly</u> because <u>most</u> of the nuclei don't decay <u>for a long time</u> — they just sit there, <u>basically unstable</u>, but kind of <u>biding their time</u>.

When the activity's really low, the randomness of radioactive decay becomes more noticeable.

Half-Life can be Calculated from Numbers or from a Graph

You could be asked to <u>calculate</u> how you'd expect the <u>activity</u> of a source to <u>change over time</u>:

A <u>sample</u> of a radioactive isotope has an <u>activity of 1000 Bq</u> and a <u>half-life of 5 years</u>:

- After <u>1 half-life</u> (<u>5 years</u>) the activity will be 1000 ÷ 2 = <u>500 Bq</u>.

- After <u>2 half-lives</u> (<u>10 years</u>) the activity will be 500 ÷ 2 = <u>250 Bq</u>.

You can also find the <u>net decline of a sample</u> — <u>how much</u> the activity (or the number of undecayed nuclei) decreases by over a period of time — normally a <u>ratio</u>.

For this example, the <u>net decline of the sample after 2 half-lives</u> (10 years) is 1000 − 250 = 750 Bq. Or as a <u>ratio</u>: decrease in activity/ original activity = 750/1000 = <u>3/4</u>.

You also need to be able to find the half-life of a sample from a <u>graph</u>...

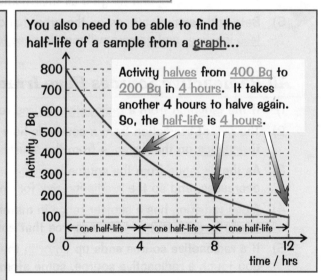
Activity <u>halves</u> from <u>400 Bq</u> to <u>200 Bq</u> in <u>4 hours</u>. It takes another 4 hours to halve again. So, the <u>half-life</u> is <u>4 hours</u>.

If you're given count rates rather then activity, you can find the half-life in exactly the same way.

EXAMPLE: The count rate of a radioactive sample is measured as 640 counts per minute. Two hours later it has fallen to 40 counts per minute. Find its half-life.

1) Count how many half-lives it took to fall to 40 counts per minute.

Initial count:		after 1 half-life:		after 2 half-lives:		after 3 half-lives:		after 4 half-lives:
640	(÷2) →	320	(÷2) →	160	(÷2) →	80	(÷2) →	40

2) Calculate the half-life of the sample. Two hours is four half-lives — so the half-life is 2 hours ÷ 4 = 30 min

Half-life of a box of chocolates — about five minutes...

To measure half-life, you time how long it takes for the counts per minute (or second) to halve.

Q1   The half-life of a radioactive source is 60 hr. Find its activity after 240 hr, if it is initially 480 Bq.   [2 marks]

Dangers of Radioactivity

Time to find out about the hazards of ionising radiation — it damages living cells when it ionises atoms.

Ionising Radiation Harms Living Cells

1) Some materials absorb ionising radiation — it can enter living cells and interact with molecules.

2) These interactions cause ionisation (they produce charged particles called ions).

3) Lower doses of ionising radiation damage living cells by causing mutations in the DNA. This can cause the cell to divide uncontrollably — which is cancer.

4) Higher doses tend to kill cells completely, which causes radiation sickness if a lot of cells all get blasted at once.

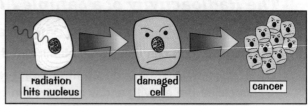

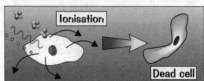

Which Radiation is the Most Dangerous Depends on Where it is

1) OUTSIDE the body, beta and gamma sources are the most dangerous.

2) This is because beta and gamma can still get inside to the delicate organs — they can pass through skin.

3) Alpha is much less dangerous because it can't penetrate the skin.

4) INSIDE the body, an alpha source is the most dangerous because they're the most ionising and they do all their damage in a very localised area.

5) Beta and gamma sources on the other hand are less dangerous inside the body because they are less ionising, and gamma will mostly pass straight out without doing much damage.

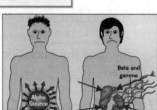

All Radioactive Sources Have Irradiation and Contamination Risks

1) If the radiation from a radioactive source reaches an object, the object is said to be irradiated.

2) The risk of irradiation from a source is how likely it is that an object will be irradiated by the source. It depends on the distance from the source and the type of radiation that the source emits.

3) As the distance from the source increases, the amount of radiation reaching that point decreases, and so the irradiation risk for any source is lower at larger distances.

4) Alpha radiation has a shorter range in materials compared to gamma radiation, so the irradiation risk is lower for a source that emits alpha radiation (at a given distance).

5) If a radioactive source ends up on or in the object, we say the object is contaminated — e.g. if you touch a radioactive source, some atoms of it might rub off onto your hand, contaminating you.

6) The contamination risk is how likely it is that an object could get contaminated. If a radioactive source is a solid, then there's no contamination risk for an object that doesn't touch the source. But if the source is a gas, then it could move and come into contact with the object, increasing the contamination risk. Gases are particularly dangerous for people as they can be inhaled, contaminating you from the inside.

7) If an object becomes contaminated, then the irradiation risk due to the source is very high as the distance between the source and object is so small.

8) Irradiation is temporary — if the source is taken away, any irradiation it's causing stops. Contamination lasts longer — if the original source is taken away, the atoms causing the contamination are left behind, potentially causing more harm.

Top tip number 364 — if something is radioactive, don't lick it...

If you're working with radioactive sources, read about the safety risks and make experiments as safe as possible.

Q1   Give two effects that ionising radiation can have on living cells.   [2 marks]

Q2   Compare the irradiation risks and the contamination risks of a radioactive solid that emits alpha radiation and a radioactive solid that emits beta radiation when they are the same distance from a person.   [4 marks]

Revision Questions for Topic P4

It's not quite time to wave goodbye to those pesky waves yet — have a go at these revision questions.

- Try these questions and <u>tick off each one</u> when you <u>get it right</u>.
- When you've done <u>all the questions</u> under a heading and are <u>completely happy</u> with it, tick it off.

Wave Basics (p.188-189) ☑

1) Sketch a diagram of a wave. Label the amplitude, wavelength and rest position, and a crest and a trough. ☑

2) What is the difference between a transverse wave and a longitudinal wave? Give one example of each. ☑

3) Describe an experiment to measure the speed of sound. ☑

4) Describe an experiment to measure the wavelength of a water wave. ☑

Reflection and Refraction (p.190-192) ☑

5) What three things can happen to a wave at a boundary between materials? ☑

6) What is the one simple rule for all reflected waves? ☑

7) What causes waves to refract? ☑

8) Describe what happens to a beam of white light if you shine it through a triangular prism. ☑

E.M. Waves (p.193-195) ☑

9) What type of wave are EM waves? ☑

10) List the waves in the EM spectrum, in order of increasing wavelength. ☑

11) Explain why ultra-violet waves are dangerous. ☑

12) Give one use of each type of EM wave. ☑

Radiation (p.196-198) ☑

13) What is the atomic number of an atom? What is the mass number of an atom? ☑

14) Define an isotope. ☑

15) When is nuclear radiation produced? ☑

16) What is an alpha particle? What is a beta particle? ☑

17) Which of alpha, beta and gamma radiation has the longest range in air? ☑

18) What happens to the count rate of radiation with an increasing distance from the source of radiation? ☑

19) Which types of radiation are stopped by: a) paper,   b) thin aluminium,   c) thick lead? ☑

20) State what happens to the mass number and atomic number of a nucleus that undergoes alpha decay. ☑

21) State what happens to the mass number and atomic number of a nucleus that undergoes beta decay. ☑

22) What is electron excitation and when does it occur? ☑

23) List alpha, beta and gamma radiation in the order of how strongly ionising they are. ☑

Half-life and Dangers of Radioactivity (p.199-200) ☑

24) What is meant by the activity of a radioactive source and what are its units? ☑

25) Define the half-life of a radioactive source. ☑

26) What is meant by the net decline in activity for a radioactive source? ☑

27) Explain how radiation can lead to cancer. ☑

28) What is the irradiation risk of a radioactive source? ☑

29) What is the contamination risk of a radioactive source? ☑

Conservation of Energy

Energy. Might seem a tricky little beast, but know this — it can be transferred and stored in different ways.

Energy is Transferred Between Energy Stores

Energy can be held in different stores. Here are the stores you need
to learn, plus examples of objects with energy in each of these stores:

1) **KINETIC**............................. — anything moving has energy in its kinetic energy store.
2) **THERMAL**............................ — any object — the hotter it is, the more energy it has in this store.
3) **CHEMICAL** .... — anything that can release energy by a chemical reaction, e.g. food, fuels.
4) **GRAVITATIONAL POTENTIAL**... — anything in a gravitational field (i.e. anything which can fall).
5) **ELASTIC POTENTIAL**............. — anything stretched, like springs and rubber bands.
6) **ELECTROSTATIC**.................. — e.g. two charges that attract or repel each other.
7) **MAGNETIC** .... — e.g. two magnets that attract or repel each other.
8) **NUCLEAR**............................ — atomic nuclei release energy from this store in nuclear reactions.

Energy can be transferred between stores in four main ways:

Mechanically — an object moving due to a force acting on it, e.g. pushing, pulling, stretching or squashing.
Electrically — a charge moving through a potential difference, e.g. charges moving round a circuit.
By heating — energy transferred from a hotter object to a colder object, e.g. heating a pan of water on a hob.
By radiation — energy transferred e.g. by light/sound waves, e.g. energy from the Sun reaching Earth by light.

There is a Law of Conservation of Energy

There are plenty of different stores of energy, but energy always obeys the law below:

> Energy can be stored, transferred between stores, and dissipated — but it can never
> be created or destroyed. The total energy of a closed system has no net change.

Dissipated is a fancy way of saying the energy is spread out and lost.

A closed system is just a system (a collection of objects) that can be treated completely
on its own, without any matter being exchanged with the surroundings.

Energy Transfers Show... well... the Transfer of Energy

In the exam, they might ask you about any situation where energy is transferred. If you understand
a few different examples, it'll be easier to think through whatever they ask you about in the exam.

A BALL ROLLING UP A SLOPE: energy is transferred mechanically from the kinetic energy store
of the ball to its gravitational potential energy store.

A BAT HITTING A BALL: some energy in the kinetic energy store of the bat is transferred mechanically to the
thermal energy stores of the bat, the ball and their surroundings. Some energy
is transferred mechanically from the kinetic energy store of the bat to the kinetic
energy store of the ball. The rest of the energy is carried away by sound.

A CAR SLOWING DOWN (without braking): energy in the kinetic energy store of the car is transferred
mechanically (due to friction between the tyres and road) and
then by heating to the thermal energy stores of the car and road.

AN ELECTRIC KETTLE BOILING WATER: energy is transferred electrically from the mains to the thermal
energy store of the kettle's heating element. It is then transferred
by heating to the thermal energy store of the water.

Energy can't be created or destroyed — only talked about a lot...

This is important, so remember it. Energy can only be transferred to a different store, never destroyed.

Q1   Describe the energy transfers for a falling ball landing on the ground without bouncing.   [3 marks]

Q2   Describe the energy transfers that occur when a piece of wood is burning.   [2 marks]

Efficiency

So energy is <u>transferred</u> between different <u>stores</u>. But not all of the energy is transferred to <u>useful</u> stores.

Most Energy Transfers Involve Some Losses, Often by Heating

1) You've already met the <u>law of conservation of energy</u> on the previous page, but another <u>important principle</u> you need to know is:

> Energy is <u>only useful</u> when it is <u>transferred</u> from one store to a <u>useful store</u>.

2) <u>Useful devices</u> can <u>transfer energy</u> from <u>one store</u> to a <u>useful store</u>.

3) However, some of the <u>input energy</u> is always <u>lost or wasted</u>, often to <u>thermal energy stores</u> by <u>heating</u>. For example, a <u>motor</u> will transfer energy to its <u>kinetic energy store</u> (useful), but will also transfer energy to the <u>thermal energy stores</u> of the motor and the surroundings (<u>wasted</u>).

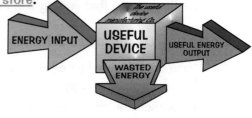

4) The law of conservation of energy means that:
<u>total energy input = useful energy output + wasted energy</u>.

5) The <u>less energy</u> that's <u>wasted</u>, the <u>more efficient</u> the device is said to be.

> The amount of energy wasted can often be reduced — see page 205.

You can Calculate the Efficiency of an Energy Transfer

The <u>efficiency</u> of any device is defined as:

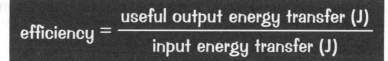

$$\text{efficiency} = \frac{\text{useful output energy transfer (J)}}{\text{input energy transfer (J)}}$$

> This will give the efficiency as a decimal. To give it as a percentage, you need to multiply the answer by 100, e.g. 0.75 = 75%.

EXAMPLE:

A toaster transfers 216 000 J of energy electrically from the mains. 84 000 J of energy is transferred to the bread's thermal energy store. Calculate the efficiency of the toaster.

$$\text{efficiency} = \frac{\text{useful output energy transfer}}{\text{input energy transfer}} = \frac{84\ 000}{216\ 000} = 0.38888... = 0.39 \text{ (to 2 s.f.)}$$

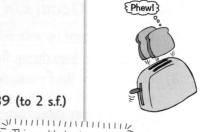

{Phew!}

> This could also be written as 39% (to 2 s.f.).

All devices have an efficiency, but because some energy is <u>always wasted</u>, the efficiency <u>can never be</u> equal to or higher than <u>1 (or 100%)</u>.

We Generally Can't Do Anything Useful with Wasted Energy

1) <u>The wasted energy</u> that's <u>output</u> by a device is transferred to less useful stores — normally by <u>heating</u>, or by <u>light</u> or <u>sound</u>. As the energy is <u>transferred</u> away from the device to its surroundings, the <u>energy</u> often spreads out and becomes <u>less concentrated</u> — we say it <u>dissipates</u>.

> For example, a <u>pan of water</u> on a <u>hob</u> — the hob will transfer energy to the water, but <u>some energy</u> will be <u>dissipated</u> to the surrounding air by heating.

2) According to the <u>law of conservation of energy</u> (see page 202), the <u>total</u> amount of <u>energy</u> stays the <u>same</u>. So the energy is still there, but it <u>can't be easily used</u> or <u>collected back in</u> again.

Make sure your revising efficiency is high...

So one really important thing to take from here — devices that transfer energy from one store to other stores will always transfer energy to stores that aren't useful. And when I say always, I mean always. <u>Always</u>. (Always.)

Q1 An electrical device wastes 420 J of energy when it has an input energy of 500 J. Calculate the efficiency of the device as a percentage.

[3 marks]

Energy Transfer by Heating

So you know energy can be transferred <u>by heating</u>, but what does that actually <u>mean</u>? I'm glad you asked...

Energy is Transferred by Heating in Three Different Ways

1) When an object is <u>heated</u>, <u>energy is transferred</u> to its <u>thermal energy store</u> and its <u>temperature increases</u>. The energy transferred is equal to: <u>$m \times$ specific heat capacity $\times$ temperature change</u>.

2) If energy is transferred by heating from a <u>hotter</u> object to a <u>cooler</u> object, the hotter object's <u>temperature</u> will <u>decrease</u> and the cooler object's <u>temperature</u> will <u>increase</u>.

3) The three ways that energy can be transferred <u>by heating</u> are: <u>conduction</u>, <u>convection</u> or <u>radiation</u>.

Conduction Occurs Mainly in Solids

1) When an object is <u>heated</u> the energy transferred to the object is shared across the <u>kinetic</u> energy stores of the <u>particles</u> in the object.

2) The particles in the <u>hotter</u> part of the object <u>vibrate</u> more and <u>collide</u> with each other, transferring energy from their <u>kinetic energy stores</u> to <u>neighbouring particles</u>. These then also vibrate faster, <u>increasing</u> the <u>temperature</u> of that part of the object. This continues until the extra energy is <u>spread out evenly</u> across all the particles, and the <u>temperature</u> of the object is the <u>same</u> everywhere.

> <u>CONDUCTION</u> is the process where <u>vibrating particles</u> pass extra <u>energy</u> in their kinetic energy stores to the <u>kinetic energy stores</u> of <u>neighbouring particles</u>.

3) Generally conduction occurs mainly in <u>solids</u>, as particles are held tightly together. Particles in <u>liquids</u> and <u>gases</u> are <u>further apart</u>, so conduction of energy is a lot <u>slower</u>.

Air is a good insulator.

4) All objects have a <u>thermal conductivity</u> — it describes <u>how well</u> an object transfers energy by conduction. <u>Metal</u> has a <u>high thermal conductivity</u>, and <u>liquids and gases</u> have a <u>low thermal conductivity</u>.

Convection Occurs in Fluids (Liquids and Gases)

1) When you <u>heat up</u> a liquid or gas, the particles <u>move faster</u>, and the fluid <u>expands</u>, becoming <u>less dense</u>.

2) The <u>warmer</u>, <u>less dense</u> fluid <u>rises</u> above its <u>colder</u>, <u>denser</u> surroundings.

3) As the warm fluid rises, cooler fluid takes its place. The process continues until you end up with a <u>circulation</u> of fluid (<u>convection currents</u>).

Convection can't happen in solids because the particles can't move (just vibrate on the spot).

> <u>CONVECTION</u> occurs when the particles with <u>more</u> energy in their <u>kinetic energy stores</u> move from the <u>hotter region</u> to the <u>cooler region</u> — and take their kinetic energy stores with them.

4) <u>Radiators</u> in buildings rely on convection to make the warm air <u>circulate</u> round the room.

5) To <u>reduce convection</u>, you need to <u>stop the fluid moving</u>. Clothes, blankets and foam cavity wall insulation all work by <u>trapping pockets of air</u>. The air can't move so the energy has to conduct <u>very slowly</u> through the pockets of air, as well as the material in between.

Radiation can Travel Through a Vacuum

1) For energy to be transferred by conduction or convection, you need <u>particles</u>. But energy can also be transferred by <u>radiation</u>, which can travel through a <u>vacuum</u>. When energy is transferred by <u>heating</u> by radiation, the energy is carried by <u>infra-red waves</u> (see page 194).

2) <u>All</u> objects <u>continually</u> emit and absorb <u>radiation</u> — the <u>hotter</u> an object gets, the <u>more</u> radiation it <u>emits</u>.

3) <u>Cooler objects</u> will <u>absorb</u> the radiation emitted by hotter things, so their <u>temperature increases</u>.

4) <u>Matt black</u> surfaces are very <u>good absorbers and emitters</u> of radiation.

5) <u>Light-coloured, smooth</u> and <u>shiny</u> objects are very <u>poor absorbers and emitters</u> of radiation.

Conduction — nothing to do with organising an orchestra...

Sometimes I'm just too funny for my own good. Pure gold this stuff.

Q1   Why would hot water in a black mug cool down faster than if the mug was white?   [2 marks]

Reducing Unwanted Energy Transfers

It's always best not to throw energy away willy-nilly, so we try to increase the efficiency of everything.

Insulating Your House Reduces Energy Loss

1) Energy in the home can be transferred usefully (e.g. by radiators) and wasted (e.g. by windows).

2) To save energy, a house can be designed to lose less energy (see below). You can also make things more efficient, so they waste less energy, e.g. use energy-saving light bulbs instead of normal ones.

Loft Insulation

Fibreglass 'wool' laid on the loft floor and ceiling reduces energy loss from the house by conduction and convection.

Hot Water Tank Jacket

Reduces conduction, keeping the water hot.

Cavity Walls & Cavity Wall Insulation

Two layers of bricks with a gap between them reduce conduction, but energy is also transferred across the gap by convection. Squirting insulating foam into the gap traps pockets of air to minimise this convection.

Double Glazing

Two layers of glass with an air gap between reduce conduction.

Thick Curtains

Reduce heat loss by convection and conduction through the windows.

Energy is still lost from the walls by radiation though. Also, if there are any spaces where air is not trapped there'll still be some convection too.

Draught-proofing

Strips of foam and plastic around doors and windows stop hot air going out — reducing convection.

3) The energy loss from hot water pipes (e.g. connecting the boiler to the radiators) can also be reduced by:

- Covering the pipes with insulation to reduce conduction and convection.
- Painting the pipes white to reduce energy loss by radiation.
- Making the pipes as short as possible, so the water spends less time in the pipes.
- Making the pipes as wide as possible, so they have a smaller surface area to volume ratio. This means a smaller fraction of the water in the pipes is next to the surface of the pipe, and so less energy is lost by conduction.

4) The thickness of walls affects how quickly energy is transferred out of a building. The thicker the walls, the lower the rate of energy transfer. The thermal conductivity of the material the walls are made from also affects the rate of energy transfer. A high thermal conductivity means a high rate of energy transfer.

Reducing Friction Reduces Energy Loss

1) Friction within a system also leads to energy being lost through heating.

2) This can be reduced with lubrication, for example, using oil on a bike chain.

3) Changing the shape of an object, e.g. making a car more streamlined, reduces friction from air resistance.

Now I just need to buy a hot water tank shirt, socks and trousers...

I know what you're thinking — what about underwear for the hot water tank? Don't be so ridiculous.

Q1 State three ways that you could reduce the amount of energy loss from a house. [3 marks]

Q2 State two properties that affect how quickly energy is transferred through a wall. [2 marks]

Topic P5 — Energy

Mechanical Energy Transfers

Cast your mind back to p.171 — when a <u>force</u> is applied to an object, <u>work is done</u> and <u>energy is transferred</u>.

Falling Objects Transfer Energy Between Stores

1) When an object <u>falls</u>, <u>work</u> is done on the object by the force due to <u>gravity</u> (this is <u>weight</u>, see p.169). Some of the energy in its <u>gravitational potential energy store</u> is <u>transferred</u> to its <u>kinetic energy store</u>.

2) If something is <u>thrown upwards</u> by applying a force to it, the <u>work done</u> by the force causes it to <u>gain height</u>, and energy in its <u>kinetic energy store</u> is transferred to its <u>gravitational potential energy store</u>.

3) In practice, some of the energy will be <u>dissipated</u> through <u>heating</u> due to <u>air resistance</u>, but in the exam they'll likely say you can <u>ignore</u> air resistance, in which case you'll just need to remember this <u>really quite obvious</u> formula:

This is because of the law of conservation of energy (p.202).

> Energy transferred to/from an object's kinetic energy store
> = Energy transferred from/to the object's gravitational potential energy store

4) The <u>equation</u> for calculating the energy in the <u>kinetic energy store</u> of an object is:
<u>kinetic energy = ½ × mass × (speed)^2 = ½ × mv^2</u>.

5) The <u>equation</u> for calculating the energy in the <u>gravitational potential energy store</u> of an object is:
<u>gravitational potential energy = mass × height × gravitational field strength = m × h × g</u>. If an object moves, you can use its <u>change in height</u> for *h* to calculate the <u>energy transferred</u> to or from this store.

> **EXAMPLE:**
>
> The diagram shows a roller coaster carriage with mass 500 kg falling between points A and B. The height difference between A and B is 20 m. You can ignore air resistance and friction for this question.
>
>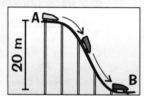
>
> a) How much energy is transferred to the kinetic energy store of the carriage in moving from A to B?
>
> As you're ignoring friction and air resistance, you know that <u>all</u> of the energy transferred from the gravitational potential energy store of the carriage is <u>transferred</u> to its kinetic energy store.
>
> So kinetic energy = gravitational potential energy
> = *m* × *h* × *g*
> = 500 × 20 × 10
> = 100 000 J
>
> *You should know that g = 10 N/kg for the exam.*
>
> b) The roller coaster was stationary at the top of the track. Calculate its speed at the bottom.
>
> 1) 100 000 J is the energy in the carriage's kinetic energy store at the bottom of the track, so <u>rearrange</u> the kinetic energy equation to find *v*^{2}.
>
> v^2 = kinetic energy ÷ (½ × *m*)
> = 100 000 ÷ (½ × 500) = 400
>
> 2) Take the <u>square root</u> of the answer to find *v*.
>
> $v = \sqrt{400}$ = 20 m/s
>
> *If you know the mass of an object and how much energy is in its kinetic energy store, you can calculate its speed. Handy.*

Elastic Objects Have Elastic Potential Energy Stores

1) When an elastic object, e.g. a <u>spring</u>, is <u>squashed</u> by a moving object, work is done on the spring and energy is <u>transferred</u> from the object's <u>kinetic energy store</u> to the spring's <u>elastic potential energy store</u>.

2) As the spring pushes the object <u>back out</u>, the spring transfers the energy back to the <u>kinetic energy store</u> of the object.

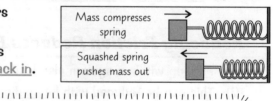
Mass compresses spring

Squashed spring pushes mass out

3) The <u>same</u> energy <u>transfers</u> would take place if the object was <u>stretching</u> the spring and then the spring <u>pulled</u> the object <u>back in</u>.

4) The <u>energy transferred</u> to the elastic potential energy store of a <u>stretched</u> or <u>squashed</u> spring is equal to <u>0.5 × spring constant × (extension)^2</u>.

> *When an elastic object is stretched or compressed, energy can be lost as some energy is transferred to the thermal energy store of the object, causing it to heat up.*

Transfer this information to your exam knowledge stores...

So, down to the real important stuff. Make sure you know the equations here, or this will be a bit of a struggle.

Q1   A spring with spring constant 6.50 N/m is squashed by 0.120 m.
     Calculate the energy transferred to the elastic potential energy store of the spring.   [2 marks]

Electrical Energy Transfers

More energy transfers eh? Well, you know the saying — <u>practice</u> makes perhaps the most prepared student.

Electrical Circuits Transfer Energy Electrically

1) When a device is <u>plugged</u> into a <u>socket</u> in the wall, it's connected to the <u>mains</u> (i.e. the <u>national grid</u>). <u>Energy</u> is <u>transferred electrically</u> from the <u>mains</u> to the <u>device</u>.

2) A <u>battery</u> has energy in its <u>chemical energy store</u> — this energy can be <u>transferred electrically</u> to <u>devices</u> in a circuit. Here are some <u>examples</u> of electrical devices and how they <u>transfer</u> the energy <u>supplied</u>:

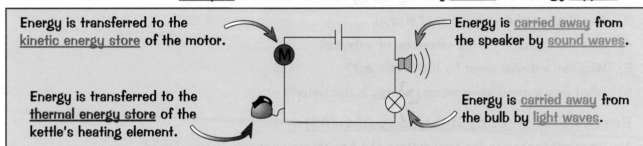

Energy is transferred to the <u>kinetic energy store</u> of the motor.

Energy is <u>carried away</u> from the speaker by <u>sound waves</u>.

Energy is transferred to the <u>thermal energy store</u> of the kettle's heating element.

Energy is <u>carried away</u> from the bulb by <u>light waves</u>.

4) Not all of the <u>energy transferred</u> by the battery will be transferred <u>usefully</u> — some is <u>wasted</u> .

5) Some energy is <u>lost</u> as it's <u>transferred</u> to the device — e.g. energy is transferred to the <u>thermal energy stores</u> of the <u>wires</u> by <u>heating</u>.

6) Some energy is also lost in the device itself, for example:
   - a <u>motor heats up</u> as energy is transferred to its <u>thermal energy store</u> (due to <u>friction</u>),
   - a <u>heating element</u> within a <u>kettle</u> will also transfer energy to the <u>thermal energy stores</u> of the <u>kettle</u> and the <u>surroundings</u>.

Electrical Appliances Have Power Ratings

1) The amount of <u>energy transferred</u> to a device is the same as the <u>work done</u> by the battery or mains when a <u>current flows</u> (minus any energy lost to the wires, see above).

2) The energy transferred to a device is equal to <u>energy transferred = power × time</u> (where <u>power = current × potential difference</u>). Remember — power is measured in <u>watts</u>, **W**.

3) The <u>power rating</u> of electrical appliances (bulbs, kettles, hair dryers etc.) is often written on the appliance — it tells you how much <u>energy</u> is <u>transferred</u> to the appliance <u>per second</u> (the <u>rate</u> of energy transfer):

A <u>850 W microwave</u> will transfer <u>850 J</u> of energy from the <u>mains per second</u>. But this <u>doesn't mean</u> 850 J of energy is transferred <u>to the food</u> by heating every second, because <u>no</u> device is <u>100%</u> efficient and some energy is <u>wasted</u> by the device (see above).

The energy transferred to a device can also be measured in kilowatt-hours, kWh — the amount of energy transferred to a 1000 W device in 1 hour.

EXAMPLE: A kettle has a current of 12.5 A when a voltage of 230 V is applied across it.

a) Calculate the power rating of the kettle.   power = current × potential difference = 12.5 × 230 = **2875 W**

b) How much energy is transferred to the kettle from the mains in 4.0 minutes? Give your answer in standard form. *Standard form is on p.150.*

4 min in seconds is 4 × 60 = 240 s, so energy transferred = power × time = 2875 × 240 = 690 000 J

690 000 = 6.9̆0̆0̆0̆0̆ × 10⁵ = **6.9 × 10⁵ J**

Go and put the kettle on, you deserve a brew...

The power rating tells you how much energy is transferred to a device per second, and the efficiency tells you what fraction of this energy is usefully transferred by the device. Remember — no device is 100% efficient.

Q1   A light bulb with a power rating of 35 W is connected to a battery for 2.0 minutes.
Calculate the energy transferred to the bulb during this time, and explain why the
energy transferred from the bulb by light waves will be less than your calculated value.   **[3 marks]**

Revision Questions for Topic P5

Well, that wraps up <u>Topic P5</u> — but now to find out how much has sunk in, and how much is left to learn...
- Try these questions and <u>tick off each one</u> when you <u>get it right</u>.
- When you've done <u>all the questions</u> under a heading and are <u>completely happy</u> with it, tick it off.

Energy Stores and Efficiency (p.202-203) ☑

1) State the eight types of energy stores. ☑
2) State the four ways of transferring energy between energy stores. ☑
3) Give the law of conservation of energy. ☑
4) Give the equation for the efficiency of a device. ☑
5) Why can a device never be 100% efficient? ☑
6) What do we mean when we say energy is dissipated? ☑

Energy Transfers by Heating (p.204-205) ☑

7) What will happen to the temperature of a hot object as energy is transferred
   from its thermal energy store to the thermal energy store of a cooler object? ☑
8) Give the three ways that energy could be transferred by heating. ☑
9) Explain how energy is transferred by conduction. ☑
10) Explain how energy is transferred by convection. ☑
11) Will a black surface absorb radiation more or less quickly than a white surface? ☑
12) Explain how cavity walls and cavity wall insulation reduce energy loss from buildings. ☑
13) Give two ways that energy loss through windows can be reduced. ☑
14) What effect does increasing the thermal conductivity of
    a wall have on the rate of energy transfer through it? ☑

Mechanical and Electrical Energy Transfers (p.206-207) ☑

15) Describe the energy transfers for a falling object, ignoring friction. ☑
16) Describe the energy transfers for an object thrown in the air, ignoring friction. ☑
17) Give the equation for the energy in the kinetic energy store of a moving object. ☑
18) Give the equation for the energy transferred to the gravitational potential
    energy store of an object that is lifted a height, h, above the ground. ☑
19) Give the equation for the energy in the elastic potential energy store of a stretched spring. ☑
20) Describe the energy transfers for a squashed spring being released and moving a mass. ☑
21) Describe how energy is usefully transferred when a motor is connected to a battery. ☑
22) Describe how energy is usefully transferred when a loudspeaker is connected to a battery. ☑
23) How is energy lost in a motor? ☑
24) How is energy lost in a heating device? ☑
25) Give an equation in terms of power and time for the energy transferred by a component in a circuit. ☑
26) Give an equation in terms of current and potential difference for the energy transferred by a circuit. ☑
27) What is the power rating of an electrical appliance? ☑

Everyday Speeds and Accelerations

Are you ready for a super speedy page? Get set... gooooooooooo!!

Speeds can be Given in Different Units

The unit for speed you'll mainly use in science is metres per second, m/s. In the real world speeds are often measured in miles per hour, mph or kilometres per hour, km/hr. Make sure you can convert between them.

> **Convert mph to km/hr:**
> There are about 1.6 kilometres to every mile. So multiply by 1.6.
> So 30 mph = 30 × 1.6 = 48 km/hr.

> **Convert km/hr into m/s:**
> Divide by 3600 (i.e. 60 × 60) to turn hr into s, then multiply by 1000 to change from km to m. Or just divide by 3.6.
> So 48 km/hr = 48 ÷ 3.6 = 13.33... ≈ 13 m/s (to 2 s.f.).

Learn these Typical Speeds

1) Walking — 1.4 m/s (5 km/hr)
2) Running — 3 m/s (11 km/hr)
3) Cycling — 5.5 m/s (20 km/hr)
4) Cars in a built-up area — 13 m/s (47 km/hr or 30 mph)
5) Cars on a motorway — 31 m/s (112 km/hr or 70 mph)

6) Trains — up to 55 m/s (200 km/hr)
7) A breeze — 5 m/s
8) A gale — 20 m/s
9) The speed of sound in air is 340 m/s

You Need to be Able to Estimate Acceleration

To estimate an acceleration, you may need to estimate the time a change in speed takes, then use the equation: acceleration = change in velocity ÷ time taken.

>  A car starts from rest and accelerates up to 50 km/hr as quickly as possible. Estimate its acceleration in m/s^2.
>
> First, change the speed to m/s: 50 km/hr = 50 ÷ 3.6 = 13.88... m/s.
> This is a fairly typical speed for a car in town. From experience you'd guess it takes a few seconds for most cars to get up to this speed — say it takes 2 seconds.
> Acceleration = change in velocity ÷ time taken = 13.88... ÷ 2 = 6.94... ≈ 7 m/s^2 (to 1 s.f.)
>
> *Give your answer to 1 s.f. for rough estimates like this.*

Large Decelerations can be Dangerous

1) Large decelerations of objects and people (e.g. in car crashes), and the forces involved can cause injuries. This is because a large deceleration requires a large force (since $F = ma$).

2) The force on an object can be lowered by slowing the object down over a longer time, i.e. decreasing its deceleration (since a = change in speed ÷ t, and $F = ma$ again). You can also think of this in terms of momentum — the longer it takes for a change in momentum, the smaller the forces acting.

3) Safety features in cars are designed to increase collision times, which reduces the deceleration and forces, and so reduces the risk of injury. For example, seat belts stretch slightly and air bags slow you down gradually. Crumple zones are areas at the front and back of a car which crumple up easily in a collision, increasing the time taken to stop.

   Some safety features also work by stopping you hitting hard surfaces like the dashboard or the road.

4) This stuff's not just about car collisions — for example bike helmets contain a crushable layer of foam which increases the time taken for your head to stop, reducing the deceleration and forces acting. Shin pads work this way too — if something hits a shin pad, the pad deforms, reducing deceleration and the force on your leg.

My acceleration towards the kettle is about 10 m/s^2...

This stuff is pretty dull, but it's important for the next few pages, so make sure you know it all.

Q1   A car pulls onto a motorway slip-road and accelerates from 50 mph to 70 mph as quickly as possible.
     Estimate its acceleration in m/s^2.   [3 marks]

Stopping Distances and Reaction Times

The <u>stopping distance</u> is the distance covered between the driver <u>spotting</u> a hazard and the vehicle <u>stopping</u>.

Stopping Distance = Thinking Distance + Braking Distance

The <u>longer</u> it takes a car to <u>stop</u> after seeing a hazard, the <u>higher</u> the risk of <u>crashing</u>. The distance it takes to stop a car (<u>stopping distance</u>) is divided into the <u>thinking distance</u> and the <u>braking distance</u>:

The <u>thinking distance</u> is the distance the car travels in the driver's <u>reaction time</u> (the time between <u>noticing the hazard</u> and <u>applying the brakes</u>). It's affected by <u>two main factors</u>:

1) Your <u>reaction time</u> — this is affected by <u>tiredness</u>, <u>alcohol</u>, <u>drugs</u> and <u>distractions</u>.

2) Your <u>speed</u> — the <u>faster</u> you're going, the <u>further</u> you travel during your reaction time.

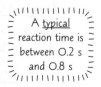

A <u>typical</u> reaction time is between 0.2 s and 0.8 s

The <u>braking distance</u> is the distance taken to stop <u>once the brakes have been applied</u>. It's affected by:

1) Your <u>speed</u> — the <u>faster</u> you're going, the <u>further</u> it takes to stop (see next page).

2) The <u>mass</u> of the car — a car full of <u>people</u> and <u>luggage</u> won't stop as quickly as an empty car.

3) The condition of the <u>brakes</u> — <u>worn</u> or <u>faulty</u> brakes won't be able to brake with <u>as much force</u>.

4) How good the <u>grip</u> of your tyres is — you're more likely to <u>skid</u> when the road is <u>dirty</u>, if it's <u>icy or wet</u> and if the <u>tyres</u> are <u>bald</u> (tyres must have a minimum <u>tread depth</u> of <u>1.6 mm</u>).

<u>Thinking</u> and <u>braking distance</u> can be seen on *v-t* graphs.

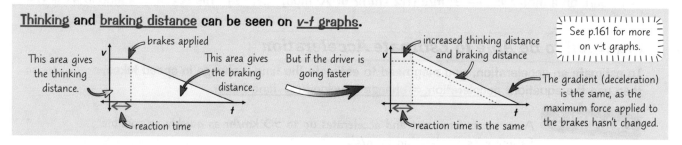

brakes applied

This area gives the thinking distance.

This area gives the braking distance.

But if the driver is going faster

reaction time

increased thinking distance and braking distance

See p.161 for more on v-t graphs.

The gradient (deceleration) is the same, as the maximum force applied to the brakes hasn't changed.

reaction time is the same

The Ruler Drop Experiment Measures Reaction Times

1) Stand with your hand open. Get someone else to hold a ruler so it <u>hangs between</u> your thumb and forefinger, and your forefinger's lined up with <u>zero</u>.

2) Without giving any warning, the person holding the ruler <u>drops it</u>. Close your thumb and finger to try to <u>catch the ruler as quickly as possible</u>.

3) The <u>measurement on the ruler</u> at the point where it was caught is <u>how far</u> the ruler dropped in the time it took you to react.

4) The <u>longer</u> the <u>distance</u>, the <u>longer</u> the <u>reaction time</u>.

5) You can calculate <u>how long</u> the ruler was falling for (the <u>reaction</u> time) because its <u>acceleration</u> is <u>constant</u> (and equal to *g*, 10 m/s²).

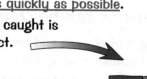

finger in line with zero

ruler is dropped without warning

distance fallen

Say you caught the ruler at 20 cm. From page 158 you know: $v^2 - u^2 = 2ad$. $u = 0$, $a = 10$ m/s² and $d = 0.2$ m, so: $v = \sqrt{2 \times 10 \times 0.2} = 2$ m/s. *v* is equal to the <u>change in speed</u> of the ruler.

From page 158 you also know $a = $ change in v $\div$ t, so $t = 2 \div 10 = 0.2$ s — your <u>reaction time</u>.

6) It's <u>hard</u> to do this experiment <u>accurately</u>, so do a lot of <u>repeats</u> and find the <u>mean distance</u> that the ruler fell. Use this mean in the calculation above.

7) Make sure it's a <u>fair test</u>, e.g. use the <u>same ruler</u> each time and have the <u>same person</u> dropping it.

8) You could investigate factors that <u>affect</u> reaction time, e.g. introduce <u>distractions</u>.

There are other ways to measure reaction times, e.g. pressing a button when a computer screen changes.

Stop right there — and learn this page...

Bad visibility also causes accidents — if it's foggy, it's harder to notice a hazard, so there's less room to stop.

Q1 Drivers on long journeys should take regular breaks. Explain why, in terms of stopping distance. [3 marks]

Non-Renewable Energy Sources

We use **A LOT** of electricity — I bet you're reading this in a room with an <u>electric light</u>, with your <u>phone</u> on in your pocket, and maybe the <u>radio</u> in the background. The energy to power it all has to come from <u>somewhere</u>.

Non-Renewable Energy Sources Will Run Out One Day

1) We get <u>most</u> of our energy from <u>non-renewable</u> sources.

2) These are sources that will <u>run out</u> one day and they <u>damage</u> the <u>environment</u>.

3) The main non-renewables are the three <u>fossil fuels</u> (<u>coal</u>, <u>oil</u> and <u>natural gas</u>) and <u>nuclear fuels</u> (<u>uranium</u> and <u>plutonium</u>).

Peat is often called a non-renewable source too, because it can't be quickly replaced.

Most Power Stations Use Steam to Drive a Turbine

We currently generate most of our electricity from burning <u>fossil fuels</u> in power stations, like this:

1) As the fossil fuel <u>burns</u> (in oxygen) the energy in its <u>chemical energy store</u> is transferred to the <u>thermal energy store</u> of the <u>water</u>.

2) The water <u>boils</u> to form <u>steam</u>, which <u>turns</u> a <u>turbine</u>, transferring energy to the <u>kinetic energy store</u> of the turbine.

3) As the turbine revolves, so does the <u>generator</u> — as it turns it <u>generates electricity</u>.

4) The generator transfers the energy <u>electrically</u> away from the power station, via the <u>national grid</u>.

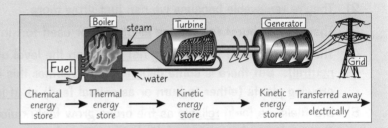

Nuclear Reactors Are Just Fancy Boilers

1) A <u>nuclear power station</u> is mostly the same as the one above, but the energy from <u>nuclear fission</u> is used to <u>heat</u> water to make <u>steam</u> to drive <u>turbines</u>, etc. The difference is in the <u>boiler</u>:

2) Nuclear power stations take the <u>longest</u> time of all the power stations to start up. <u>Natural gas</u> power stations take the <u>shortest</u> time.

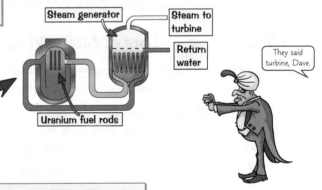
They said turbine, Dave.

Non-Renewable Sources Cause Environmental Problems

1) All three <u>fossil fuels</u> (coal, oil and natural gas) release CO_2 — coal releases the most, then oil, then natural gas. This CO_2 contributes to <u>climate change</u> and <u>global warming</u>.

2) Burning coal and oil releases <u>sulfur dioxide</u>, which causes <u>acid rain</u>. This is reduced by taking the sulfur out <u>before</u> it's burned, or cleaning up the <u>emissions</u>.

3) <u>Coal mining</u> makes a <u>mess</u> of the landscape, especially "<u>open-cast mining</u>".

4) <u>Oil spillages</u> cause <u>serious environmental problems</u>.

5) <u>Nuclear waste</u> (from nuclear power stations) is very <u>dangerous</u> and difficult to <u>dispose of</u>. This means that, even though nuclear <u>fuel</u> (i.e. uranium) is <u>relatively cheap</u>, the <u>overall cost</u> of nuclear power is <u>high</u> due to the cost to <u>build</u> and <u>decommission</u> the <u>power plant</u>.

6) <u>Nuclear power</u> also carries the risk of a <u>major catastrophe</u> like the <u>Fukushima disaster</u> in Japan.

It all boils down to steam...

Steam engines were invented as long ago as the 17th century, yet we're still using that idea to produce most of our electricity over 300 years later. Pretty impressive, eh?

Q1 Describe how a coal-fired power station works. [2 marks]

Renewable Energy Sources

Renewable energy sources, unlike non-renewables, <u>don't run out</u> (funny that).

Renewable Energy Sources Will Never Run Out

1) A <u>renewable energy source</u> is one that will <u>never run out</u>.
2) Most of them do some <u>damage to the environment</u>, but in <u>less nasty</u> ways than non-renewables.
3) They <u>don't</u> provide as much energy as <u>non-renewables</u> and the <u>weather-dependent</u> ones can be <u>unreliable</u>.
4) Renewable sources include <u>bio-fuels</u>, <u>wind</u> power, the <u>Sun</u>, <u>hydro-electricity</u> and the <u>tides</u>.

Bio-fuels are Made from Plants and Waste

1) <u>Bio-fuels</u> can be made from anything from <u>farm waste</u>, <u>animal droppings</u> and <u>landfill rubbish</u> to <u>specially grown crops</u> (e.g. sugar cane, vegetable oils or trees).
2) They're renewable because we can just <u>grow more</u>.
3) They can be burnt to produce <u>electricity</u> or used to run <u>cars</u> in the same way as <u>fossil fuels</u>.
4) They aren't meant to have any <u>net effect</u> on the level of CO_2 in the atmosphere (they're <u>carbon neutral</u>). But there is some <u>debate</u> about whether this is true, as this only really works if you keep growing plants (either to burn or as animal feed) at <u>at least the rate</u> that you're burning things.
5) Bio-fuels are fairly <u>reliable</u> as the crops grow fairly quickly. But it's harder to respond to <u>immediate energy demands</u>, as crops <u>take time</u> to grow (you can <u>stockpile</u> bio-fuels to combat this).
6) The <u>cost</u> to make <u>bio-fuels</u> is <u>very high</u> and some worry that growing crops specifically for bio-fuels will mean there isn't enough <u>space</u> or <u>water</u> to meet the demands for crops that are grown for <u>food</u>.
7) In some places, large areas of <u>land</u> have been <u>cleared</u> to grow <u>bio-fuels</u>, resulting in species losing their <u>habitats</u>. The <u>decay</u> and <u>burning</u> of this vegetation also increases CO_2 and <u>methane</u> emissions.

Wind Power — Lots of Little Wind Turbines

1) Each wind turbine has a <u>generator</u> inside it — the rotating <u>blades</u> turn the generator and produce <u>electricity</u>.
2) There's <u>no pollution</u> (except for a little bit when they're manufactured).
3) But some people think they <u>spoil the view</u>. And they can be <u>very noisy</u>, which can be annoying for people living nearby.
4) They <u>only</u> work when it's <u>windy</u>, so you can't always <u>supply</u> electricity, or respond to <u>high demand</u>.

Solar Cells — Expensive but No Environmental Damage

(well, there may be a bit caused by <u>making</u> the cells)

1) Solar cells are made from <u>special materials</u> that release <u>electrons</u> when light falls on them, generating an <u>electric current</u>.
2) Solar power is often used in <u>remote places</u> where there's not much choice (e.g. the Australian outback) and to power electric <u>road signs</u> and <u>satellites</u>.
3) There's <u>no pollution</u>. (Although they do use quite a lot of energy to make.)
4) Solar cells are mainly used to generate electricity on a relatively <u>small scale</u>, e.g. in <u>homes</u>.
5) Solar power is most suitable for <u>sunny countries</u>, but it can be used in <u>cloudy countries</u> like Britain.
6) And of course, you <u>can't</u> make solar power at <u>night</u> or <u>increase production</u> when there's extra demand.

Time to recharge.

Burning poo.... lovely...

Given our electricity-guzzling ways, it's pretty important we find ways to generate electricity without destroying the planet. Burning cow pats may not be the ultimate fix, but it's a start. See the next page for more ways.

Q1   State two renewable energy sources.   [2 marks]

Q2   State two disadvantages of using wind power to generate electricity.   [2 marks]

More On Energy Sources

Two more renewable energy sources to learn, then we'll look at trends in the crazy world of energy production.

Hydro-electricity — Building Dams and Flooding Valleys

1) Producing hydro-electricity usually involves flooding a valley by building a big dam.

2) Rainwater is caught and allowed out through turbines.

3) There is a big impact on the environment due to the flooding of the valley and possible loss of habitat for some species.

4) A big advantage is immediate response to increased electricity demand — more water can be let out through the turbines to generate more electricity.

5) Initial costs are often high but there are minimal running costs and it's a reliable energy source.

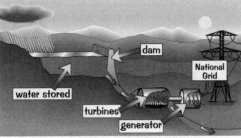

Tidal Barrages — Using the Sun and Moon's Gravity

1) Tidal barrages are big dams built across river estuaries with turbines in them.

2) As the tide comes in it fills up the estuary. The water is then let out through turbines at a set speed.

3) There is no pollution but they affect boat access, can spoil the view and they alter the habitat for wildlife, e.g. wading birds.

4) Tides are pretty reliable (they always happen twice a day). But the height is variable and they don't work when the water level is the same either side.

5) Even though it can only be used in some estuaries, tidal barrages have great potential.

Renewables are Growing, but we Still Depend on Coal and Gas

1) Over the 20th century, the electricity use of the UK hugely increased, as the population got bigger and people began to use electricity for more and more things.

2) Most of this electricity was generated using fossil fuels (mostly coal and gas) and from nuclear power.

3) Over time, we've become more aware that these fuels will run out one day and that they cause environmental damage.

> Nuclear power is another option for decreasing fossil fuels use and the UK is investing in nuclear power. But some people worry about the possibility of nuclear accidents and the dangers of nuclear waste.

4) So we're investing time and money in developing renewable energy sources, but progress is slow.

5) In the UK, renewable sources still only account for generating around 20% of the electricity we use — most of our electricity still comes from burning coal and gas. This is partly because most renewable sources generate less electricity than a big coal-fired power station, and many renewable energy sources are weather-dependent (e.g. wind and solar) so the amount they supply fluctuates a lot.

6) It's not just about generating electricity renewably — we're also trying to use less. Since the beginning of the 21st century, our electricity use has been decreasing (slowly), as we get better at making appliances more efficient and people have become more aware of the need to save energy.

7) We don't just burn fossil fuels to generate electricity — we use oil (diesel and petrol) to fuel our cars, and gas to heat our homes and cook our food.

8) We're investigating other ways to power cars, e.g. electric cars.

Trends in energy use — light bulbs wearing sunglasses...

There are problems with every kind of electricity production, and no one wants any of them happening in their backyard. But if we want to carry on living the way we are, we're going to need to make some compromises.

Q1   Give one advantage and one disadvantage of producing hydro-electricity.   [2 marks]

Q2   Many people want to replace non-renewable energy sources for generating electricity with renewable energy sources. Suggest why.   [2 marks]

Electricity and the National Grid

There are two types of current — <u>alternating</u> and <u>direct</u>. The <u>national grid</u> supplies alternating current.

Alternating Voltage Keeps Changing Direction

1) An <u>alternating current</u> (a.c.) is produced by an <u>alternating voltage</u> (or <u>alternating potential difference</u>, <u>p.d.</u>) — the p.d. and current <u>constantly change direction</u>.

2) The <u>UK mains electricity</u> (in your home) is <u>a.c.</u> at <u>50 Hz</u> and around <u>230 V</u>.

3) <u>Direct current</u> (d.c.) is produced by a <u>direct voltage</u> — the current and the p.d. <u>don't change direction</u>.

4) You get d.c. from <u>batteries</u> and <u>cells</u>.

5) A <u>cathode ray oscilloscope (CRO)</u> trace can show how the <u>p.d.</u> of a supply <u>changes with time</u>.

6) If you connect an <u>alternating voltage</u> to the CRO, you see a <u>wave</u> — it goes up and down in a <u>regular pattern</u>.

7) <u>Direct voltage</u> gives a <u>horizontal line</u> — it <u>doesn't vary</u>.

8) The <u>height</u> at any point shows the <u>input p.d.</u> at that point.

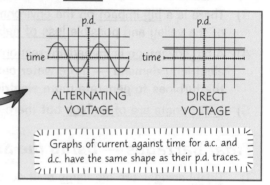

Graphs of current against time for a.c. and d.c. have the same shape as their p.d. traces.

Electricity Gets Around via the National Grid...

1) The <u>national grid</u> is a network of <u>wires</u> and <u>transformers</u> that connects UK <u>power stations</u> to <u>consumers</u> (anyone who uses electricity).

2) It transfers energy electrically from <u>power stations</u> (the <u>supply</u>) to where it's needed in <u>homes</u> and <u>industry</u> (the <u>demand</u>).

3) To transmit the <u>huge</u> amount of <u>power</u> needed, you need either a <u>high p.d.</u> or a <u>high current</u> (as $P = IV$).

4) The <u>problem</u> with a <u>high current</u> is that you lose <u>loads of energy</u> as the wires <u>heat up</u> and energy is transferred to the <u>thermal</u> energy store of the <u>surroundings</u>. The power lost is given by $\underline{P = I^2R}$, where R is the resistance of the wires (so you can reduce losses by using wires of a lower resistance).

5) Wasted energy and power <u>costs money</u>, so it's <u>cheaper</u> to <u>boost the p.d.</u> up <u>really high</u> (to 400 000 V) and keep the current <u>very low</u> — this makes the national grid an <u>efficient</u> way of transferring energy.

Power is the energy transferred in a given time, so a higher power means more energy is transferred.

...With a Little Help from Transformers

1) To get the voltage up to 400 000 V for <u>efficient transmission</u> we use <u>transformers</u> (and <u>big pylons</u> with <u>huge insulators</u>).

2) Transformers all have two coils, a <u>primary coil</u> and a <u>secondary coil</u>, joined with an <u>iron core</u>.

3) <u>Potential difference</u> (p.d.) is <u>increased</u> using a <u>step-up transformer</u>. They have <u>more</u> turns on the <u>secondary</u> coil than the primary coil. As the p.d. is increased by the transformer, the <u>current</u> is <u>decreased</u>.

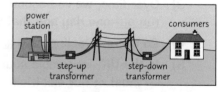

Remember — potential difference and voltage are the same thing.

4) The p.d. is then <u>reduced</u> again at the local consumer end using a <u>step-down transformer</u> (the <u>current</u> is therefore <u>increased</u> by this transformer). They have <u>more</u> turns on the <u>primary</u> coil than the secondary.

5) The <u>power</u> of a primary coil is given by <u>power = p.d. × current</u>. Transformers are nearly <u>100% efficient</u>, so the <u>power in primary coil = power in secondary coil</u>. This mean that:

p.d. across primary coil (V)	×	current in primary coil (A)	=	p.d. across secondary coil (V)	×	current in secondary coil (A)

Transformers — there's more than meets the eye...

Fun fact — the step-down transformers on power lines get a bit warm, so birds love to nest on them.

Q1   An electrician wants to increase the voltage that is supplied to a device using a transformer. State what type of transformer she should use and what effect it will have on the current.

[2 marks]

Wiring in the Home

Now then, did you know... electricity is <u>dangerous</u>. It can kill you. Well just <u>watch out</u> for it, that's all.

Plugs Contain Three Wires

Appliances usually contain <u>three wires</u>.
You need to know what each of them is for:

2) NEUTRAL WIRE — blue.
The neutral wire <u>completes</u> the circuit — electricity normally flows <u>in</u> through the <u>live</u> wire and <u>out</u> through the <u>neutral</u> wire. The neutral wire is always at <u>0 V</u>.

1) LIVE WIRE — brown.
The live wire carries the voltage (potential difference, p.d.). It alternates between a <u>high +ve and −ve voltage</u> of about <u>230 V</u>.

FUSE (see below)

3) EARTH WIRE — green and yellow.
The earth wire is for <u>safety</u>. It carries the current away if something goes wrong. It's <u>also</u> at 0 V.

1) The <u>p.d.</u> between the <u>live wire</u> and the <u>neutral wire</u> equals the <u>supply p.d.</u> (<u>230 V</u> for the mains).

2) The <u>p.d.</u> between the <u>live wire</u> and the <u>earth wire</u> is also <u>230 V</u> for a mains-connected appliance.

3) There is <u>no p.d.</u> between the <u>neutral wire</u> and the <u>earth wire</u> — they're both at 0 V.

4) Your <u>body</u> is also at <u>0 V</u>. This means if you touched the <u>live wire</u>, there'd be a <u>large p.d.</u> across your body and a <u>current</u> would flow through you. This large <u>electric shock</u> could injure or even kill you.

5) Even if a plug socket is <u>off</u> (i.e. the switch is <u>open</u>) there is still a <u>danger</u> of an electric shock. A current <u>isn't flowing</u>, but there is still a p.d. in the live part of the socket, so your body could provide a <u>link</u> between the supply and the earth if you made <u>contact</u> with it.

Earthing and Fuses Prevent Fires and Shocks

1) Electricity will flow through anything that <u>conducts</u>. So if the live wire accidentally connects with something <u>metal</u> (e.g. the <u>case of an appliance</u>) <u>current</u> will <u>flow</u>. This could cause serious <u>electric shocks</u> and <u>fires</u>.

2) All appliances with <u>metal cases</u> must be "<u>earthed</u>" for safety. This means the case must be attached to an <u>earth wire</u>.

3) If a <u>fault</u> develops so the <u>live</u> wire touches the <u>metal case</u>, then a current will flow down the <u>earth wire</u>.

4) The earth wire is <u>very thick</u>, to give it a <u>low resistance</u>. This means the <u>total resistance</u> of the circuit decreases. Current = p.d. ÷ resistance, so this causes a <u>big current</u> to flow through the <u>live</u> wire, the <u>case</u>, and out down the <u>earth wire</u>.

5) This surge in current <u>melts</u> the fuse, <u>breaking the circuit</u> and cutting off the live supply. This <u>isolates</u> the appliance, so it's <u>impossible</u> to get an <u>electric shock</u> from the case. It also <u>prevents fires</u> caused by the heating effect of a large current.

6) Fuses and earthing also <u>protect the circuits and wiring</u> in your appliances from getting <u>fried</u> if there is a <u>current surge</u>.

7) If the appliance has a <u>casing</u> that's <u>non-conductive</u> (e.g. <u>plastic</u>) then it's <u>double insulated</u>. Anything with double insulation <u>doesn't need an earth wire</u> as it can't become live.

normal toaster — current flows from live to neutral

coil becomes loose, live wire touches casing

resistance of the earth wire and casing is low, so current increases

current flows from casing through the earth wire

surge of current melts the fuse, breaking the circuit

Electricity rule number 1 — don't stick your fingers in the socket...

So wiring's fun isn't it? Unfortunately, it could be in your exams so you'd best get it learnt.

Q1   A metal kettle is plugged into the mains electricity supply (230 V, 50 Hz).
       a) Explain why the kettle needs an earth wire and how it works.   [3 marks]
       b) State the potential difference between the kettle's earth and neutral wires.   [1 mark]

Revision Questions for Topic P6

Congratulations! That's it for the theory. There's just the practical stuff to go now. Oh, and these questions...

- Try these questions and <u>tick off each one</u> when you <u>get it right</u>.
- When you've done <u>all the questions</u> under a heading and are <u>completely happy</u> with it, tick it off.

Everyday Transport (p.209-210) ☐

1) Estimate typical speeds for
   a) walking,
   b) running,
   c) sound.

2) Explain how crumple zones reduce the risk of injury in a crash. ☑

3) What is meant by a driver's reaction time? ☑

4) Give examples of two things that might affect a driver's reaction time. ☑

5) List four things that will affect the braking distance of a car. ☑

6) Describe an experiment to measure reaction times. ☑

Generating and Using Electricity (p.211-215) ☐

7) List four non-renewable energy sources. ☑

8) Describe how electricity is generated in a nuclear power station. ☑

9) List three environmental problems associated with non-renewable energy resources. ☑

10) What's the difference between renewable and non-renewable energy sources? ☑

11) Describe how electricity is generated using wind power. ☑

12) Give one disadvantage of generating electricity from the tides. ☑

13) What is the voltage and frequency of the mains electricity supply in the UK? ☑

14) What is the difference between direct voltage and alternating voltage?
    Sketch a CRO trace for each. ☑

15) Why does the national grid carry electricity at such high voltages? ☑

16) Name the device that is used to increase the voltage
    between a power station and the cables of the national grid. ☑

17) What are the three main wires in a plug? ☑

Safety and Ethics

- <u>Topic CS7</u> covers <u>practical skills</u> you'll need to know about for your course (including 15% of your exams).
- You're required to do at least <u>16 practical activities</u> (experiments). These are covered throughout the biology, chemistry and physics topics earlier in the book and they're <u>highlighted</u> with <u>practical stamps</u> like this one.
- The following pages of this topic cover some <u>extra bits and bobs</u> you need to know about practical work. First up, safety in the lab...

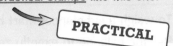

PRACTICAL

Make Sure You're Working Safely in the Lab

1) <u>Before</u> you start any experiment, make sure you know about any <u>safety precautions</u> to do with your <u>method</u> or the <u>chemicals</u> you're using. <u>Follow</u> any instructions that your teacher gives you <u>carefully</u>.

2) Make sure that you're wearing <u>sensible clothing</u> when you're in the lab (e.g. open shoes won't protect your feet from spillages). When you're doing an experiment, you should wear a <u>lab coat</u> to protect your skin and clothing. Depending on the experiment, you may need to also wear <u>safety goggles</u> and <u>gloves</u>.

3) You also need to be aware of <u>general safety</u> in the lab, e.g. keep anything <u>flammable</u> away from lit Bunsen burners, don't directly touch any <u>hot equipment</u>, handle <u>glassware</u> carefully so it doesn't <u>break</u>, etc.

4) Stop masses and equipment falling by using <u>clamp stands</u>. Make sure masses are of a <u>sensible weight</u> so they don't break the equipment they're used with, and use <u>pulleys</u> of a sensible <u>length</u>. That way, any hanging masses won't <u>hit the floor</u> during the experiment.

5) When <u>heating</u> materials, make sure to let them <u>cool</u> before moving them, or wear <u>insulated gloves</u> while handling them. If you're using an <u>immersion heater</u> to heat liquids, you should always let it <u>dry out</u> in air, just in case any liquid has leaked inside the heater.

6) If you're using a <u>laser</u>, there are a few safety rules you must follow. Always wear <u>laser safety goggles</u> and never <u>look directly into</u> the laser or shine it <u>towards another person</u>. Make sure you turn the laser <u>off</u> if it's not needed to avoid any accidents.

7) When working with electronics, make sure you use a <u>low</u> enough <u>voltage</u> and <u>current</u> to prevent wires <u>overheating</u> (and potentially melting) and avoid <u>damage to components</u>, like blowing a filament bulb.

Make Sure you Work Safely Around Hazardous Chemicals

1) The substances used in chemical reactions may be <u>hazardous</u> — for example, they might be <u>flammable</u> (<u>catch fire easily</u>), or they might <u>irritate</u> or <u>burn</u> your <u>skin</u> if it comes into contact with them.

2) Always be careful that the chemicals you're using aren't flammable before you go lighting any Bunsen burners, and make sure you're working in an area that's <u>well ventilated</u>.

3) If you're doing an experiment that might produce nasty <u>gases</u> (such as chlorine), you should carry out the experiment in a <u>fume hood</u> so that the gas can't escape out into the room you're working in.

4) Never directly touch any chemicals (even if you're wearing gloves). Use a <u>spatula</u> to transfer <u>solids</u> between containers. Carefully <u>pour</u> liquids between different containers, using a <u>funnel</u> to avoid spillages.

5) Be careful when you're <u>mixing</u> chemicals, as a reaction might occur. If you're <u>diluting</u> a liquid, add the <u>concentrated substance</u> to the <u>water</u> (not the other way around) or the mixture could get very <u>hot</u>.

You Need to Think About Ethical Issues In Your Experiments

1) Any <u>organisms</u> involved in your investigations need to be treated <u>safely</u> and <u>ethically</u>.

2) <u>Animals</u> need to be treated <u>humanely</u> — they should be <u>handled carefully</u> and any wild animals captured for studying (e.g. during an investigation of the distribution of an organism) should be <u>returned to their original habitat</u>. Any animals kept in the lab should also be <u>cared for</u> in a humane way, e.g. they should not be kept in <u>overcrowded conditions</u>.

3) If you're carrying out an experiment involving other <u>students</u> (e.g. investigating the effect of caffeine on reaction time), they should not be forced to participate <u>against their will</u> or feel <u>pressured</u> to take part.

Proper lab attire includes golden fur and a waggy tail...

Have a good think about safety and ethics before you start any experimental work — it's all important stuff.

Apparatus and Techniques

Get your lab coats on, it's time to find out about the skills you'll need in experiments...

You can Measure Substances Using a Balance

1) To weigh a substance, start by putting the container you're weighing your substance into on the balance.

2) Set the balance to exactly zero and then start weighing out your substance.

3) If you're weighing solids, it's no good carefully weighing out your solid if it's not all transferred to your reaction vessel — the amount in the reaction vessel won't be the same as your measurement. Here's a couple of methods you can use to make sure that none gets left in your weighing container...

- If you're dissolving a solid in a solvent to make a solution, wash any remaining solid into the new container using the solvent. This way you know all the solid you weighed has been transferred.

- You could set the balance to zero before you put your weighing container on to it, then reweigh the weighing container after you've transferred the solid. You can use the difference in mass to work out exactly how much you added to your experiment.

Three Ways to Measure Liquids

There are a few methods you might use to measure the volume of a liquid. Whichever method you use, always read the volume from the bottom of the meniscus (the curved upper surface of the liquid) when it's at eye level.

Read volume from here — the bottom of the meniscus.

pipette filler

Pipettes are long, narrow tubes that are used to suck up an accurate volume of liquid and transfer it to another container. A pipette filler attached to the end of the pipette is used so that you can safely control the amount of liquid that you're drawing up. Pipettes are often calibrated to allow for the fact that the last drop of liquid stays in the pipette when the liquid is ejected from it. This reduces transfer errors.

If you only want a couple of drops of liquid, and don't need it to be accurately measured, you can use a dropping pipette to transfer it. For example, this is how you'd add a couple of drops of indicator into a mixture.

Burettes measure from top to bottom (so when they're filled to the top of the scale, it reads zero). They have a tap at the bottom which is used to release the liquid into another container (you can even release it drop by drop). To use a burette, take an initial reading. Then once you've released as much liquid as you want, take a final reading. The difference between the readings tells you how much liquid you used.

Measuring cylinders are the most common way to measure out a liquid. They come in all different sizes. Make sure you choose one that's the right size for the measurement you want to make. It's no good using a huge 1000 cm³ cylinder to measure out 2 cm³ of a liquid — the graduations will be too big, and you'll end up with massive errors. It'd be much better to use one that measures up to 10 cm³.

You May Have to Measure the Time Taken for a Change

1) If your experiment involves timing something (e.g. how long a reaction takes) or taking measurements at regular intervals, it's probably best to use a stopwatch. Using a stopwatch that measures to the nearest 0.1 s will make your results more accurate.

2) Always make sure you start and stop the stopwatch at exactly the right time. E.g. if you're investigating the rate of a reaction, you should start timing at the exact moment you mix the reagents and start the reaction.

3) If you're carrying out experiments involving acceleration or speed, you could use a light gate (see p.224).

4) It's a good idea to get the same person to do the timing so the results are as precise as possible.

Topic CS7 — Practical Skills

Apparatus and Techniques

Measure Temperature Accurately with a Thermometer

1) Make sure the <u>bulb</u> of your thermometer is <u>completely submerged</u> in any substance you're measuring.
2) Wait for the temperature to <u>stabilise</u> before you take your initial reading.
3) Again, read your measurement off the <u>scale</u> on a thermometer at <u>eye level</u>.

bulb

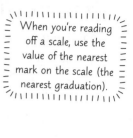

When you're reading off a scale, use the value of the nearest mark on the scale (the nearest graduation).

Measure Most Lengths with a Ruler

1) In most cases a bog-standard <u>centimetre ruler</u> can be used to measure <u>length</u>. It depends on what you're measuring though — <u>metre rulers</u> or <u>long measuring tapes</u> are handy for <u>large</u> distances, while <u>micrometers</u> are used for measuring tiny things like the <u>diameter of a wire</u>.
2) You'll also need to decide on the <u>appropriate level of accuracy</u> for your experiment. For example, the length of a <u>leaf</u> would be better measured in <u>millimetres</u>, but the <u>distance travelled by a bus</u> in a certain time would be better measured in <u>metres</u>.
3) A ruler should always be <u>parallel to</u> what you want to measure.
4) If you're dealing with something where it's <u>tricky</u> to measure just <u>one</u> thing accurately, e.g. waves in water, you can measure the length of <u>ten</u> of them and then <u>divide</u> to find the <u>length of one</u>.
5) If you're taking <u>multiple measurements</u> of the <u>same</u> object (e.g. to measure changes in length) then make sure you always measure from the <u>same point</u> on the object. It can help to put a <u>marker</u> or <u>pointer</u> onto the object to line up your ruler against.
6) Make sure the ruler and the object are always at <u>eye level</u> when you take a reading. This stops <u>parallax</u> affecting your results, e.g. if you're doing the ruler drop experiment (p.210).
7) <u>Parallax</u> is where a measurement appears to <u>change</u> based on <u>where you're looking from</u>. The <u>blue line</u> in the diagram on the right shows the <u>real position</u> of the <u>hand</u> relative to the <u>ruler</u>. If the eye <u>isn't level</u> with this line, it looks like the hand is <u>too low</u> or <u>too high</u>.

ruler — spring

pointer

ruler

eye

correct level to see the hand's position

hand

Measuring the Area of Something in Biology

In biology, you might need to measure the <u>area</u> of something (e.g. part of a habitat, a living thing). Living things are usually quite <u>complex shapes</u>, but you can make their area easier to work out by comparing them to a <u>simpler shape</u> and working out the area of that (e.g. <u>clear zones</u> in bacterial lawns are roughly <u>circular</u> — see p.73). To find the area of something:

1) First, you'll need to take <u>accurate measurements</u> of its dimensions.

> If you want to <u>measure</u> the area of a <u>field</u> that is <u>rectangular</u>, you'll need to use a <u>tape measure</u> or a <u>trundle wheel</u> to measure the <u>length</u> and <u>width</u> of the field. Record your readings in metres.

2) Then you can <u>calculate</u> its <u>area</u>.

> Area of a <u>rectangle</u> = <u>length</u> × <u>width</u>.
> So, if your field is 30 m by 55 m, the <u>area</u> would be 30 × 55 = <u>1650 m^2</u>.

Don't forget the units of area are always something squared, e.g. mm^2.

Here are some examples of other area formulas that may come in useful:

- Area of a triangle = ½ × base × height
- Area of a circle = πr^2

Apparatus and Techniques

Measure pH to Find Out How Acidic or Alkaline a Solution Is

You need to be able to decide the best method for measuring pH, depending on what your experiment is.

1) Indicators are dyes that change colour depending on whether they're in an acid or an alkali. You use them by adding a couple of drops of the indicator to the solution you're interested in. They're useful for titration reactions, when you want to find the point at which a solution is neutralised.

2) Single indicators are one colour in acids and another colour in alkalis. Examples of single indicators include litmus (red in acids, blue in alkalis) and phenolphthalein (colourless in acids, pink in alkalis).

3) Universal indicator is a mixed indicator — it's made by mixing together several single indicators. This means it changes through a whole series of colours as you go along the pH scale (it doesn't show one sudden colour change). It's useful for estimating the pH of a solution based on its colour.

4) Indicators can be soaked into paper and strips of this paper can be used for testing pH. If you use a dropping pipette to spot a small amount of a solution onto some indicator paper, it will change colour depending on the pH of the solution.

There's lots more about pH on page 113.

5) Indicator paper is useful when you don't want to change the colour of all of the substance, or if the substance is already coloured (so it might obscure the colour of the indicator). You can also hold a piece of damp indicator paper in a gas sample to test its pH.

6) pH probes are attached to pH meters which have a digital display that gives a numerical value for the pH of a solution. They're used to give an accurate value of pH.

Draw Your Observations Neatly with a Pencil

1) You should draw what you see under the microscope using a pencil with a sharp point.

2) Make sure your drawing takes up at least half of the space available and that it is drawn with clear, unbroken lines.

3) Your drawing should not include any colouring or shading.

4) If you are drawing cells, the subcellular structures should be drawn in proportion.

5) Remember to include a title of what you were observing and write down the magnification that it was observed under.

6) You should also label the important features of your drawing (e.g. nucleus, chloroplasts), using straight lines. Make sure that none of these lines cross each other because this can make them hard to read.

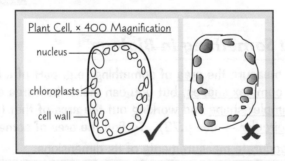

Use a Protractor to Find Angles

1) First align the vertex (point) of the angle with the mark in the centre of the protractor.

2) Line up the base line of the protractor with one line that forms the angle and then measure the angle of the other line using the scale on the protractor.

3) If the lines creating the angle are thick, align the protractor and measure the angle from the centre of the lines. Using a sharp pencil to trace light rays or draw diagrams helps to reduce errors when measuring angles.

4) If the lines are too short to measure easily, you may have to extend them. Again, make sure you use a sharp pencil to do this.

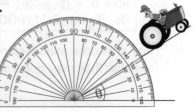

Topic CS7 — Practical Skills

Apparatus and Techniques

Organisms Should Be Sampled At Random Sites in an Area

1) It's generally <u>not possible</u> to count <u>every single organism</u> in an area. So if you're interested in the <u>distribution</u> of an organism in an area, or its <u>population size</u>, you need to take <u>samples</u> of the population in the area you're interested in.

2) You can use <u>quadrats</u> or <u>transects</u> to take population samples — see pages 59 and 61.

3) If you only take samples from <u>one part</u> of an area, your results will be <u>biased</u> — they may not give an <u>accurate representation</u> of the <u>whole area</u>.

4) To make sure that your sampling isn't biased, it needs to be <u>random</u>. This means you need to use a method of <u>choosing sampling sites</u> in which every site has an <u>equal chance</u> of being chosen. For example:

If you're looking at plant species in a field...

1) <u>Divide</u> the field into a <u>grid</u>.

2) <u>Label the grid</u> along the bottom and up the side with numbers or letters.

3) Use a <u>random number generator</u> (e.g. on a computer or calculator) to select coordinates, e.g. 2,4; 7,3.

4) Take your samples at these coordinates.

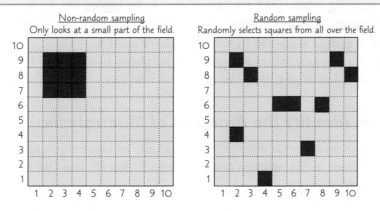

Non-random sampling
Only looks at a small part of the field.

Random sampling
Randomly selects squares from all over the field.

Colorimeters Measure the Intensity of Colour

Colorimeters are <u>machines</u> that measure <u>colour</u>. They work like this:

1) <u>Light</u> is passed through a solution.

2) Some of the light is <u>absorbed</u> by the solution — <u>darker</u> colours absorb <u>more</u> light than lighter colours.

3) The colorimeter <u>measures</u> the amount of light that <u>passes through</u> the solution and uses this to <u>work out</u> how much light was absorbed.

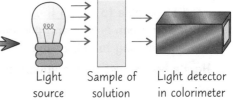

Light source   Sample of solution   Light detector in colorimeter

4) A <u>reading of absorbance</u> is given (the amount of light absorbed). The <u>higher</u> the absorbance, the <u>darker the colour</u> of the solution.

5) You can use the <u>absorbance value</u> for a particular <u>colour</u> to determine a <u>colour change</u>. For example:

- If you are investigating the <u>rate</u> at which amylase breaks down starch into maltose (see p.17), you may want to know the <u>exact point</u> at which <u>all</u> the starch has been <u>broken down</u>.

- This is shown in the experiment by the <u>colour change</u> from <u>blue-black</u> to <u>browny-orange</u>.

- If you measure the <u>absorbance value</u> with a colorimeter for pure maltose (<u>browny-orange colour</u>), you can compare the absorbance readings for other samples taken <u>during</u> the experiment to this to determine <u>when exactly</u> that <u>colour change</u> takes place.

- If you have a <u>data logger</u> you can take <u>continuous samples</u> of the changing absorbance of a solution during a reaction.

Apparatus and Techniques

To Collect Gases, the System Needs to be Sealed

1) There are times when you might want to <u>collect</u> the gas produced by a reaction. For example, to investigate the <u>rate</u> of reaction.

2) The most accurate way to measure the volume of a gas that's been produced is to collect it in a <u>gas syringe</u> (see page 129).

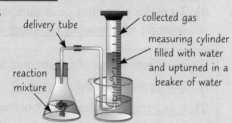

delivery tube
collected gas
gas syringe
reaction mixture

3) You could also collect it by <u>displacing water</u> from a measuring cylinder. Here's how you do it...

- Fill a <u>measuring cylinder</u> with <u>water</u>, and carefully place it <u>upside down</u> in a container of water. Record the <u>initial level</u> of the water in the measuring cylinder.

- Position a <u>delivery tube</u> coming <u>from</u> the reaction vessel so that it's <u>inside</u> the measuring cylinder, pointing upwards. Any gas that's produced will pass <u>through</u> the delivery tube and <u>into</u> the <u>measuring cylinder</u>. As the gas enters the measuring cylinder, the <u>water</u> is <u>pushed out</u>.

- Record the <u>level of water</u> in the measuring cylinder and use this value, along with your <u>initial value</u>, to calculate the <u>volume</u> of gas produced.

delivery tube
collected gas
measuring cylinder filled with water and upturned in a beaker of water
reaction mixture

4) When you're measuring a gas, your equipment has to be <u>sealed</u> or some gas could escape and your results wouldn't be <u>accurate</u>.

If the delivery tube is underneath the measuring cylinder rather than inside it then some of the gas might escape out into the air.

5) If you just want to <u>collect</u> a sample to test (and don't need to measure a volume), you can collect it over water as above using a <u>test tube</u>. Once the test tube is full of gas, you can stopper it and store the gas for later.

There's more about electrolysis on pages 117-118.

You May Have to Identify the Products of Electrolysis

1) When you electrolyse an <u>aqueous solution</u>, the products of electrolysis will depend on how reactive the ions in the solution are compared to the H^+ and OH^- ions that come from water.

2) At the <u>cathode</u> you'll either get a <u>pure metal</u> coating the electrode or bubbles of <u>hydrogen gas</u>.

3) At the <u>anode</u>, you'll get bubbles of <u>oxygen gas</u> unless a <u>halide ion</u> is present, when you'll get the <u>halogen</u>.

4) You may have to identify what's been made in an electrolysis experiment. To do this, you need to be able to <u>set up the equipment</u> correctly so that you can <u>collect</u> any gas that's produced. The easiest way to collect the gas is in a <u>test tube</u>.

5) Here's how to set up the equipment...

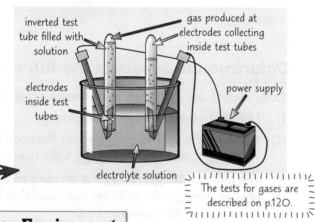

inverted test tube filled with solution
gas produced at electrodes collecting inside test tubes
electrodes inside test tubes
power supply
electrolyte solution

The tests for gases are described on p.120.

Make Sure You Can Draw Diagrams of Your Equipment

When you're writing out a <u>method</u> for your experiment, it's always a good idea to draw a <u>labelled diagram</u> showing how your apparatus will be <u>set up</u>. The easiest way to do this is to use a scientific drawing, where each piece of apparatus is drawn as if you're looking at its <u>cross-section</u>. For example:

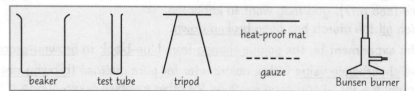

beaker   test tube   tripod   heat-proof mat   gauze   Bunsen burner

The pieces of glassware are drawn without tops so they aren't sealed. If you want to draw a closed system, remember to draw a bung in the top.

Experimentus apparatus...

Wizardry won't help you here, unfortunately. It's best you just get your head down and learn this stuff.

Heating Substances

Heating a reaction isn't as simple as wrapping it up in a lumpy wool jumper and a stripy scarf.
There's more than one way to do it, and you need to be able to decide on the <u>best</u>, and the <u>safest</u>, method.

Bunsen Burners Have a Naked Flame

Bunsen burners are good for heating things quickly. You can easily adjust how strongly they're heating. But you need to be careful not to use them if you're heating <u>flammable</u> compounds as the flame means the substance would be at risk of <u>catching fire</u>.

Here's how to use a Bunsen burner...

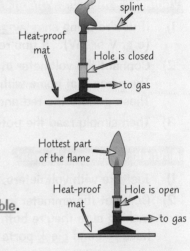

- Connect the Bunsen burner to a gas tap, and check that the hole is <u>closed</u>. Place it on a <u>heat-proof mat</u>.

- Light a <u>splint</u> and hold it over the Bunsen burner. Now, turn on the gas. The Bunsen burner should light with a <u>yellow flame</u>.

- The <u>more open</u> the hole is, the <u>more strongly</u> the Bunsen burner will heat your substance. Open the hole to the amount you want. As you open the hole more, the flame should turn more <u>blue</u>.

- The <u>hottest</u> part of the flame is just above the <u>blue cone</u>, so you should heat things here.

- If your Bunsen burner is alight but not heating anything, make sure you <u>close</u> the hole so that the flame becomes <u>orange</u> and <u>clearly visible</u>.

- If you're heating something so that the container (e.g. a test tube) is <u>in</u> the flame, you should hold the vessel at the <u>top</u>, furthest away from the substance (and so the flame) using a pair of <u>tongs</u>.

- If you're heating something <u>over</u> the flame (e.g. an evaporating dish), you should put a <u>tripod and gauze</u> over the Bunsen burner before you light it, and place the vessel on this.

The Temperature of Water Baths & Electric Heaters Can Be Set

1) A <u>water bath</u> is a container filled with water that can be heated to a <u>specific temperature</u>.

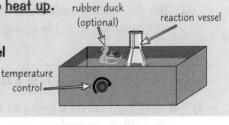

- <u>Set</u> the temperature on the water bath, and allow the water to <u>heat up</u>.

- Place the vessel containing your substance in the water bath using a pair of tongs. The level of the water outside the vessel should be <u>just above</u> the level of the substance inside the vessel. The substance will then be warmed to the <u>same temperature</u> as the water.

As the substance in the vessel is surrounded by water, the heating is very <u>even</u>. Water boils at <u>100 °C</u> though, so you <u>can't</u> use a water bath to heat something to a higher temperature than this — the water <u>won't</u> get <u>hot</u> enough.

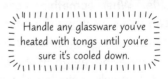
Handle any glassware you've heated with tongs until you're sure it's cooled down.

2) <u>Electric heaters</u> are often made up of a metal <u>plate</u> that can be heated to a certain temperature. The vessel containing the substance you want to heat is placed on top of the hot plate. You can heat substances to <u>higher temperatures</u> than you can in a water bath but, as the vessel is only heated from <u>below</u>, you'll usually have to <u>stir</u> the substance inside to make sure it's <u>heated evenly</u>.

A bath and an electric heater — how I spend my January nights...

You know, I used to have a chemistry teacher who'd play power ballads when the Bunsen burners were alight and sway at the front of the class like he was at a gig. You think I made that up, but it's true.

Working with Electronics

Electrical devices are used in a bunch of experiments, so make sure you know how to use them.

You Have to Interpret Circuit Diagrams

Before you get cracking on an experiment involving any kind of electrical devices, you have to plan and build your circuit using a circuit diagram. Make sure you know all of the circuit symbols on page 177 so you're not stumped before you've even started.

There Are a Couple of Ways to Measure Potential Difference and Current

Voltmeters Measure Potential Difference

1) If you're using an analogue voltmeter, choose the voltmeter with the most appropriate unit (e.g. V or mV). If you're using a digital voltmeter, you'll most likely be able to switch between them.

2) Connect the voltmeter in parallel across the component you want to test. The wires that come with a voltmeter are usually red (positive) and black (negative). These go into the red and black coloured ports on the voltmeter. Funnily enough.

3) Then simply read the potential difference from the scale (or from the screen if it's digital).

Ammeters Measure Current

1) Just like with voltmeters, choose the ammeter with the most appropriate unit.

2) Connect the ammeter in series with the component you want to test, making sure they're both on the same branch. Again, they usually have red and black ports to show you where to connect your wires.

3) Read off the current shown on the scale or by the screen.

Turn your circuit off between readings to prevent wires overheating and affecting your results.

Multimeters Measure Both

1) Instead of having a separate ammeter and voltmeter, many circuits use multimeters. These are devices that measure a range of properties — usually potential difference, current and resistance.

2) If you want to find potential difference, make sure the red wire is plugged into the port that has a 'V' (for volts).

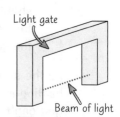

3) To find the current, use the port labelled 'A' or 'mA' (for amps).

4) The dial on the multimeter should then be turned to the relevant section, e.g. to 'A' to measure current in amps. The screen will display the value you're measuring.

Light Gates Measure Time, Speed and Acceleration

1) A light gate sends a beam of light from one side of the gate to a detector on the other side. When something passes through it, the light beam is interrupted. The gate can measure when the beam was interrupted and how long it was interrupted for.

2) To find the speed of an object, connect the light gate to a computer. Measure the length of the object and input this using the software. It will then automatically calculate the speed of the object as it passes through the beam.

3) To measure acceleration, you can use an object that interrupts the signal twice in a short period of time, e.g. a piece of card with a gap cut into the middle.

4) The light gate measures the speed for each section of the object and uses this to calculate its acceleration. This can then be read from the computer screen.

Have a look at page 159 and page 164 for some examples of light gates being used.

Light gate

Beam of light

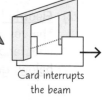

Card interrupts the beam

A light gate is better than a heavy one...

After finishing this page, you should be able to take on any electrical experiment that they throw at you... ouch.

Answers

p.11 — Cells and Microscopy
Q1 It provides a selective barrier to control what goes in and out of the cell *[1 mark]*. It contains receptor molecules that are used for cell communication *[1 mark]*.

p.12 — Light Microscopy
Q1 Place a drop of mountant/water on the slide *[1 mark]*. Use tweezers to place the specimen on the mountant *[1 mark]*. Add a drop of stain *[1 mark]*. Carefully apply a cover slip over the specimen *[1 mark]*.

p.13 — More on Light Microscopy
Q1 total magnification = eyepiece lens magnification × objective lens magnification
8 × 15 = 120
so the total magnification is ×120 *[1 mark]*.

p.14 — DNA
Q1 It's a large, complex molecule made up of nucleotides (monomers) joined together in a long chain *[1 mark]*.
Q2 a) G *[1 mark]*
b) Each base forms cross links to a base on the opposite strand *[1 mark]*. This keeps the two DNA strands wound tightly together *[1 mark]*.

p.15 — Enzymes
Q1 C *[1 mark]*
Q2 Enzymes have an active site *[1 mark]*, which the substrate has to fit into in order for the reaction to be catalysed *[1 mark]*. This means that enzymes usually only work with one substrate so they are very specific *[1 mark]*.

p.16 — More on Enzymes
Q1 The enzyme's activity may slow down/ stop *[1 mark]* because the enzyme may be irreversibly denatured *[1 mark]*. A pH higher than pH 4 will interfere with the bonds holding the enzyme together *[1 mark]*. This may change the shape of the active site *[1 mark]* so the substrate can no longer fit *[1 mark]*.

p.17 — Investigating Enzyme Activity
Q1 33 ÷ 60 = 0.55 cm³/second *[1 mark]*

p.18 — Respiration
Q1 glucose + oxygen → carbon dioxide + water *[1 mark for correct reactants, 1 mark for correct products]*

p.19 — More on Respiration
Q1 Ethanol and carbon dioxide *[1 mark]*.
Q2 E.g. aerobic respiration produces much more ATP than anaerobic respiration *[1 mark]*.

p.20 — Biological Molecules
Q1 a) (simple) sugars *[1 mark]*
b) amino acids *[1 mark]*
Q2 E.g. so that energy can be transferred from their breakdown during respiration *[1 mark]*.

p.21 — Photosynthesis
Q1 Photosynthesis produces glucose *[1 mark]*, which is used to make larger, complex molecules that make up the mass of the plant's living material/the plant's biomass *[1 mark]*.

p.22 — The Rate of Photosynthesis
Q1 Initially, as the temperature increases, the rate of photosynthesis increases *[1 mark]* because the enzymes needed for photosynthesis work faster at higher temperatures *[1 mark]*. However, if the temperature gets too hot, the enzymes start to denature *[1 mark]* so the rate of photosynthesis decreases dramatically beyond this point *[1 mark]*.

p.24 — The Cell Cycle and Mitosis
Q1 When the cell divides during mitosis, the two new cells will contain identical DNA *[1 mark]*.
Q2 Mitosis is when a cell reproduces itself by splitting to form two identical offspring *[1 mark]*.

p.25 — Cell Differentiation and Stem Cells
Q1 Differentiation is the process by which a cell changes to become specialised for its job *[1 mark]*.

p.26 — Diffusion and Active Transport
Q1 a) The net movement of particles from an area of higher concentration to an area of lower concentration *[1 mark]*.
b) The movement of particles across a membrane against a concentration gradient/from an area of lower to an area of higher concentration *[1 mark]* using ATP released during respiration *[1 mark]*.

p.27 — Osmosis
Q1 Osmosis is the net movement of water molecules across a partially permeable membrane from a region of higher water concentration to a region of lower water concentration / Osmosis is the diffusion of water molecules across a partially permeable membrane down a water potential gradient (i.e. from an area of higher water potential to an area of lower water potential) *[1 mark]*.
Q2 E.g. the piece of carrot will shrivel and become floppy *[1 mark]*. This is because the cells become flaccid/lose water as a result of osmosis *[1 mark]*.

p.28 — Exchanging Substances
Q1 surface area = 5 × 5 × 6 = 150 cm²
volume = 5 × 5 × 5 = 125 cm³
surface area : volume ratio
= 150 : 125
= 6 : 5 *[1 mark]*

p.29 — Exchange Surfaces
Q1 It means that substances only have to travel a short distance *[1 mark]*.

p.30 — More on Exchange Surfaces
Q1 Any three from: leaves are broad, so there's a large surface area for diffusion. / Leaves are thin, which means gases only have to travel a short distance. / There are air spaces inside the leaf, which let carbon dioxide and oxygen move easily between cells. / Air spaces inside the leaf increase the surface area for gas exchange. / The lower surface is full of little holes called stomata, which let carbon dioxide and oxygen diffuse in and out *[1 mark for each correct answer, up to 3 marks]*.
Q2 Each branch of a plant's roots is covered in millions of root hair cells *[1 mark]*, which gives the plant a big surface area for absorbing water and mineral ions from the soil *[1 mark]*.

p.31 — The Circulatory System
Q1 the right ventricle *[1 mark]*

p.32 — The Blood Vessels
Q1 They have a big lumen to help the blood flow despite the low pressure *[1 mark]* and they have valves to keep the blood flowing in the right direction *[1 mark]*.
Q2 E.g. networks of capillaries carry blood to every cell in the body to exchange substances with them *[1 mark]*. They have permeable walls, so that substances can easily diffuse in and out of them *[1 mark]*. Their walls are only one cell thick, which increases the rate of diffusion *[1 mark]*.

p.33 — The Blood
Q1 E.g. red blood cells have a large surface area to volume ratio for absorbing oxygen *[1 mark]*. They don't have a nucleus, which allows more room for carrying oxygen *[1 mark]*. They contain haemoglobin, which can combine with oxygen in the lungs and release it in body tissues *[1 mark]*.

p.34 — Plant Transport Systems and Transpiration
Q1 Water evaporates and diffuses from a plant's surface, creating a slight shortage of water in the leaf *[1 mark]*. This draws more water up from the rest of the plant through the xylem vessels to replace it *[1 mark]*. This in turn means more water is drawn up from the roots *[1 mark]*.

p.35 — More on Transpiration
Q1 guard cells *[1 mark]*
Q2 In low light conditions, the stomata begin to close *[1 mark]*. This means that very little water can escape and the rate of transpiration decreases *[1 mark]*.
Q3 As it gets warmer, the rate of transpiration increases *[1 mark]* because when it's warm the water particles have more energy to evaporate and diffuse out of the stomata *[1 mark]*.

p.36 — Investigating Transpiration
Q1 Any two from: e.g. air humidity / light intensity / air movement *[2 marks]*.

p.38 — The Nervous System
Q1 brain *[1 mark]*, spinal cord *[1 mark]*

p.39 — Hormones and Negative Feedback Systems
Q1 Endocrine glands secrete hormones *[1 mark]*. These act as chemical messengers *[1 mark]* and travel in the bloodstream *[1 mark]* to target cells / organs *[1 mark]*. These have receptors so they can respond to the hormone *[1 mark]*.

p.40 — Hormones in Reproduction
Q1 LH stimulates the release of an egg/ovulation *[1 mark]*. It also indirectly stimulates progesterone production *[1 mark]*.

p.41 — Hormones for Fertility and Contraception
Q1 The hormones FSH and LH *[1 mark]* can be injected by women with naturally low FSH levels *[1 mark]* to stimulate ovulation *[1 mark]*.

p.42 — More on Contraception
Q1 E.g. oral contraceptives can have unpleasant side-effects *[1 mark]*. / She might find it difficult to remember to take a pill every day *[1 mark]*.
Q2 Any two from: e.g. IUDs are more effective. / IUDs are longer acting. / There's less chance of IUDs not working as they are intended *[1 mark for each correct answer, up to 2 marks]*.

p.43 — Controlling Blood Sugar Level
Q1 In type 1 diabetes, the person produces little or no insulin *[1 mark]*, whereas in type 2 diabetes, the person still produces insulin but they are resistant to it/don't respond properly to it *[1 mark]*.

p.44 — The Carbon Cycle
Q1 E.g. not as much CO_2 in the air is being used for photosynthesis *[1 mark]*. Microorganisms involved in the decomposition of the dead trees release CO_2 into the atmosphere through respiration *[1 mark]*.

p.45 — The Nitrogen Cycle and the Water Cycle

Q1 Decomposers turn proteins in dead leaves into ammonia, which goes on to form ammonium ions *[1 mark]*. Then nitrifying bacteria turn the ammonium ions into nitrates *[1 mark]*.

p.46 — Ecosystems and Interactions Between Organisms

Q1 All the organisms (different species) living in a habitat *[1 mark]*.

Q2 Any two from: e.g. temperature / moisture level / light intensity / pH of the soil *[1 mark for each correct answer, up to 2 marks]*.

p.47 — More On Interactions Between Organisms

Q1 Mutualism *[1 mark]* as the relationship benefits both the cow and the microorganisms *[1 mark]*.

p.49 — Genes and Variation

Q1 Your height is partly influenced by your genome because your genes control how tall you can grow *[1 mark]*. But your height will also be affected by environmental factors, such as your diet, because if you don't take in enough food you won't be able to grow as tall *[1 mark]*.

p.50 — More on Variation and Genetic Variants

Q1 A gene mutation alters the base sequence of DNA in a gene *[1 mark]*, which may affect the order of amino acids in the chain *[1 mark]*. This may lead to changes in the protein produced, leading to a possible change in phenotype *[1 mark]*.

p.51 — Sexual Reproduction and Meiosis

Q1 During fertilisation, a male gamete fuses with a female gamete to form a fertilised egg *[1 mark]*. The gametes need to be haploid so that the fertilised egg ends up with the diploid number of chromosomes, and not twice as many *[1 mark]*.

Q2 When the cell divides, some of the father's chromosomes and some of the mother's chromosomes go into each new cell *[1 mark]*. The mixing up of the chromosomes/genes creates genetic variation *[1 mark]*.

p.52 — Sex Determination and Asexual Reproduction

Q1 E.g.

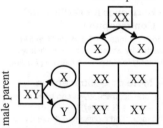

female parent

male parent

So, 50% of the possible genotypes are XX (girls) and 50% are XY (boys) so the probability of the baby being a boy or girl is equal.
[1 mark for correctly identifying the parents' gametes, 1 mark for correctly completing the diagram]

p.53 — Genetic Diagrams

Q1 a) E.g.

Parents' phenotype: no albinism   albinism

Parents' genotype: Aa   aa

Gametes' genotype: A   a   a   a

Possible genotypes of offspring: Aa   aa   Aa   aa

Phenotypes: no albinism   albinism   no albinism   albinism

[1 mark for correctly identifying the parents' genotypes, 1 mark for correctly completing a genetic diagram.]

b) 50% *[1 mark]*

p.54 — Classification

Q1 An artificial classification system sorts organisms into groups depending on their observable features *[1 mark]*, whereas a natural classification system sorts organisms into groups based on their evolutionary relationships/ common ancestors and common structural features *[1 mark]*.

p.55 — Evolution and Natural Selection

Q1 Some of the musk oxen may have had a gene variant/allele which gave them thicker fur *[1 mark]*. Those musk oxen would have been more likely to survive and reproduce *[1 mark]* and so pass on their gene variants/alleles for thicker fur *[1 mark]*. This process of natural selection may have continued over many generations, leading to all musk oxen having thick fur *[1 mark]*.

p.56 — Evidence for Evolution

Q1 D *[1 mark]*

Q2 Fossils can show what organisms that lived a long time ago looked like *[1 mark]*. Arranging them in chronological/date order shows how organisms gradually changed/developed *[1 mark]*.

p.58 — Investigating Distribution and Abundance

Q1 E.g. the student could use a pitfall trap in each area of woodland *[1 mark]*. Each trap could be set up and left overnight *[1 mark]*. The next day, insects present in the traps could be counted and the student could compare what was found in the two traps *[1 mark]*.

p.59 — More on Investigating Distribution and Abundance

Q1 Population size = (number in first sample × number in second sample) ÷ number in second sample previously marked
= (22 × 26) ÷ 4
= 143 crabs *[2 marks for correct answer, otherwise 1 mark for correct working]*

p.60 — Using Keys and Factors Affecting Distribution

Q1 Any two from: e.g. air temperature / sand temperature / sand moisture level / sand pH *[1 mark for each correct answer, up to 2 marks]*.

p.61 — Using Transects

Q1 E.g. mark out a line/transect across the field using a tape measure *[1 mark]*. Place a quadrat at the start of the line and count and record the organisms you find in the quadrat *[1 mark]*. Then place your quadrat at the next sampling point on the transect and count and record the organisms you find in the quadrat *[1 mark]*. The second sampling point could be at an interval along the line (e.g. every 2 metres) or directly after the first quadrat *[1 mark]*. Carry on sampling until you reach the end of your transect *[1 mark]*.

p.62 — Human Impacts on Ecosystems

Q1 E.g. the building of houses on a meadow would involve destruction of the habitats provided by the meadow *[1 mark]*. This is likely to reduce the number of species that can live in the area, therefore reducing biodiversity *[1 mark]*.

p.63 — More Human Impacts on Ecosystems

Q1 E.g. individual plants grown in the botanical gardens could be reintroduced into the wild *[1 mark]*.
By reintroducing plants into the protected habitat areas it's more likely that they'll survive as the habitat is protected from damage *[1 mark]*.

p.64 — Maintaining Biodiversity

Q1 E.g. undiscovered plant species may contain new medicinal chemicals *[1 mark]*. If these plants are allowed to become extinct we could miss out on valuable medicines *[1 mark]*.

p.65 — Selective Breeding

Q1 He should choose the bean plants that are best at surviving the drought *[1 mark]* and let them reproduce *[1 mark]*. He should then continue this process over several generations *[1 mark]*.

Q2 E.g. it reduces the gene pool which can lead to health problems developing, such as genetic disorders *[1 mark]*.
It means that if a new disease appears, the whole population could be affected because there's not much variation between individuals *[1 mark]*.

p.66 — Genetic Engineering

Q1 They are used to identify which host cells have taken up the vector/new DNA *[1 mark]*.

p.67 — More on Genetic Engineering

Q1 Any two from: e.g. transplanted genes may get out into the environment creating 'superweeds'. / Genetically engineered crops could adversely affect food chains/human health. / Genetically engineered crops could create unforeseen problems, which would then be passed on to future generations. / Genetically engineered crops might affect the number of weeds and flowers that live in and around the crops, reducing biodiversity *[1 mark for each correct answer, up to 2 marks]*.

p.68 — Health and Disease

Q1 A non-communicable disease is one that cannot be passed from one organism to another *[1 mark]*. They generally last for a long time and progress slowly *[1 mark]*. They are often linked to unhealthy lifestyles *[1 mark]*.

p.69 — How Disease Spreads

Q1 Any three from: e.g. in water / by air / by contact / in body fluids / by animal vectors / in soil / in food *[1 mark for each correct answer, up to 3 marks]*.

p.70 — Reducing and Preventing the Spread of Disease

Q1 E.g. by getting rid of the mosquitoes you can prevent the disease from being passed on *[1 mark]*. This could be done by using insecticides/by destroying their habitat so they can no longer breed *[1 mark]*.

p.71 — The Human Immune System

Q1 When you damage a blood vessel, platelets clump together forming a blood clot *[1 mark]*. This prevents microorganisms from entering the wound *[1 mark]*.

p.72 — Vaccines and Medicines

Q1 The antigens on the dead pathogens in the vaccine trigger an immune response *[1 mark]* so your white blood cells produce antibodies to attack the pathogens *[1 mark]*. Some of the white blood cells remain as memory cells in the blood *[1 mark]* so if the same pathogens appear, the antibodies to help destroy them can be produced immediately *[1 mark]*.

p.73 — Investigating Antimicrobials

Q1 Hot air rises, so microbes in the air should be drawn away from the culture *[1 mark]* preventing contamination by unwanted microorganisms *[1 mark]*.

p.74 — Comparing Antimicrobials

Q1 a) A *[1 mark]*

b) diameter = 13 mm
radius = 13 ÷ 2 = 6.5 mm *[1 mark]*
$\pi r^2 = \pi \times 6.5^2 = 132.7...$
= 133 mm² *[1 mark]*

c) E.g. a disc soaked in sterile water *[1 mark]*.

d) To show that any difference in the growth of the bacteria is only due to the effect of the antiseptic *[1 mark]*.

Answers

p.75 — Developing New Medicines

Q1 a) A substance that looks like the real drug but doesn't do anything *[1 mark]*.

b) So scientists can see the actual difference the drug makes *[1 mark]*. It allows for the placebo effect, where the patient expects the treatment to work and so feels better, even though the treatment isn't doing anything *[1 mark]*.

p.76 — Non-Communicable Diseases

Q1 Exercise increases the amount of energy used by the body and decreases the amount of stored body fat *[1 mark]*. It also builds muscle so it helps to boost your metabolic rate *[1 mark]*.

p.77 — More on Non-Communicable Diseases

Q1 Any two from: e.g. cirrhosis / cardiovascular disease / cancers (e.g. mouth, throat, bowel, liver) *[1 mark for each correct answer, up to 2 marks]*.

p.78 — Treating Cardiovascular Disease

Q1 E.g. they can cause excessive bleeding if the person taking them is hurt in an accident *[1 mark]*.

p.79 — Stem Cells in Medicine

Q1 a) The patient's immune system recognises the cells as foreign and attacks them *[1 mark]*.

b) Use the patient's own adult stem cells *[1 mark]*.

Q2 E.g. some people feel that human embryos shouldn't be used for experiments since each is a potential human life *[1 mark]*.

p.80 — Using Genome Research in Medicine

Q1 If doctors know which genes predispose people to type 2 diabetes *[1 mark]*, they could provide individually tailored advice on the best diet and lifestyle to reduce the risk of type 2 diabetes developing *[1 mark]*.

p.82 — States of Matter

Q1 a) In a solid, the particles are held by strong forces *[1 mark]* in fixed positions in a regular lattice arrangement *[1 mark]*. The particles don't move but vibrate about their positions *[1 mark]*.

b) In a gas, there's almost no force of attraction between the particles *[1 mark]*. The particles move constantly with random motion *[1 mark]*, travel in straight lines and only interact when they collide *[1 mark]*.

c) In a liquid, there are some forces of attraction between the particles *[1 mark]*. The particles move constantly with random motion *[1 mark]* but they do tend to stick to each other *[1 mark]*.

p.83 — The History of the Atom

Q1 The plum pudding model predicted that most of the alpha particles would pass straight through the sheet or be deflected slightly at most *[1 mark]*. In fact, though most of the particles did pass straight through the gold atoms, a few were deflected more than expected and a small number were deflected straight back *[1 mark]*. This suggested that most of the atom is made up of empty space, with a positive nucleus in the centre *[1 mark]*.

Q2 E.g.

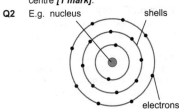

[1 mark for correct structure, 1 mark for correct labels]

p.84 — The Atom

Q1 a) +1

b) 0

c) −1

[1 mark for all three parts correct]

Q2 In the nucleus *[1 mark]*.

Q3 nuclear radius, atomic radius, simple molecule *[1 mark]*

p.85 — Atoms, Ions and Isotopes

Q1 a) 16 − 8 = 8 neutrons *[1 mark]*

b) 40 − 20 = 20 neutrons *[1 mark]*

c) 127 − 53 = 74 neutrons *[1 mark]*

Q2 a) Chlorine-35: 17 protons, 17 electrons and (35 − 17 =) 18 neutrons *[1 mark]*. Chlorine-37: 17 protons, 17 electrons and (37 − 17 =) 20 neutrons *[1 mark]*.

b) 17 + 1 = 18 electrons *[1 mark]*

p.86 — The Periodic Table

Q1 2 *[1 mark]*

Q2 Potassium and sodium are both in Group 1. Potassium and calcium are in different groups. So the chemical properties of potassium should be closer to those of sodium than calcium *[1 mark]*, because elements in the same group have similar chemical properties *[1 mark]*.

p.87 — Electron Shells

Q1 2.8.3 or

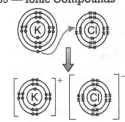

[1 mark]

Q2 Group 2 *[1 mark]*
Period 4 *[1 mark]*

p.88 — Ionic Bonding

Q1 Each potassium atom loses an electron to form a K^+ ion *[1 mark]*. Each chlorine atom gains an electron to form a Cl^- ion *[1 mark]*. The oppositely charged ions are attracted to each other by electrostatic forces to form an ionic bond *[1 mark]*.

p.89 — Ionic Compounds

Q1

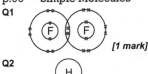

[1 mark for arrow showing electron transferred from potassium to chlorine, 1 mark for correct outer shell electron configurations, 1 mark for correct charges]

Q2 When melted, the ions are free to move, so they can carry an electric current *[1 mark]*.

p.90 — Simple Molecules

Q1

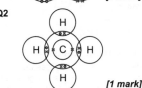

[1 mark]

Q2

[1 mark]

p.91 — Giant Covalent Structures and Fullerenes

Q1 Similarities: any two from, e.g. giant covalent structure / covalent bonding / high melting point *[1 mark for each similarity]*.
Differences: any two from, e.g. diamond is colourless, graphite is black / graphite conducts electricity, diamond doesn't / carbon atoms form 4 covalent bonds in diamond, and 3 in graphite *[1 mark for each difference]*.

p.92 — Polymers and Properties of Materials

Q1 The properties of polymers depend on the forces between the chains *[1 mark]*. The properties of polymers A and B suggest that B has only weak intermolecular forces between its chains *[1 mark]*, while it is likely that A has stronger links such as covalent bonds/cross-links between the chains *[1 mark]*.

p.93 — Metals

Q1 Copper is a good electrical conductor *[1 mark]* as it contains delocalised electrons which are free to move and carry an electrical current *[1 mark]*.

p.94 — States, Structure and Bonding

Q1 a) A — gas *[1 mark]*, B — solid *[1 mark]*, C — liquid *[1 mark]*.

b) A is likely to be a simple molecular structure *[1 mark]*, since simple molecular substances have low melting and boiling points *[1 mark]*. B is likely to be a metal *[1 mark]*, as metals have high melting points and are good electrical conductors *[1 mark]*. D is likely to be ionic *[1 mark]*, as ionic compounds have high melting and boiling points, and conduct electricity when molten, but not when solid *[1 mark]*.

p.95 — Purity

Q1 Under the scientific definition, a pure substance is a substance completely made up of a single element or compound *[1 mark]*. Orange juice is not chemically pure, since it is a mixture (of water, sugars and other compounds) *[1 mark]*.

Q2 Steel has a lower melting point than pure iron *[1 mark]*. The carbon in the iron makes it impure, and impurities lower the melting point *[1 mark]*.

p.96 — Distillation

Q1 Ethanol will be collected in the second fraction *[1 mark]*, because it has the second lowest boiling point of the three compounds in the mixture *[1 mark]*.

p.97 — Filtration and Crystallisation

Q1 Slowly heat the solution to evaporate off some of the water *[1 mark]*. Stop heating once some of the water has evaporated, or once copper sulfate crystals start to form *[1 mark]*. Allow the solution to cool until copper sulfate crystals form *[1 mark]*. Filter the crystals out of the solution and dry them in a warm place / desiccator / drying oven *[1 mark]*.

p.98 — Chromatography

Q1 Chemical A will end up closer to the solvent front than B *[1 mark]*. A is more soluble in the solvent, so it will spend more time dissolved in the mobile phase, and move further up the plate *[1 mark]*.

p.99 — Interpreting Chromatograms

Q1 R_f of Y = distance travelled by Y ÷ distance travelled by solvent front
= 3.6 cm ÷ 6.0 cm *[1 mark]* = 0.60 *[1 mark]*

p.100 — Relative Masses

Q1 M_r of NaCl = 23.0 + 35.5 = 58.5 *[1 mark]*.

Q2 M_r of C_2H_5OH = (2 × C) + (6 × H) + O
= (2 × 12.0) + (6 × 1.0) + 16.0
= 24.0 + 6.0 + 16.0 = 46.0 *[1 mark]*

Q3 M_r of $Cu(NO_3)_2$ = Cu + 2 × (N + (3 × O))
= 63.5 + 2 × (14.0 + (3 × 16.0)) *[1 mark]*
= 63.5 + 2 × (14.0 + 48.0)
= 63.5 + (2 × 62.0)
= 63.5 + 124.0 = 187.5 *[1 mark]*

Answers

p.101 — Molecular and Empirical Formulas
Q1 4, 8 and 2 all divide by 2.
$4 \div 2 = 2$, $8 \div 2 = 4$, $2 \div 2 = 1$
So the empirical formula of this compound is
C_2H_4Cl *[1 mark]*.

p.103 — Conservation of Mass
Q1 M_r(reactants) = $M_r(H_2SO_4)$ + 2 × M_r(NaOH).
= ((2 × 1.0) + 32.1 + (4 × 16.0)) + 2 × (23.0 +
16.0 + 1.0) = 98.1 + (2 × 40.0) = 178.1 *[1 mark]*
M_r(products) = $M_r(Na_2SO_4)$ + 2 × $M_r(H_2O)$
= ((2 × 23.0) + 32.1 + (4 × 16.0)) + 2 × ((2 × 1.0)
+ 16.0) = 142.1 + (2 × 18.0) = 178.1 *[1 mark]*
M_r(products) = M_r(reactants), so the mass is
conserved *[1 mark]*.

p.104 — Chemical Formulas
Q1 a) Br^- *[1 mark]*
b) CO_3^{2-} *[1 mark]*
c) Li^+ *[1 mark]*
d) NO_3^- *[1 mark]*
Q2 $Mg(OH)_2$ *[1 mark]*

p.105 — Chemical Equations
Q1 $2Fe + 3Cl_2 \rightarrow 2FeCl_3$ *[1 mark]*
Q2 a) water → hydrogen + oxygen *[1 mark]*
b) $2H_2O \rightarrow 2H_2 + O_2$
*[1 mark for correct reactants and products,
1 mark for a correctly balanced equation]*

p.106 — More on Chemical Equations
Q1 $H^+_{(aq)} + OH^-_{(aq)} \rightarrow H_2O_{(l)}$ *[1 mark]*
Q2 $Cl_2 + 2e^- \rightarrow 2Cl^-$
*[1 mark for correct reactants and products,
1 mark for a correctly balanced equation]*

p.107 — Moles
Q1 moles = mass ÷ M_r = 90 ÷ 18.0 = 5.0 moles
[1 mark]
Q2 mass = moles × M_r
= 0.200 × 119.0 = 23.8 moles *[1 mark]*
Q3 M_r = mass ÷ moles = 87.0 ÷ 0.500 = 174 *[1 mark]*

p.108 — Calculating Masses
Q1 M_r(KBr) = 39.1 +79.9 = 119
$M_r(Br_2)$ = 79.9 × 2 = 159.8 *[1 mark]*
moles of KBr = mass ÷ M_r
= 23.8 ÷ 119 = 0.200 moles *[1 mark]*
From the equation, 2 moles of KBr react to
produce 1 mole of Br_2. So 0.200 moles of KBr
will produce (0.200 ÷ 2 =) 0.100 moles of Br_2
[1 mark]. So mass of Br_2
= 0.100 × 159.8 = 16.0 g *[1 mark]*.

p.109 — More Mole Calculations
Q1 $M_r(N_2)$ = 2 × 14.0 = 28.0
$M_r(H_2)$ = 2 × 1.0 = 2.0 *[1 mark]*
Ratio: N_2 = 84 ÷ 28.0 = 3.0
H_2 = 12 ÷ 2.0 = 6.0
Divide by the smallest (3) gives a ratio of N_2 : H_2
of 1 : 2 *[1 mark]*.
The balanced equation gives a ratio of N_2 : H_2 of
1 : 3, so H_2 must be the limiting reactant
[1 mark].

p.110 — Concentration
Q1 200 cm³ = (200 ÷ 1000) dm³ = 0.2 dm³ *[1 mark]*
mass = concentration × volume
= 55 × 0.2 = 11 g *[1 mark]*

p.111 — Endothermic and Exothermic Reactions
Q1 a) exothermic *[1 mark]*
b)

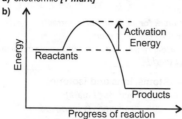

*[1 mark for correct shape, 1 mark for correctly
labelled axes, 1 mark for correctly labelled
products, reactants and activation energy]*

p.112 — Bond Energies
Q1 Energy required to break original bonds:
(1 × N≡N) + (3 × H–H)
= 941 + (3 × 436) = 941 + 1308
= 2249 kJ/mol *[1 mark]*
Energy released by forming new bonds:
(6 × N–H)
= 6 × 391 = 2346 kJ/mol *[1 mark]*
Overall energy change:
= 2249 – 2346 = –97 kJ/mol *[1 mark]*

p.113 — Acids and Bases
Q1 a) Acidic *[1 mark]*
b) Yellow *[1 mark]*

p.114 — Strong and Weak Acids
Q1 A strong acid ionises/dissociates completely in
water *[1 mark]*. A weak acid only dissociates a
small amount in water *[1 mark]*.
Q2 It increased *[1 mark]* by a factor of 1000
[1 mark].

p.115 — Reactions of Acids
Q1 $2HCl + CaCO_3 \rightarrow CaCl_2 + H_2O + CO_2$
*[1 mark for correct reactants and products,
1 mark for a correctly balanced equation]*

p.116 — Making Salts
Q1 E.g. React the base, iron oxide, with the acid,
nitric acid. Keep on adding base until all the
acid has been neutralised — at this point, no
more base will react and it will sink to the bottom
of the flask *[1 mark]*. Then, filter out the excess
solid using filter paper, and collect the solution of
salt and water *[1 mark]*. Then, gently evaporate
off some of the water from your salt and water
solution and leave to allow the salt to crystallise
[1 mark].

p.117 — Oxidation and Reduction
Q1 H^+ *[1 mark]*
Q2 positive ions/cations *[1 mark]*

p.118 — Electrolysis
Q1 $2Br^- \rightarrow Br_2 + 2e^-$ *[1 mark]*

p.119 — Electrolysis of Copper Sulfate
Q1 The mass of the anode should decrease
[1 mark] as copper from the anode decomposes
to Cu^{2+} ions in the electrolyte *[1 mark]*.

p.120 — Tests for Gases
Q1 Check to see if the gas will relight a glowing
splint *[1 mark]*. If the splint will relight, the gas
is oxygen *[1 mark]*.
Q2 Gas A is chlorine *[1 mark]*.
Gas B is hydrogen *[1 mark]*.

p.122 — Group 1 — Alkali Metals
Q1 When the alkali metals react, they lose their
single outer electron *[1 mark]*. As you go down
Group 1, the outer electron gets further from the
nucleus *[1 mark]* so less energy is needed to
remove it/it is more easily lost *[1 mark]*.
Q2 $2Li + 2H_2O \rightarrow 2LiOH + H_2$
*[1 mark for correct reactants and products,
1 mark for correctly balanced equation]*

p.123 — Group 7 — Halogens
Q1 Bromine would be a solid at this temperature
[1 mark]. The melting points of the halogens
increase as you go down the group, so at the
melting point of chlorine, bromine would still be
solid *[1 mark]*.
Q2 $2Na + I_2 \rightarrow 2NaI$
*[1 mark for correct reactants and products,
1 mark for correctly balanced equation]*

p.124 — Halogen Displacement Reactions
Q1 Bromine water *[1 mark]*.

p.125 — Group 0 — Noble Gases
Q1 Any answer between –130 °C and –93 °C
[1 mark].

p.126 — Reactivity of Metals
Q1 a) Metal B, Metal C, Metal A *[1 mark]*
b) Metal A is copper. Metal B is magnesium.
Metal C is zinc *[1 mark for all three correct]*.

p.127 — The Reactivity Series and Displacement
Q1 Magnesium would displace iron from iron sulfate
solution, because it's higher up than iron in the
reactivity series/more reactive than iron *[1 mark]*.
Q2 Tin would not displace zinc from zinc sulfate
solution, as it's lower than zinc in the reactivity
series/it's less reactive than zinc *[1 mark]*.

p.129 — Reaction Rates
Q1 E.g. mix the two solutions and place the reaction
vessel over a sheet of paper with a mark on it
[1 mark]. Time how long it takes for the mark to
be obscured *[1 mark]*.
Q2 E.g. it releases the gas straight into the room,
so if the gas is harmful you'll need to take safety
precautions *[1 mark]*.

p.130 — Rate Experiments
Q1 E.g. place a measured volume of hydrochloric
acid of a known concentration in a conical
flask on a mass balance. Add a known mass
of magnesium metal *[1 mark]*. Take readings
of the total mass of the flask at regular time
intervals *[1 mark]*. Repeat the experiment with
the same volume and concentration of acid and
the same mass of magnesium. Increase the
surface area of the magnesium by cutting it into
smaller pieces *[1 mark]*.

p.131 — Calculating Rates
Q1 E.g.

[1 mark]
Change in y = 23 – 11 = 12
Change in x = 45 – 5 = 40
Gradient = 12 ÷ 40 = 0.3 cm³/s *[1 mark]*

p.132 — Collision Theory
Q1 It would be faster with calcium carbonate
powder than with calcium carbonate chips
[1 mark]. The powder has a higher surface
area to volume ratio than the chips *[1 mark]*.
This means that the frequency of collisions will
increase and so the rate will increase *[1 mark]*.
Q2 As the temperature increases, the speed that
the particles move at increases, so there are
more collisions *[1 mark]*. Higher temperatures
also increase the energy of the collisions
[1 mark]. So at higher temperatures there
are more successful collisions / more particles
collide with enough energy to react *[1 mark]*.

p.133 — Catalysts

Q1 A catalyst is a substance that increases the speed of reaction *[1 mark]*, without being chemically changed or used up in the reaction *[1 mark]*.

Q2 At the end of the reaction, the same amount of dark brown PbO_2 powder should still be visible at the bottom of the flask *[1 mark]*.

p.134 — Dynamic Equilibrium

Q1 A reversible reaction is one where the products can react with each other to produce the reactants *[1 mark]*.

Q2 Dynamic equilibrium occurs when the forwards and backwards reactions in a reversible reaction occur at the same rate *[1 mark]*.

Q3 Temperature, *[1 mark]* pressure *[1 mark]* and concentration *[1 mark]*.

p.135 — Le Chatelier's Principle

Q1 The position of equilibrium will shift to the right (towards the products) *[1 mark]*. The forward reaction is endothermic, so when the temperature is increased the equilibrium position will move to the right to absorb the excess heat *[1 mark]*.

Q2 Decreasing the pressure would shift the equilibrium position to the left (towards the reactants) *[1 mark]* as there are more fewer moles of gas on the reactant side than on the products side *[1 mark]*. So the yield of SO_3 would decrease *[1 mark]*.

p.137 — Extracting Metals from their Ores

Q1 Tin is less reactive than carbon *[1 mark]* so you could extract tin from its ore by reducing it with carbon *[1 mark]*.

Q2 $2ZnO + C \rightarrow 2Zn + CO_2$
[1 mark for correct reactants and products, 1 mark for balanced equation]

p.138 — Extracting Metals with Electrolysis

Q1
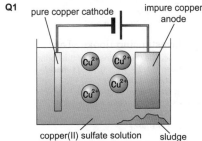

copper(II) sulfate solution — sludge

[1 mark for correct cathode, 1 mark for correct anode, 1 mark for correct labels]

Q2 Bioleaching uses bacteria to separate metals from their ores *[1 mark]*. The bacteria get energy from some of the bonds between the atoms in the metal ore and separate the metal from the ore. The leachate contains the metal ions, which can be extracted (by, e.g. electrolysis or by displacement with a more reactive metal) *[1 mark]*. Phytoextraction involves growing plants in soils that contain metal compounds *[1 mark]*. The metals build up in the plants (since the plant can't use or get rid of them). The plants can be harvested, dried and burnt, and the metal compounds collected from the ash left in the furnace *[1 mark]*.

p.139 — Life-Cycle Assessments

Q1 Any four from e.g. the energy required to extract the raw materials / whether the raw materials are renewable or not / whether other harmful emissions (e.g. CO/HCl) are produced / whether the waste products are harmful or not / how environmentally friendly the cars are to dispose of *[1 mark for each]*.

p.140 — Recycling Materials

Q1 E.g. Metals are non-renewable, so recycling metals is important to conserve finite resources of the metal *[1 mark]*. Also, non-recycled material has to be disposed of in landfill sites, which take up space and can pollute the surroundings *[1 mark]*.

p.141 — Crude Oil

Q1 LPG, Petrol, Naphtha, Kerosene/Paraffin, Diesel, Oil and Bitumen
[5 marks for all correct and in the correct order, otherwise lose 1 mark for each error]

Q2 Propane and butane *[1 mark]*.

p.142 — Hydrocarbons

Q1 Alkane B will have the higher boiling point *[1 mark]* as it has a longer hydrocarbon chain, so has stronger intermolecular forces between the chains *[1 mark]*.

Q2 E.g. generate electricity / as fuel / make chemicals *[1 mark for each correct use]*.

p.143 — Cracking

Q1 Powdered aluminium oxide catalyst *[1 mark]*, 400 °C - 700 °C and 70 atm *[1 mark]*.

Q2 C_9H_{18} *[1 mark]*

p.144 — The Atmosphere

Q1 Nitrogen gas was formed by the reaction between ammonia and oxygen *[1 mark]* and was also released by denitrifying bacteria *[1 mark]*. The proportion of nitrogen in our atmosphere increased because it's unreactive, so it wasn't reacted as it was made *[1 mark]*.

p.145 — The Greenhouse Effect

Q1 Electromagnetic radiation, from the Sun, passes through the atmosphere where it is absorbed. This warms the Earth *[1 mark]*. The Earth gives out some of the heat radiation it absorbs *[1 mark]*. Some of this radiation is re-emitted back into space, but some is absorbed or reflected back to Earth by greenhouse gases *[1 mark]*. This is the greenhouse effect and works to keep the Earth warm.

Q2 E.g. carbon dioxide, water vapour and methane *[1 mark for each]*

p.146 — Global Warming

Q1 Global warming is the increase in the average temperature of the Earth *[1 mark]*. It is caused by the enhanced greenhouse effect / the increase in the proportion of greenhouse gases in the atmosphere *[1 mark]*.

p.147 — Pollutants

Q1 Acid rain forms when nitrogen oxides and sulfur dioxide *[1 mark]*, mix with clouds to form dilute nitric acid and dilute sulfuric acid *[1 mark]*. (This falls as acid rain.)

Q2 E.g. carbon monoxide *[1 mark]*, (carbon) particulates *[1 mark]*.

p.148 — Water Treatment

Q1 Surface water is first filtered through a wire mesh to filter out large impurities, and then through gravel and sand to filter out any further solid impurities *[1 mark]*. Then, a sedimentation process, which involves adding aluminium sulfate or iron sulfate to the water, causes fine particles to clump together and settle at the bottom *[1 mark]*. Finally, chlorine gas is bubbled through the water to kill any microbes or harmful bacteria *[1 mark]*.

Q2 Nitrate residues come from excess fertiliser that is run off into rivers and lakes *[1 mark]*. They're dangerous as, in high quantities, they can cause serious health problems by preventing the blood from carrying oxygen properly *[1 mark]*.

p.150 — The History of the Atom and Atomic Structure

Q1 In the Thomson model, atoms are made of negatively charged electrons spread through a positively charged 'pudding' *[1 mark]*.

Q2 An atom is made up of a small central nucleus *[1 mark]* containing neutrons and positively charged protons *[1 mark]* surrounded by negatively charged electrons orbiting it in shells *[1 mark]*.

p.151 — Density

Q1 E.g. use a mass balance to find the mass of the object *[1 mark]*. Fill a eureka can with water to just below the spout, then immerse the object in the can *[1 mark]*. Collect the water displaced by the object as it flows out of the spout in a measuring cylinder and record its volume *[1 mark]*. Then calculate the density of the object using density = mass ÷ volume *[1 mark]*.

Q2 volume in $m^3 = 75 \div (100^3)$
$= 7.5 \times 10^{-5} m^3$ *[1 mark]*
density = mass ÷ volume *[1 mark]*
$= (4.5 \times 10^{-2}) \div (7.5 \times 10^{-5}) = 600$ kg/m³ *[1 mark]*

p.152 — Particle Theory and States of Matter

Q1 As a typical substance changes from solid to liquid to gas, its density will decrease *[1 mark]* as its mass will stay the same *[1 mark]* but its volume will increase *[1 mark]* as the particles have more energy to overcome the forces between them *[1 mark]*.

p.153 — Specific Heat Capacity

Q1 change in thermal energy = mass × specific heat capacity × change in temperature, so:
change in temperature = change in thermal energy ÷ (mass × specific heat capacity) *[1 mark]*
$= 1680 \div (0.20 \times 420) = 20$ °C *[1 mark]*

p.154 — Specific Latent Heat

Q1

[1 mark for showing the line as flat at 0 °C, 1 mark for showing the line as flat at 100 °C. 1 mark for drawing a straight line with a positive gradient for temperatures below 0 °C, between 0 and 100 °C, and above 100 °C.]

p.155 — Pressure of Gases

Q1 When gas particles collide with the walls of their container, they exert a force on it *[1 mark]*. Across many particles, this force causes an outward pressure *[1 mark]*.

Q2 When the temperature of a gas decreases, the energy in the kinetic store of its particles decreases so their velocities decrease *[1 mark]*. This means they hit the walls of the container less hard *[1 mark]* and less often *[1 mark]* which decreases the pressure *[1 mark]*.

p.157 — Speed and Velocity

Q1 First convert minutes into seconds:
$2.0 \times 60 = 120$ s *[1 mark]*

Then substitute this into the equation for speed:
$$speed = \frac{distance\ travelled}{time}$$
$$= \frac{660}{120} = 5.5 \text{ m/s } [1\ mark]$$

Q2 First convert 54 km/hr into m/s:
54 km/hr ÷ (60 × 60) = 0.015 km/s
0.015 km/s × 1000 = 15 m/s *[1 mark]*
Then substitute into the equation for distance travelled:
distance travelled = speed × time
= 15 × 24 = 360 m *[1 mark]*

p.158 — Acceleration

Q1 $$acceleration = \frac{change\ in\ velocity}{time}$$
So change in velocity = acceleration × time
= 8.25 × 4.0 *[1 mark]* = 33 m/s
As the initial speed is 0 m/s,
the maximum speed is: 33 m/s *[1 mark]*
To find distance covered, rearrange the equation $v^2 - u^2 = 2 \times a \times d$ for distance:
$d = (v^2 - u^2) \div (2 \times a)$
$= (33^2 - 0^2) \div (2 \times 8.25)$ *[1 mark]*
= 66 m *[1 mark]*

p.159 — Investigating Motion

Q1 Use the light gates to time how long it takes the object to pass between the two light gates *[1 mark]*. Measure the distance between the two light gates *[1 mark]*. Divide the distance by the time taken for the object to travel between the two light gates *[1 mark]*.

Q2 Using a stopwatch introduces human errors like reaction times, which aren't present with light gates *[1 mark]*. This matters more for short intervals, as the reaction time is a larger proportion of the interval being timed *[1 mark]*.

p.160 — Distance-Time Graphs

Q1 E.g.

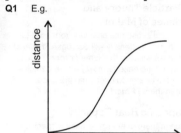

[1 mark for a continuous line that initially curves upwards, and which curves downwards at the end until it becomes horizontal. 1 mark for a straight middle section.]

p.161 — Velocity-Time Graphs

Q1 E.g.

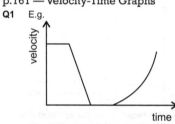

[1 mark for line which is initially horizontal, then bends to give a straight line with a negative gradient, continuing until it meets the time axis. 1 mark for showing the line then continuing horizontally along the time axis, and 1 mark for then showing the line curving upwards.]

p.162 — Forces and Free Body Force Diagrams

Q1 a)

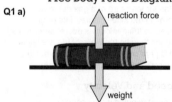

[1 mark for arrows pointing in the right direction and labelled correctly, 1 mark for arrows being the same length]

b)

[1 mark for arrows pointing in the right direction and labelled correctly, 1 mark for the weight arrow being longer than the drag arrow]

p.163 — Scale Diagrams and Forces

Q1 E.g.

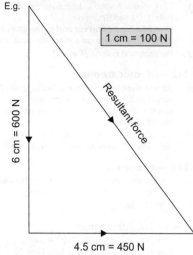

1 cm = 100 N

6 cm = 600 N

Resultant force

4.5 cm = 450 N

[1 mark for a scale drawing, drawn accurately using any sensible scale.]

In this scale drawing:
length of resultant force vector = 7.5 cm
1 cm = 100 N
Therefore, resultant force = 750 N *[1 mark]*

p.164 — Newton's First and Second Laws of Motion

Q1 $F = ma = 26\,000 \times 1.5$
$= 39\,000$ N *[1 mark]*

p.165 — Friction and Terminal Velocity

Q1 Initially, the thrust is much larger than the drag acting on the boat *[1 mark]*, so the boat accelerates *[1 mark]*. As the velocity of the boat increases, the drag increases, but the thrust remains the same, reducing the acceleration *[1 mark]*. Eventually the thrust is balanced out by the drag and the boat travels at a constant (terminal) velocity *[1 mark]*.

p.166 — Inertia and Newton's Third Law of Motion

Q1 An object with a smaller mass (in this case the empty trolley) will have a smaller inertia, so less force is needed to stop it *[1 mark]*.

p.167 — Momentum

Q1 momentum = mass × velocity
$= 220\,000 \times 250$
$= 55\,000\,000$ kg m/s *[1 mark]*

Q2 First, convert quantities to the correct units:
58 g = 0.058 kg
11.6 ms = 0.0116 s *[1 mark]*
Then calculate the change in momentum:
change in momentum
= momentum after − momentum before
$= (m \times v) - (m \times u)$
$= (0.058 \times 34) - (0.058 \times 0)$ *[1 mark]*
= 1.972 kg m/s *[1 mark]*
Then substitute this into the equation for force:
$$force = \frac{change\ in\ momentum}{time}$$
$$= \frac{1.972}{0.0116} = 170 \text{ N } [1 mark]$$
(NB: You could also use the alternative method of calculating the acceleration of the ball first (from acceleration = change in velocity ÷ time) and then calculating the force using $F = ma$. If you have got the correct answer using this alternative method, you still get all 4 marks.)

p.168 — Conservation of Momentum

Q1 Total momentum before collision
$= (2.0 \times 1.5) + (3.0 \times 0)$
= 3 kg m/s *[1 mark]*
The total momentum before the collision is equal to the total momentum after the collision.
Total momentum after collision
= total mass of trolleys × final velocity
$3 = (2.0 + 3.0) \times$ velocity
velocity = 3 ÷ (2.0 + 3.0) *[1 mark]*
= 0.6 m/s *[1 mark]*

p.169 — Mass, Weight and Gravity

Q1 weight = $m \times g$
$= 67 \times 10$
= 670 N *[1 mark]*

Q2 Rearrange equation for mass:
mass = $\frac{w}{g}$ = 820 ÷ 10 *[1 mark]*
= 82 kg *[1 mark]*

p.170 — Mechanical Energy Stores

Q1 $PE = m \times h \times g$
$= 0.80 \times 1.5 \times 10$
= 12 J *[1 mark]*

Q2 $KE = 0.5 \times m \times v^2$
$= 0.5 \times 4.9 \times (2.0)^2$
= 9.8 J *[1 mark]*

p.171 — Work Done and Power

Q1 For the book to stop, it will need to do work against friction equal to the energy in its kinetic energy store. Rearrange the work done equation for distance:
distance = work done ÷ force *[1 mark]*
= 1.25 ÷ 5.0 = 0.25 m *[1 mark]*

p.172 — Forces and Elasticity

Q1 The extension of the spring
= 0.20 − 0.16 = 0.04 m *[1 mark]*
Rearrange $F = x \times k$
So $k = \frac{F}{x} = \frac{3.0}{0.04}$
= 75 N/m *[1 mark]*

p.173 — Investigating Hooke's Law

Q1 First calculate the extension of the spring:
extension = 1.3 − 1.2 = 0.1 m *[1 mark]*
Then substitute this into:
energy transferred in stretching
$= 0.5 \times$ spring constant × (extension)^2
$= 0.5 \times 54 \times 0.1^2$
= 0.27 J *[1 mark]*

p.175 — Static Electricity

Q1 E.g. hold the object near some small scraps of paper *[1 mark]*. If the object is charged, the scraps of paper will be attracted to it, making them 'jump' towards it *[1 mark]*. / Touch the object against the plate of a gold leaf electroscope *[1 mark]*. If the object is carrying a charge, the gold leaf on the electroscope will rise *[1 mark]*.

p.176 — Current and Potential Difference

Q1 charge = current × time, so
time = charge ÷ current = 120 ÷ 2.5 *[1 mark]*
= 48 s *[1 mark]*

Q2 energy transferred = charge × potential difference so:
potential difference = energy transferred ÷ charge
= 360 ÷ 75 *[1 mark]* = 4.8 V *[1 mark]*

p.177 — Circuits — the Basics

Q1

[1 mark]

Q2

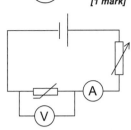

[1 mark for a complete circuit with a power supply showing a thermistor in series with a variable resistor, 1 mark for a voltmeter connected across the thermistor and an ammeter connected in series with the thermistor.]

p.178 — Resistance and $V = I \times R$

Q1 potential difference = current × resistance, so
resistance = potential difference ÷ current
= 4.25 ÷ 0.25
= 17 Ω *[1 mark]*

p.179 — Circuit Devices

Q1 a)

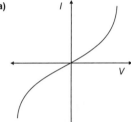

[1 mark]

b) As the current through the thermistor increases (in either direction), the thermistor warms up *[1 mark]*. This decreases the resistance of the thermistor, causing the *I-V* graph to curve *[1 mark]*.

p.180 — Series and Parallel Circuits

Q1 3.6 ÷ 3 = 1.2 V *[1 mark]*

p.181 — More on Series and Parallel Circuits

Q1 3.5 V *[1 mark]*

p.182 — Energy and Power in Circuits

Q1 11 × 60 = 660 seconds *[1 mark]*
energy transferred = power × time
= 1500 × 660 = 990 000 J *[1 mark]*

Q2 Power = potential difference × current, so
current = power ÷ potential difference
= 8.5 ÷ 2.5 *[1 mark]* = 3.4 A *[1 mark]*

Q3 power = current² × resistance, so
current = √power ÷ resistance *[1 mark]*
= √375 ÷ 15 *[1 mark]* = 5 A *[1 mark]*

p.183 — Magnets and Magnetic Fields

Q1 Put the magnet on a piece of paper and put a compass next to it, marking on the piece of paper the point at which the compass needle is pointing *[1 mark]*. Then move the compass so that the tail of the compass needle is where the tip of the needle was previously, and mark again where the needle is pointing *[1 mark]*. Repeat this several times and then join up the markings for a complete sketch of a field line around the magnet *[1 mark]*. Do this several times for different points around the magnet to get several field lines *[1 mark]*.

Q2 Copper is not a magnetic material *[1 mark]*.

p.184 — Electromagnetism

Q1 a) E.g.

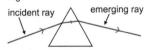

[1 mark for correct shape of field lines, 1 mark for correctly showing the direction of both the current and the magnetic field lines]

b) E.g.

[1 mark for correct shape of field lines, 1 mark for correctly showing the direction of both the current and the magnetic field lines]

p.185 — Magnetic Forces

Q1 Thumb — direction of the force *[1 mark]*.
First finger — direction of the magnetic field *[1 mark]*.
Second finger — direction of the current *[1 mark]*.

Q2 35 cm = 0.35 m
Rearrange $F = B \times I \times l$
for the magnetic flux density, B:
$B = F \div (I \times L)$
= 9.8 ÷ (5.0 × 0.35) *[1 mark]*
= 5.6 T *[1 mark]*

p.186 — Motors

Q1 Any two from: decrease the current / decrease the number of turns on the coil / decrease the magnetic flux density.
[1 mark for each correct answer]

p.188 — Wave Basics

Q1 7.5 ÷ 100 = 0.075 m *[1 mark]*
wave speed = frequency × wavelength, so
frequency = wave speed ÷ wavelength
= 0.15 ÷ 0.075 *[1 mark]* = 2 Hz *[1 mark]*

p.189 — Wave Experiments

Q1 E.g. attach a motor to a dipper and place it in a ripple tank filled with water to create some waves *[1 mark]*. Place a cork in the water and count how many times it bobs up in 20 seconds *[1 mark]*. Divide this number by 20 to give the frequency of the wave *[1 mark]*.

p.190 — Reflection and Refraction

Q1 The light will bend away from the normal *[1 mark]*.

p.191 — More on Reflection

Q1 27° *[1 mark]*.

p.192 — More on Refraction

Q1 E.g.

incident ray   emerging ray

[1 mark for both rays correctly labelled. 1 mark for the ray bending towards the normal as it enters the glass. 1 mark for the ray bending away from the normal as it leaves the glass.]

p.193 — Electromagnetic Waves

Q1 E.g. gamma rays are ionising so they can cause tissue damage and cancer, but visible light isn't ionising *[1 mark]*. Visible light is reflected or absorbed by the skin, but gamma rays can pass through the skin and so can damage deeper tissues *[1 mark]*.

p.194 — Uses of EM Waves

Q1 An alternating current of a set frequency in an electric conductor causes charges to oscillate *[1 mark]*, creating an oscillating electric and magnetic field (an EM wave) of the same frequency — a radio wave *[1 mark]*.

Q2 E.g. infra-red cameras / night-vision cameras / medical imaging / heating / cooking *[1 mark]*

p.195 — More Uses of EM Waves

Q1 Any two from, e.g: sterilising medical instruments / sterilising food / treating cancer / medical imaging *[2 marks]*

p.196 — Isotopes and Radioactive Decay

Q1 Number of protons in isotope B = 7
(the same as isotope A).
So mass number
= number of protons + number of neutrons
= 7 + 7 = 14 *[1 mark]*

p.197 — Radiation Properties and Decay Equations

Q1 $^{238}_{92}\text{U} \longrightarrow ^{234}_{90}\text{Th} + ^{4}_{2}\alpha$

[1 mark for the correct mass number of uranium, 1 mark for correct alpha particle symbol and mass and atomic numbers and 1 mark for the correct mass number for thorium]

p.198 — Electron Energy Levels

Q1 A positive ion is an atom that has lost one or more electrons *[1 mark]*. An ion is formed when an outer electron absorbs enough energy that it leaves the atom *[1 mark]*.

p.199 — Half-Life

Q1 The number of half-lives in 240 hours is
240 ÷ 60 = 4 half-lives *[1 mark]*
Initial count = 480
after 1 half-life = 480 ÷ 2 = 240
after 2 half-lives = 240 ÷ 2 = 120
after 3 half-lives = 120 ÷ 2 = 60
after 4 half-lives = 60 ÷ 2 = 30
So the activity after 240 hours
= 30 counts per minute *[1 mark]*

p.200 — Dangers of Radioactivity

Q1 Radiation can cause minor damage to a cell that causes it to mutate / radiation can cause cells to divide uncontrollably / causes cancer *[1 mark]*. Radiation can also kill a cell completely *[1 mark]*.

Q2 The alpha-emitting radioactive source has a lower irradiation risk than the beta-emitting radioactive source *[1 mark]*, as alpha particles have a lower range in materials compared to beta particles *[1 mark]*. There is no contamination risk for both sources *[1 mark]*, as they are both solids and so an object wouldn't become contaminated if it didn't touch the sources *[1 mark]*.

p.202 — Conservation of Energy

Q1 As the ball falls, energy is transferred mechanically from its gravitational potential energy store to its kinetic energy store *[1 mark]*. When the ball hits the ground, energy is transferred away by sound waves *[1 mark]*. The rest of the energy is carried away by heating to the thermal energy stores of the ball, the ground and the surroundings *[1 mark]*.

Q2 Energy in the chemical energy store of the wood is transferred by heating to the thermal energy stores of the surroundings *[1 mark]*. The rest of the energy is transferred away by light waves *[1 mark]*.

p.203 — Efficiency

Q1 Useful output energy transfer
= 500 − 420 = 80 J *[1 mark]*

Efficiency = $\dfrac{\text{useful output energy transfer}}{\text{input energy transfer}}$

= $\dfrac{80}{500}$ = 0.16 *[1 mark]*

0.16 × 100 = 16% *[1 mark]*

Answers

p.204 — Energy Transfer by Heating

Q1 Black surfaces are better emitters of radiation, so a black mug would radiate energy more quickly than a white mug *[1 mark]*. So energy would be carried away more quickly from the thermal energy store of the water *[1 mark]*.

p.205 — Reducing Unwanted Energy Transfers

Q1 Any three from: install loft insulation / install a hot water tank jacket / introduce cavity walls and cavity wall insulating foam / install draught-proofing / install double glazing / put up thick curtains / make the walls thicker / replace walls with walls that have a lower thermal conductivity / decrease the length of the hot water pipes / increase the width of the hot water pipes / insulate the hot water pipes / paint the hot water pipes white.
[1 mark for each correct answer]

Q2 Its thickness *[1 mark]* and its thermal conductivity *[1 mark]*.

p.206 — Mechanical Energy Transfers

Q1 energy transferred in stretching
$= 0.5 \times$ spring constant $\times$ (extension)^2 *[1 mark]*
$= 0.5 \times 6.50 \times 0.120^2$
$= 0.0468$ J *[1 mark]*

p.207 — Electrical Energy Transfers

Q1 Energy transferred to bulb
$=$ power $\times$ time *[1 mark]*
$= 35 \times (2.0 \times 60)$
$= 4200$ J *[1 mark]*
The energy transferred by the bulb as light waves will be less than the energy transferred to the bulb by the battery, as the bulb transfers some energy by heating to the thermal energy stores of its surroundings/energy is transferred to the thermal energy stores of the wires by heating *[1 mark]*.

p.209 — Everyday Speeds and Accelerations

Q1 $70 - 50 = 20$ mph
$20 \times 1.6 = 32$ km/hr
$32 \div 3.6 = 8.88...$ m/s
[1 mark]
Estimate 4 seconds to accelerate.
[1 mark for any value in the range 2 s to 5 s.]
acceleration = change in velocity ÷ time
$= 8.88... \div 4 = 2.22...$
$= 2$ m/s^2 (to 1 s.f.)
[1 mark for dividing 8.88... m/s by the time that you estimated.]

p.210 — Stopping Distances and Reaction Times

Q1 If you're tired, e.g. from a long journey, your reaction time is likely to be longer *[1 mark]*, which would increase thinking distance and so stopping distance *[1 mark]*. This would make an accident more likely if you were forced to brake *[1 mark]*.

p.211 — Non-Renewable Energy Sources

Q1 As the coal burns it heats the water in the boiler. The water boils, making steam *[1 mark]*. The steam drives a turbine, which in turn drives a generator, generating electricity *[1 mark]*.

p.212 — Renewable Energy Sources

Q1 Any two from: e.g. bio-fuels / wind power / the sun/solar power, hydro-electricity / the tides *[2 marks]*

Q2 Any two from: e.g. some people think wind turbines spoil the view / wind turbines can be quite noisy / you can only generate electricity when it's windy/the electricity supply is unreliable / you can't generate more electricity in response to high demand. *[2 marks]*

p.213 — More On Energy Sources

Q1 Advantage, e.g. the electricity supply is reliable / you can generate more electricity in response to high demand / it has minimal running costs. *[1 mark]*
Disadvantage, e.g. it has a big impact on the environment / the initial cost is high / you need to flood a valley / it can lead to a loss of habitat. *[1 mark]*

Q2 Renewable sources won't run out but non-renewable will *[1 mark]*. Also, renewable energy sources tend to cause less damage to the environment than non-renewables, so it's better to try to use more of these sources *[1 mark]*.

p.214 — Electricity and the National Grid

Q1 A step-up transformer *[1 mark]*. It will decrease the current *[1 mark]*.

p.215 — Wiring in the Home

Q1 a) The kettle needs an earth wire because the live wire may develop a fault and come into contact with the metal body of the kettle, which could cause electric shocks or fires *[1 mark]*. If this happened, the earth wire has low resistance, so the resistance of the circuit will fall and the current will increase *[1 mark]*. The surge in current would melt the fuse, isolating the appliance, preventing shocks and fires *[1 mark]*.

b) 0 V *[1 mark]*

Index

Index

Index

SRHR45